UNITED STATES DEPARTMENT OF COMMERCE
C. R. Smith, *Secretary*
NATIONAL BUREAU OF STANDARDS ● A. V. Astin, *Director*

Technology of

Liquid Helium

R. H. Kropschot, B. W. Birmingham, and
D. B. Mann, Editors

Institute for Basic Standards
National Bureau of Standards
Boulder Laboratories
Boulder, Colorado 80302

National Bureau of Standards Monograph 111

Issued October 1968

Abstract

The discovery of the element helium was made just 100 years ago in 1868. Today helium is produced in large quantities and used in many technological applications. This treatise is a source document containing information on helium resources, production, conservation, thermodynamic properties, liquefaction and refrigeration techniques, transportation and storage of liquid and safety requirements. It also contains a discussion of uses for liquid and cold gas in cryoelectronics, superconductivity, bubble chambers, cryopumping and missile and space systems. The book brings together articles by noted authorities in cryogenic technology in which they discuss their specialized field in great depth.

Key Words: Conservation, cryoelectronics, cryogenics, cryopumping, helium, liquefaction, magnets, purification, refrigeration, safety, storage, thermodynamic properties, transportation.

Library of Congress Catalog Card No. 68–61553

Foreword

One hundred years ago, in 1868, J. N. Lockyer discovered a mysterious element in the chromosphere of the sun. Since Lockyer and other well-known scientists of the time thought that it existed nowhere else, the element was given the name "helium" from the Greek word "helios" or "sun."

Less than 25 years later, however, W. F. Hillebrand of the U.S. Department of the Interior obtained an unidentified gas from the mineral uraninite. Sir William Ramsay, learning of Hillebrand's work, obtained a similar gas from the mineral cleveite. Ramsay removed the oxygen and nitrogen he found present in this gas and examined the residue. This residue, helium, proved, after 27 years of uncertainty, that the sun element did indeed exist on earth.

But the work of these three pioneers of science remained relatively unheralded until a method was developed to obtain and use this substance in volume. The key to this development came in 1905, when a natural gas discovered in Kansas was found to contain nearly two percent helium. In 1918, exactly 50 years after its discovery, helium was first extracted in volume from natural gas. From then until today, the use and importance of helium has expanded at an ever-increasing rate.

Helium has many uses; for example, as a gas in lighter-than-air ships, as a pressurant and control gas in aerospace vehicles, as a shielding gas in welding, and as a coolant gas in reactors. One of the most interesting uses is in the field of cryogenics.

Because of its very low boiling point, 4.2 K, helium is needed in liquid form to provide the refrigeration for all types of cryoelectronic and other devices, especially those involving the phenomenon of superconductivity. Helium itself is scientifically interesting because of its transformation to helium II at 2.18 K and the absence of a triple point. The unusual behavior of helium II, such as superfluid creep, abnormal viscosity, and sound propagation, has been studied extensively by low temperature physicists.

This book, however, is aimed at articulating the developments in the last decade in the technology of liquid helium, for much has been written previously on the physics of liquid helium. In fact it is now becoming apparent that the 1960's will be remembered as the era of a developing liquid helium technology.

I am pleased, therefore, to have this book available at this time not only to share in the Helium Centennial Celebration but hopefully to act as a stimulus to an increasingly rapid development of the technology.

Washington, D.C.,   W. R. HIBBARD, *Director*,
March 1968.   U.S. Bureau of Mines.

Preface

When one thinks of liquid helium and its associated technology, the names of two pioneers come immediately to mind. The first, of course, is the Dutch scientist Kamerlingh Onnes, since he first succeeded in liquefying helium at the University of Leiden in The Netherlands in 1908.

Several attempts were made prior to 1908 to liquefy helium, notably by Olszewski and Dewar, but these were unsuccessful. In fact, Kamerlingh Onnes was to make several abortive attempts to liquefy helium by using a technique of cooling compressed helium gas with liquid hydrogen and then making a rapid expansion. He finally used a circulation technique where compressed helium gas was cooled to near the triple point temperature of hydrogen and then piped through a regenerative heat exchanger prior to expansion. By this "boot-strap" cooling in the regenerative heat exchanger he eventually obtained helium cold enough to form liquid upon expansion.

It was not until the early and middle 1920's that several other laboratories reported success in liquefying helium. Simon and Kapitza made contributions in the early 1930's, but their developments did not seem to have the impact on liquid helium technology as did our second pioneer—Samuel C. Collins of the Massachusetts Institute of Technology. Collins developed a highly successful helium liquefier after World War II, and over 350 have now been sold commercially, putting liquid helium within reach of virtually every low-temperature physicist.

Collins was successful, with what we now know as the "Collins Cryostat," because he perceived that there were two major problems associated with earlier attempts to produce liquefiers, and he provided solutions to these problems.

One problem pertained to imperfect vacuum technology, which would probably be considered trivial today but was most troublesome two decades ago. Collins circumvented the need for a high vacuum, and thus leak-tight joints, by suspending the regenerative heat exchangers of the liquefier in an atmosphere of gaseous helium with the cold end in the downward position. In this manner he was able to depend on convective equilibrium for insulation, and small leaks to the helium atmosphere made little difference.

Another problem pertained to the life and effectiveness of the expansion engine. Earlier developers had used material combinations such as a bronze piston in a stainless steel cylinder, and we now realize that these combinations were relatively poor from the standpoint of both wear and clearance. Collins chose nitrided steel for both the piston and cylinder, with the result that not only was the metal better from an operational standpoint but clearances could be reduced by an order of magnitude, yielding an overall improvement in performance.

I would like now to identify another individual who is not nearly as well known as Kamerlingh Onnes or Collins but who I feel had a profound influence on large-scale liquid helium technology as we know it today. This individual was the late Ray E. Brown, who spent his entire professional career in the United States Department of the Navy. Since his contributions may be less well known than those of Kamerlingh Onnes or Collins, I would like to highlight just a few of them in this Introduction.

In 1927 Ray Brown became associated with the lighter-than-air ship program of the Navy Bureau of Aeronautics, and the rest of his working life was synonymous with the growth of helium as a useful material—first, as a lifting gas for airships, and finally, as an important commodity for many military, medical, industrial, and scientific applications.

Ray Brown played a prominent role in the design of railway tank cars, automotive trailers, and other methods of transportation for compressed helium. He participated in the development of storage facilities for helium at the Navy's lighter-than-air facilities. During World War II, he managed almost singlehandedly the procurement and distribution of helium for the Navy's dirigibles and for other military operations.

By virtue of his association with the gaseous helium field, he maintained a continuing awareness of all aspects of helium behavior including that of liquid helium, and after World War II he conceived the idea of using helium in the liquid phase for economy in transportation. He pointed out that when helium is shipped in the compressed form in steel cylinders the mass of helium is only one to two percent of the total mass of the container; therefore, most of the transportation charges are for transporting steel, and only a small portion is for transporting helium. Thus, he suggested that helium either in the liquid form or as a cold, dense gas could be used to increase this percentage so that a much greater portion of the transportation cost would be for the helium.

Ray Brown came to the National Bureau of Standards in the mid-1940's to propose the development of a suitable liquid helium technology to support his suggestion. However, it was not until about 1954 that the National Bureau of Standards was in a position to assist him in this venture at its then relatively young Cryogenics Laboratory in Boulder, Colo. During the next several years the National Bureau of Standards with Navy support worked on many aspects of the liquid helium problem and laid the groundwork for the large-scale liquid helium ventures which are operating today and explained in more detail in the main text of this book.

Kamerlingh Onnes, Collins, and Brown are notable for their individual efforts. In addition, the team effort of the National Bureau of Standards, and certainly the U.S. Bureau of Mines, whose many years of work resulted in the development and perfection of a cryogenic process for separating helium gas, have provided the basis for the industrial interest in a large-scale liquid helium technology. Another significant stimulus to this technology is the Bureau of Mines' conservation program for helium, which makes it economically attractive for industrial firms to consider large-scale liquefaction. Accordingly, the editors of this Monograph feel that its publication during this centennial year celebration of the discovery of the element helium is most timely.

I will not attempt to summarize either the entire book or portions of it in this Introduction; however, I would like to point out that the editors deliberately omitted discussion of superfluid helium since this topic has been amply covered in other books and articles authored by many notable scientists working in the field of low-temperature physics. We have also omitted a discussion of helium heat transfer, both superfluid and supercritical, since the data are so scanty at this time. Research efforts are currently underway to provide such data, but it will probably be at least one to two years before comprehensive articles can be written. The applications described in chapter 8 were selected on the basis of significant uses and are certainly not intended to be all-inclusive; however, it is hoped that they do include the applications which involve large expenditures.

The use of proprietary names, products, and processes in this Monograph, though contrary to the usual NBS practice, is essential to the proper understanding of the work presented. These proprietary references are made with no intent to endorse or condemn specific products or processes, but are made solely with the intent to be representative and comprehensive in the field of liquid helium technology.

The National Bureau of Standards has officially adopted the International System of Units, abbreviated SI for Systéme International. It has been the Bureau's policy to employ the SI in all its publications except where the use of these units would obviously impair communication or would reduce the usefulness of a publication to its primary recipients. This Monograph does not consistently use SI units because much of the work in the field of liquid helium technology has been based upon other systems of units. Appropriate conversion factors are included where necessary.

We urge that specialists and other users of data in this field accustom themselves to SI units as rapidly as possible.

B. W. BIRMINGHAM, *Deputy Director*,
Institute for Basic Standards/Boulder, Colo.

Contents

Contents — Continued

CHAPTER 1

Helium Resources, Production, and Conservation

William M. Deaton [1] **and Paul V. Mullins** [2]

---

[1] Formerly Chief Technologist (now retired), Helium Activity, Bureau of Mines, U.S. Department of the Interior, Amarillo, Tex. 79106.

[2] General Manager, Helium Operations, Bureau of Mines, U.S. Department of the Interior, Amarillo, Tex. 79106.

1

1.1. HELIUM RESOURCES

1.1.1. Helium Occurrence

Helium is present in the earth's atmosphere to the extent of about 1 part in 200,000 or 0.0005 mole percent. It is abundant in the sun and stars, thus is not a rare element so far as the whole universe is concerned. It is a rare element on the earth only in the sense that it is generally so widely dispersed that it would be difficult to recover it from the atmosphere as a concentrated gas. Helium is found in minor amounts in most natural gases produced in the United States. In many cases, the helium content is only a few hundredths or a few tenths of 1 percent; but natural gas produced in large volumes in some areas contains 0.4 to 0.6 percent, and some natural gas produced in smaller but significant volumes contains up to 2 percent. In a very few instances, the helium content exceeds 2 percent. The highest content observed is about 9 percent. Helium-bearing natural gases usually contain appreciable amounts of nitrogen and thus are relatively low in heating value. Helium-bearing gas from most sources, however, is marketable as fuel gas.

Helium is also found in natural gases produced outside the United States. No thorough survey of foreign natural gases has been made. Natural gases produced at some locations in Canada contain helium in significant amounts and some helium is produced there. Helium has been reported in natural gases in the U.S.S.R., in Japan and may be expected to be found, at least in small amounts, in many natural gases throughout the world.

1.1.2. Bureau of Mines Helium Survey

For more than 40 years, the Bureau of Mines has conducted a continuous "helium survey" to determine and evaluate occurrences of helium in natural gas in the United States. The survey is conducted by obtaining and analyzing samples of natural gas from new wells drilled in the exploration for oil and gas. Several hundred samples are obtained and analyzed each year, and complete analyses with well data are published periodically [1–7].[3]

---

[3] Figures in brackets indicate the literature references at the end of this chapter.

1.1.3. Estimated Helium Resources

Helium contained in the helium resources of the United States was estimated in 1966 to be about 200 billion cubic feet. (See table 1.1.)* The resources considered were limited to those where the helium content of the gas is 0.3 percent or more, and the estimated amount of helium at a particular location is 100 million cubic feet or more. The total recoverable helium in these resources, however, is less than 200 billion cubic feet.

TABLE 1.1.   *Estimated volumes of helium in the principal helium resources in the United States (as of January 1966)*

Geographical location	Billion cubic feet of helium (at 14.65 psia and 60 F)
Rocky Mountain area:	
Arizona, Colorado, Montana, New Mexico, Utah, Wyoming...	25.5
Midcontinent area:	
Kansas, Oklahoma, Texas...............................	169.2
Total...	194.7
Conservation helium stored in Cliffside structure..........	9.0
Total...	203.7

Many factors affect the recovery of helium. Helium is an inherent part of the natural gas and, in most instances, becomes available for recovery only under the conditions controlling the production of natural gas for fuel purposes. Thus, availability of helium for recovery is generally dependent on the rates of production and other conditions established in marketing natural gas. Also, it is important that the source gas be available for a long enough time to justify building a plant.

To accommodate practical and economical recovery, it is desirable and, in most cases, necessary to select a focal point where large volumes of helium-bearing natural gas have been brought together, after gathering from the source wells, and thus are available at a single point for helium extraction. These desired conditions are provided at some points on gas transmission lines that transport helium-bearing gas to market. Also,

*EDITORS' NOTE: The system of units was chosen by the authors and represents current industrial convention. Conversion tables to the mks system are given at the end of the chapter.

the potential net recovery at any point depends on optimum plant size and efficiency, on uniformity and continuity of gas availability, and on other factors. Taking into account these various factors, it is estimated that in 1966 the amount of recoverable helium in the United States was about 180 billion cubic feet.

1.1.4. Geographical Location of Resources

The geographical location of the principal sources of helium in the United States is shown in figure 1.1. Table 1.1 indicates that about 87 percent of the estimated helium resources is in the Texas Panhandle, Oklahoma Panhandle, and Southwestern Kansas. Natural gas from parts of the fields in this area has been transported to market for various periods, ranging from 15 to 35 years, and withdrawal is continuing at a rate that is expected to cause major depletion of the gas in these fields in 20–25 years. Helium extraction plants existing prior to 1962 had capacity to extract only about 10 percent of the more than 4 billion cubic feet a year of helium that was contained in the gas being withdrawn from this important area. As a result of the Government's helium conservation program (see section 1.4), much of this helium is now being extracted and saved as a conservation measure.

FIGURE 1.1. *Geographical location of principal helium resources in the United States.*

1.2. HELIUM PRODUCTION HISTORY

Helium has been produced in the United States in appreciable quantities since 1918. The quantities produced were relatively small except during World War II. In 1948, a sharp upward trend began as new uses were made of helium in some rapidly expanding Government and civilian activities. This trend has continued. The annual production of helium from 1920 to 1966 is shown in figure 1.2.

1.2.1. Production by the Bureau of Mines

The Federal Government pioneered helium production in 1918. Virtually all helium production in the period 1918–61 was by the U.S. Department of the Interior's Bureau of Mines and was to meet the needs of Federal agencies. Bureau plants are situated near Amarillo, Tex.; Exell, Tex. (30 miles north of Amarillo); Keyes, Okla.; Shiprock, N. Mex.; and Otis, Kans. All helium production has been accomplished by use of cryogenic processes, and the helium has been extracted from helium-bearing natural gas.

The enabling legislation for early helium operations of the Bureau of Mines was the Helium Act of March 3, 1925 (43 Stat. 1110). This Act was amended September 1, 1937 (50 Stat. 885), to authorize sales of

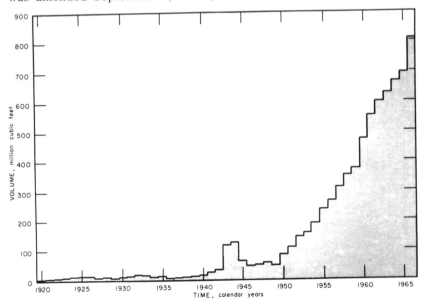

FIGURE 1.2. *Helium produced and sold by the Bureau of Mines, 1920–66.*

helium for medical, scientific, and industrial uses. A further amendment of September 13, 1960 (74 Stat. 918) provided for long-term helium purchase contracts to accommodate an extensive helium conservation program, which is described later.

1.2.2. Production by Private Industry

Private industry helium production plants were few in number and contributed little to the total volume of helium produced in the period 1918–61. Only one private company operated plants in this period. This company had two small plants — one in Kansas and one in Colorado — for short periods during 1928–37. But in the early 1960's, private industry again entered the helium production field. A private plant with a potential output of 70 million cubic feet annually was constructed in eastern Arizona and started operating in 1961. Another plant was completed near Otis, Kans., in 1966, with a planned annual output of 150 million cubic feet. A third plant near Elkhart, Kans., which has a production capacity of 140 million cubic feet, was completed and placed in operation in 1966.

In 1962–63, five large helium extraction plants were constructed in the Texas Panhandle and western Kansas by private industry under contracts with the Federal Government to extract helium from natural gas being transported to fuel markets. The product from these plants is a crude (unrefined) helium-nitrogen mixture containing 50–85 percent helium, and is purchased by the Federal Government under long-term contracts. Most of it is stored, for future use, in a natural gas underground storage reservoir near Amarillo, Tex. (see sec. 1.4).

1.2.3. Foreign Production

One helium plant with a potential output of 12 million cubic feet per year is in operation in Saskatchewan, Canada. This plant was built in 1963. Except for the production from this plant, there is no significant helium production outside the United States. Small quantities have been produced in Europe as a by-product of air separation. Some reports indicate helium has been produced from natural gas in the U.S.S.R., but few details are available.

Announcement has recently been made of expected production of helium in Europe [8]. This helium would be obtained from natural gas produced from wells in the North Sea off the coasts of England and The Netherlands. Also helium may be available in the uncondensed gas from a natural gas liquefaction plant supplying liquefied natural gas for shipment from Algeria to France and England.

1.3. HELIUM USES AND MARKETS

1.3.1. Principal Uses

With minor exceptions, all helium produced during the first 20 years of its production was used as buoyant gas for inflation of blimps, dirigibles, and balloons—principally for military operations. Small quantities were used in synthetic breathing mixtures in deep sea diving operations. Following authorization of non-Federal sales in 1937, small quantities were used in synthetic breathing mixtures for temporary relief of respiratory disorders and for reduction of explosive hazards in anesthesia. Shortly thereafter, the use of helium in shielded-arc welding began and then helium found an important use in the early nuclear energy investigations and developments. Nevertheless, about 99 percent of the annual helium production before 1946 was used in blimps, dirigibles, and balloons. Non-Federal sales were small.

In the late 1940's, helium sales increased sharply and a considerably different pattern of helium use began to develop. A major factor was the Bureau of Mines production of helium of better than 99 percent purity, rather than the former 98.3 percent purity. The higher purity was of appreciable benefit in some uses. Helium users demanded still higher purity. The purity of produced helium was raised, first to about 99.5 percent and, shortly thereafter, to nearly 100 percent. This was a strong stimulus to helium usage. Larger quantities were used for shielded-arc welding and nuclear energy development, and new uses developed and grew rapidly. In the 1950's, large volumes of helium were used in the development and operation of ballistic missiles and in the initial program for space exploration. At the same time, helium was finding a variety of uses in rapidly expanding research programs. The usefulness of helium in these applications is due to its unique physical properties, especially its inertness, its low density, and its very low liquefaction temperature. A survey in 1962 indicated that the approximate division among various uses was as shown in figure 1.3.

1.3.2. Principal Consumers

Federal agencies have always been the principal consumers of helium. Prior to and during World War II, the Federal agencies—and primarily the Navy Department—used virtually all helium produced. This pattern began to change shortly after World War II as the Atomic Energy Commission and commercial consumers began to use appreciable volumes of helium. After 1950, the development programs for ballistic missiles and space exploration resulted in the Air Force and

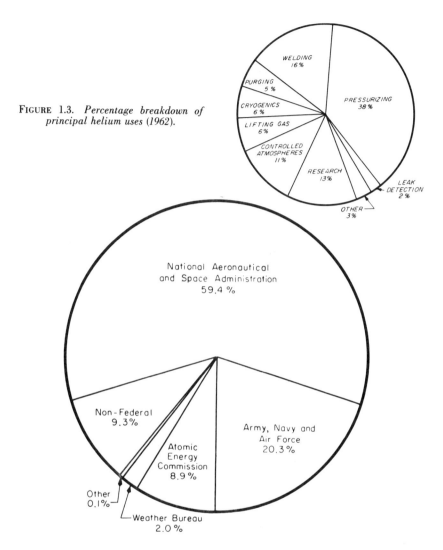

FIGURE 1.3. *Percentage breakdown of principal helium uses (1962).*

FIGURE 1.4. *Percentage breakdown of principal users of helium (1966).*

National Aeronautics and Space Administration, as well as the Atomic Energy Commission, becoming consumers of large quantities of helium. During the period 1950–66, a fairly consistent pattern prevailed of about two-thirds going to Federal consumers and one-third to non-Federal consumers. Surveys indicated that 50 percent or more of the helium sold to non-Federal distributors and consumers was used on Federal contracts, and this made Federal consumption approach 90 percent of the total market. The 1966 survey indicated the division among Federal agencies and commercial consumers was as shown in figure 1.4.

1.3.3. Geographical Distribution of Market

From the beginning of production, the geographical location of major markets has been on the east and west coasts of the United States. In 1966, about 25 percent went to points on the east coast and 45 percent to points on the west coast. The remaining 30 percent was used at locations in the Gulf Coast and interior States.

1.4. HELIUM CONSERVATION

1.4.1. Helium Conservation Program

Rapidly growing importance and use of helium prompted a critical study in the late 1950's of its future supply and demand. This led to a conclusion by the Federal Government that it should engage in an extensive helium conservation program. In September 1960, the program was approved and legislation was passed by the Congress to accommodate it. Plans for the conservation program were based primarily on the concept that helium extraction plants could be constructed at strategic points on the principal pipelines transporting helium-bearing gas to market, and that except for that portion needed to meet current demand the helium would be stored underground by the Government for future use when needed. Private industry was to be encouraged to finance, construct, and operate the plants and would sell its output to the Federal Government under long-term contracts. The product produced would be a "crude" or unpurified helium, with a composition of 50–85 percent helium and the remainder chiefly nitrogen.

The conservation program got underway in 1961 with the execution of four contracts with private industry to build and operate five plants situated near the towns of Bushton, Ulysses, and Liberal in Kansas; and in Sherman County, and near Dumas in the Texas Panhandle. All of these plants were built and in production by mid-1963. The Bureau of Mines built a 425-mile pipeline gathering system with connections to the above plants to take their full output and to deliver it to one or more of the Bureau's plants for purification and marketing, or to an underground storage reservoir in the Cliffside Gas Field near Amarillo. The storage reservoir is a partly depleted natural gas reservoir which, for over 30 years, has been the source of helium-bearing natural gas processed at the Amarillo Helium Plant.

1.4.2. Volumes to be Conserved

By the conservation program, it is estimated that about 78 billion cubic feet of helium will be extracted and saved over a 22-year period from helium-bearing gas en route to fuel markets. It is estimated that about 36 billion cubic feet of this helium will need to be purified to meet market demand during this period; and the remainder, or about 42 billion cubic feet, will be placed in the storage reservoir for use beyond 1985.

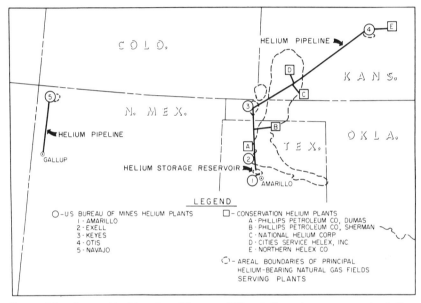

FIGURE 1.5. *Geographical location of Bureau of Mines helium plants, conservation helium plants, pipelines, and helium storage reservoir.*

1.4.3. Geographical Location of Plants, Pipelines, and Storage Field

The geographical location of helium plants, pipelines, gathering system, and the storage field for conserved helium is shown in figure 1.5.

1.4.4. Future Helium Supply

Future helium supply for important uses would seem to be assured by the helium conservation program for 30 to 50 years, and perhaps longer. The volumes extracted and saved might be increased appreciably if conditions justify and action is taken before about 1970, for there are additional quantities available which could be recovered economically.

1.5. HELIUM PRODUCTION PROCESS

1.5.1. Bureau of Mines Helium Production Plants

All of the Bureau of Mines helium production plants extract helium from natural gas and use a cryogenic process. A block diagram of the process is shown in figure 1.6. The process is described in detail later

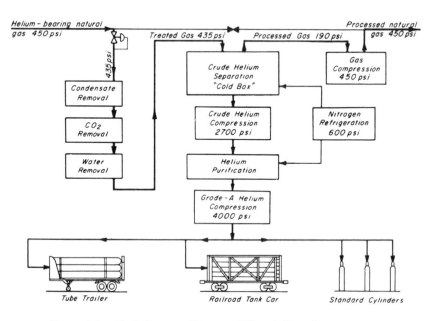

FIGURE 1.6.   *Block diagram of Bureau of Mines helium plant process.*

but briefly it consists of the following. The natural gas is supplied from the source pipeline at a pressure of about 435 psi (pounds-force per square inch gauge or lbf/in²) or, if not available at this pressure, is compressed to 435 psi upon entering the plant. The gas is pretreated to remove hydrocarbon condensate, carbon dioxide, and water before it enters the low-temperature equipment. In this equipment, called "cold boxes," the entire gas stream is cooled to about -250 F and liquefied except for the helium and a small percentage of the nitrogen; and after separating the uncondensed helium and nitrogen, the liquefied natural gas is returned through heat exchangers in counterflow to the incoming stream to the cold box outlet. Leaving at near ambient temperature, the processed gas is returned to the gas pipeline from which it was taken and goes on to fuel markets.

The helium-nitrogen product, called "crude helium," generally has a composition of about 70 percent helium and 30 percent nitrogen. It returns through heat exchangers against the incoming natural gas stream and leaves the cold box at ambient temperature and usually at 150–200 psi. This stream is further processed, as later described, to purify it to Grade-A helium quality (99.995 mole percent purity) by a high-pressure (2700 psi) and low-temperature (-320 F) cryogenic process.

The Bureau of Mines helium plants differ widely in natural gas processing capacities, which range from 6 to 130 million cubic feet of gas per day. The helium contents of the entering natural gas streams also differ greatly, ranging from 0.9 to 5.8 percent. The helium production capacities range from about 35 million to over 350 million cubic feet of helium per year.

1.5.2. Private Industry Helium Production Plants

Processes used in private industry helium plants are low-temperature processes using the same general principle as that used in Bureau of Mines plants.

Just prior to 1966, the only private industry helium plant producing Grade-A helium was the plant of Kerr-McGee Oil Industries, Inc., at Navajo, Ariz. [9]. The gas processed at this plant comes from a small gas field nearby that produces an inert gas containing about 91 percent nitrogen and 9 percent helium.

In this plant, separation of helium from the natural gas is first done at relatively low pressure (about 50 psi). After cooling to near -320 F with liquid nitrogen, the uncondensed crude helium product is warmed, compressed to 2900 psi, and then purified in the same manner as later described for Bureau of Mines plants. The designed natural gas processing rate is 2.5 million cubic feet per day and the designed purified helium production rate is 70 million cubic feet per year. Equipment is installed at this plant to liquefy helium for shipment.

A new helium plant near Otis, Kans., owned and operated by the Kansas Refined Helium Company, that processes helium-bearing natural gas produced in nearby gas fields, was placed in operation early in 1966. The designed processing capacity of this plant is 25 million cubic feet of natural gas per day. Its helium production output is estimated at about 430 thousand cubic feet per day (150 million cubic feet per year), and it contains a helium liquefier of sufficient capacity to liquefy the entire output of the plant. Shipment of the helium is scheduled to be made in liquid helium semitrailers of about 10,000-gallon capacities (see chapter 5).

The Alamo Chemical Company, a subsidiary of Phillips Petroleum Company, completed and placed in operation in 1966 a helium plant near Elkhart, Kans. [10]. It processes natural gas produced from the Greenwood Field. The designed processing capacity of this plant is 76 million cubic feet of gas per day and its helium production capacity will be about 140 million cubic feet per year. Most of the output of this plant can be liquefied and shipped in this form.

1.5.3. Private Industry Helium Conservation Plants

All the helium extraction plants producing helium for delivery to the Bureau of Mines under the Government's helium conservation program produce only a crude helium mixture of helium-nitrogen-methane having the following range of analyses: helium 50–85 percent, nitrogen 15–50 percent, methane 0–5 percent. The plants also use a low-temperature process. Their refrigeration requirements are supplied principally by Joule-Thomson cooling obtained in throttling the main natural gas stream from a pressure of 300 or 450 psi to a return-gas pressure of 150 to 200 psi, although some of the plants use auxiliary refrigeration to some extent. Unlike the Bureau of Mines plants, the private industry helium recovery plants are designed to extract liquefied petroleum gas (LPG) products from the gas being processed. These products then are

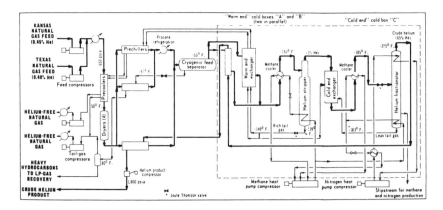

FIGURE 1.7. *Flow diagram of National Helium Corporation's helium plant.*

sold in the LPG market. This adds somewhat to the equipment needed and the refrigeration requirements. A description of the National Helium Corporation's plant, one of the conservation helium plants, showing the processing cycle has been published [11]. Figure 1.7 is reproduced from this article.

The helium content of the gases processed by these plants ranges from 0.40 percent to 0.71 percent, and the processing capacities of the plants range from 200 million to 870 million standard cubic feet of natural gas per day. The amount of helium extracted by the plants ranges from 450 million to 1,050 million standard cubic feet per year.

1.5.4. Other Helium Separation Methods

Although no plants in operation in 1966 use other than low-temperature processing to produce helium, two other methods have been suggested. One is a diffusion method involving differential diffusion of helium, in the gas to be processed, through permeable membranes or porous diffusion barriers [12–15], and the other is selective diffusion of the helium through silica glass tubing [16]. The Bureau of Mines examined both of these methods many years ago (1921–22), but at that time the problems associated with diffusion processes and equipment for them made this approach less attractive than low-temperature processing. An examination of the diffusion process, utilizing high-silica or quartz tubing, showed that this method would be workable; but to be practical would require a large area of high-silica or quartz media, which at that time was not available.

With the progress made in diffusion processes and equipment—for example, the separation of uranium isotopes in the diffusion plant at Oak Ridge, Tenn.—and the development of synthetic diffusion media and the large-scale production of fine capillary high-silica and pure quartz tubing, which is selectively permeable to helium, renewed consideration of these processes is being made.

An experimental unit using high-silica tubing has been tested by the Research Council of Alberta, Edmonton, Alberta, Canada. Its findings have been reported in the literature [17].

The Standard Oil Company of Ohio has patented a process for separating helium from natural gas that uses micro size (40–50 micron) silica-glass hollow spheres [18]. No tests using this process have thus far been reported.

1.6. HELIUM PRODUCTION BY THE BUREAU OF MINES

1.6.1. Description of Bureau of Mines Helium Plant Process

Bureau of Mines helium plants have various gas processing capacities ranging from 6 million to 130 million cubic feet of natural gas per day. The capacities are such that the plants can in most cases process the total amount of gas available to the plants. There are only a few days each year during the winter when the natural gas pipelines are carrying more gas than the plants can process. Details of the process used follow.

Gas Pretreating: Natural gas entering the plant at 435 psi passes through a separator to remove any hydrocarbon condensate or liquid water carried by the gas. At most plants, two gas treating units (fig. 1.8) are used to remove carbon dioxide and water vapor from the inlet gas. Two units are provided in order to give flexibility of operation, to accommodate seasonal fluctuations in gas supply, and to permit the Bureau to meet contractual commitments to process a fixed minimum quantity of gas. The gas processed at the various plants of the Bureau contains carbon dioxide ranging from 0.4 to about 3.0 percent. A solution of about 15 percent monoethanolamine, 76 percent diethylene glycol, and 9 per-

FIGURE 1.8.   *Carbon dioxide and water removal equipment at Keyes Helium Plant.*

FIGURE 1.9. *"Cold boxes" at Keyes Helium Plant.*

cent water is used to remove carbon dioxide. The carbon dioxide content of the natural gas is reduced to 0.005 mole percent or less. Hydrogen sulfide, if present, is also removed.

Although the primary purpose of the amine-glycol solution is to remove carbon dioxide, the gas is also partially dehydrated because of the high glycol and low water content of the solution. The gas is dried further by passing it through solid desiccant beds where the water dewpoint of the gas is reduced to about -100 F, which at 435 psi is equivalent to about 0.0025 pound per million cubic feet. Various desiccants and combinations of desiccants have been used, including activated bauxite (a naturally occurring aluminum oxide ore), activated alumina (a synthetic product), silica gel beads, and molecular sieves. The latter is used only as a trimmer bed to assist in lowering the water content of the gas to the above value. All of these desiccants have performed satisfactorily. The choice depends on their cost, performance, and length of service before having to be replaced. Inadvertent fouling of the desic-

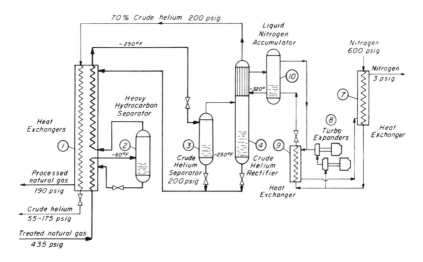

FIGURE 1.10.   *Typical crude helium extraction cycle of Bureau of Mines helium plant.*

cant beds by carryover of amine and glycol (particularly the gas entrant portion) sometimes occurs and may justify the use of a lower capacity, but less expensive, type of adsorbent, such as bauxite.

Crude Helium Separation: After pretreating the gas to remove carbon dioxide and water, it goes to low-temperature equipment housed in cold boxes (fig. 1.9) where separation of helium from the natural gas is made. The gas stream separated is a crude helium product. Steps of the process are illustrated schematically in figure 1.10. Treated natural gas enters the main gas heat exchangers, 1, at about 435 psi and is cooled first to about −60 F. It then enters a separator, 2, where the condensed heavy hydrocarbons are separated and returned through heat exchangers to the processed gas stream. Removal of heavy hydrocarbons from the inlet gas prevents the formation of plugs later in the process, due to possible solidification in the colder parts of the process equipment. The combination of adequate gas pretreating and heavy-hydrocarbon separation assures virtually trouble-free operation from freezeups. Units have been on stream without need for shutdown because of freeze-plugs for as long as one year's continuous operation.

After separation of heavy-hydrocarbons in separator, 2, the vapor phase is directed to additional heat exchangers and cooled further to about −250 F. This gas stream is then throttled into a separator, 3, maintained at a pressure of 100 to 225 psi, depending on optimum processing conditions at individual plants. The gas phase from this separator is cooled and rectified with liquid nitrogen refrigeration in the rectifier,

FIGURE 1.11. *Helium purification units at Keyes Helium Plant.*

4, before being removed as a crude helium product consisting of about 60–70 percent helium, 30–40 percent nitrogen, small amounts of methane and hydrogen, and a trace of neon. The separator pressure is maintained at the lowest pressure consistent with good helium separation efficiency and adequate to accommodate return of the processed gas through heat exchangers and redelivery to a pipeline, or other disposition. The natural gas liquids from the gas separator, 3, and rectifier, 4, are throttled to the return path of the main gas heat exchangers for counter-current heat exchange with inlet gas. The crude helium product is also returned, at about 100–200 psi, through the main gas heat exchangers in counter-current heat exchange with inlet gas.

Helium Purification: Purification of crude helium is accomplished by additional low-temperature processing steps. Prior to purification, the hydrogen content of the crude helium stream is reduced to about 0.001 percent by catalytic oxidation. This step is accomplished at 50–175 psi and ambient temperature by the addition of a small amount of air to the crude helium stream just ahead of the hydrogen removal equipment. Addition of air is controlled automatically to provide consumption of all oxygen and to leave a residual hydrogen content in the crude helium of about 0.001 percent. The provision for all oxygen to be consumed is to avoid the possibility of its accumulation in the low-temperature system where it might inadvertently become mixed with hydrocarbons to create a potentially hazardous mixture. After the hydrogen content is reduced, the crude helium is dried with activated alumina and compressed to about 2700 psi. Lubricating oil, unavoidably introduced by oil-lubricated compressors, is removed in a charcoal filter at ambient temperature and the stream is passed again through alumina-filled driers. Clean, dry, high-pressure crude helium is then fed to the purification units. These are shown in figure 1.11.

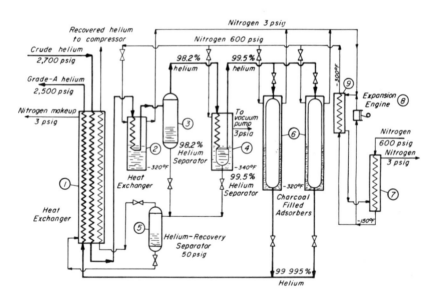

FIGURE 1.12.   *Typical cycle for crude helium purification to Grade-A helium in Bureau of Mines Helium Plant.*

Figure 1.12 shows the helium purification cycle schematically. Crude helium at 2700 psi and ambient temperature enters main heat exchanger, 1, and is cooled by counter-current heat exchange with three effluent streams. Sources of these streams are described later. The inlet crude helium stream is cooled to about −320 F, and its temperature is stabilized at this temperature by a liquid nitrogen bath in heat exchanger, 2. The liquids formed are separated in separator, 3. The vapor phase has a composition of 98.2 percent helium, 1.8 percent nitrogen, about 0.004 percent hydrogen, and 5–22 ppm of neon. This stream is cooled to about −340 F by a liquid nitrogen bath, 4, maintained at 3 psia (pounds-force per square inch absolute). Another phase separation is made, and the vapor phase has a composition of 99.5 percent helium, 0.5 percent nitrogen, 0.001 to 0.004 percent hydrogen, and a trace of neon. Condensed liquids in separator, 3, and separator, 4, are principally nitrogen, containing about 3.7 percent of dissolved helium. The liquid streams from these two separators are throttled to about 50 psi in separator, 5, where virtually all dissolved helium is released. The vapor phase from this separator is composed of about 37 percent helium and 63 percent nitrogen and is returned to main heat exchanger, 1, where it is warmed by counter-current heat exchange with inlet high-pressure crude helium. This helium-rich stream is then directed to the suction of the crude helium compressors for recycling and recovery. Liquid nitrogen from separator, 5, is also returned to the main heat exchanger where it is evaporated and warmed to ambient temperature by heat exchange with the inlet high-pressure crude helium. This stream is about 99.9 percent nitrogen and 0.1 percent helium and is the source of makeup nitrogen for the nitrogen refrigeration system.

Final purification of the 99.5 percent helium outlet stream from separator, 4, is accomplished by adsorption of the remaining impurities in one of two sets of charcoal-filled adsorbers, 6. These adsorbers are maintained at −320 F by a bath of liquid nitrogen, and the helium passed through them reaches a purity of at least 99.995 mole percent. Hydrogen remaining after the catalytic hydrogen-removal step described previously serves the purpose of signaling saturation of the charcoal used in final purification. Hydrogen is the first detectable impurity to appear in the effluent stream from the adsorbers. Detection of the first trace of hydrogen in the parts-per-million range by sensitive monitoring instruments signals the need to switch to regenerated charcoal in other adsorbers. After passage through the charcoal, the pure helium stream is directed to the main heat exchanger, warmed to ambient temperature, and sent directly to shipping containers or to diaphragm-type compressors when higher shipping container pressures are required.

Nitrogen Refrigeration Cycle: Nitrogen refrigeration required for both the crude helium separation units and the helium purification units is supplied by a Claude-type refrigeration cycle. Separate nitrogen refrigeration equipment is provided for the crude helium extraction and the crude helium purification cycles. These are shown in figures 1.10 and 1.12. The nitrogen compressors are common to both cycles, and the return low-pressure nitrogen streams from both cycles go to a common suction to the compressors.

In the nitrogen refrigeration cycle, nitrogen is compressed to about 600 psi, passed through a solid desiccant drier, and then the stream is divided, with part of it going to the crude helium separation cycle and part of it going to the helium purification cycle. Each part enters a heat exchanger, 7, where it is cooled to about −150 F by nitrogen streams leaving the cycles. Each stream is divided again with about 80 percent diverted to expansion engines or turbo expanders, 8. The remaining 20 percent goes to heat exchanger 9, where it is cooled to about −300 F. Liquid nitrogen is produced when this portion of the nitrogen stream is throttled from 600 psi to the low pressure of about 15 psi in the nitrogen accumulator, 10, (fig. 1.10) and the nitrogen baths around vessels, 2, 4, and 6 (fig. 1.12). Liquid nitrogen from accumulator, 10, flows by gravity head into the condensing section of crude helium rectifier, 4 (fig. 1.10). Flash vapors combined with nitrogen vapors from rectifier, 4, in the crude helium separation cycle and those produced from the various liquid nitrogen baths in the purification cycle join the respective expansion engine exhausts, return through nitrogen heat exchangers, 9 and 7, and are warmed to ambient temperature by counter-current heat exchange with the high-pressure inlet nitrogen.

1.6.2. Helium Quality and Quality Control

Many uses of helium require that it be of very high purity. Careful attention is given the production of helium and to the controls used to assure its quality at all of the Bureau of Mines helium plants.

Composition of Produced Helium: All helium produced at Bureau of Mines plants is 99.995 or higher mole percent helium, and is designated Grade-A helium. The total impurity is held to less than 50 ppm and is usually in the range of 20–25 ppm. The greater portion of this is neon, which is not completely removed in the purification process. It is present to the extent of about 15 ppm or less and is not considered objectionable in most helium uses.

Production Monitoring Methods: To assure that only Grade-A quality helium is produced, continuously recording instruments for checking on the presence of impurities are used. Specifically, these are supersensitive calorimeter-type instruments for detecting hydrogen in the range of 0–10 ppm and supersensitive thermal conductivity recorders capable of detecting 5 ppm nitrogen and measuring nitrogen in the range of 0–500 ppm. Chromatographic analyses of the pure helium stream with automatically programed chromatographic analyzers are also used and this use is increasing. These are capable of detecting and measuring neon, argon-oxygen, nitrogen, and methane impurities in helium when present to the extent of 5 ppm or less. The usual total impurity content of helium from the plant purification process is 20–25 ppm.

A check for water is made with a continuously recording electrolytic moisture analyzer [19]. Methods available for measuring very low water contents are not too exact, particularly near the zero ppm level; but tests made on helium from the helium purification process with the electrolytic moisture analyzer have consistently shown values of less than 1 ppm. This is to be expected, as 1 ppm is equivalent to a water dewpoint (ice point) of −105 F in a gas at atmospheric pressure, or about −55 F at 2700 psi. In the purification process, the helium emerges from charcoal adsorbers operated at a temperature of −320 F or lower while it is at a pressure of 2700 psi. Water vapor content at these conditions is less than any presently known method of testing can detect.

Methods Used to Prevent Contamination After Purification and to Assure Purity of Helium Shipped: Although helium from the purification process has a very low impurity content, careful handling is necessary to avoid introducing impurities during shipment, storage, and use.

To assist in controlling the quality of helium shipped, all shipping containers are required to be returned with a residual charge of Grade-A helium of not less than 15 psi pressure as a precaution against their becoming contaminated with air, with other gases, or with moisture.

Railway tank cars and highway tube trailers returned for filling are checked before filling by analyzing the contained residual helium. Supersensitive thermal conductivity instruments are used to determine the total impurities in the residual helium. Supersensitive gas analyzers check for traces of hydrogen and water. In addition, a sensitive chromatographic gas analyzer is used to doublecheck the presence or absence of gases other than helium.

If the results of the above checks are satisfactory, the container is filled with pure helium. If tests of residual helium in a returned tank car or trailer container show contamination, or if it is returned with valves open, the container is evacuated and purged with Grade-A helium until tests on the purging helium show that it will fill with Grade-A quality helium.

In the case of small cylinders returned for filling, it is not practical to check each cylinder before it is filled because of the large number of cylinders filled each day. In filling cylinders, they are placed on a filling rack, the residual helium contents are blown down — and recovered if tests show that it is 90 percent helium or better — and the cylinders are then evacuated to an absolute pressure of 1.25 inches of mercury. Without removing them from the rack, they are purged three times by filling them to 50 psi and then blown down to atmospheric pressure. They are then filled to about 300 psi pressure and the helium in the rack of cylinders is tested. To assure obtaining a representative sample, about 25 pounds pressure is discharged from the rack and the discharging helium is tested for impurities. If the tests show Grade-A quality helium, the cylinders are then filled to their rated shipping pressure of 1800–2600 psi. All purge helium is recovered.

To check further on the purity of helium shipped, a random sampling of about 10 percent of the cylinders filled is made, and their contents are analyzed on the aforementioned sensitive instruments. Statistical analysis applied to the results in 1966 showed that more than 99.7 percent of 208,485 cylinders shipped averaged less than 50 ppm total impurities and 91.1 percent averaged less than 25 ppm.

Helium Trace-Impurity Analysis Method: A further routine check of helium shipped in small cylinders is made by analyzing each month about 40 of these cylinders by a more precise and specific method developed by the Bureau of Mines [20]. In this method, all of the impurities contained in a sample of 1 or more liters of the helium to be tested are solidified and recovered in a trap maintained at liquid helium temperature. The impurities thus isolated and concentrated are analyzed with a mass spectrometer. From the analysis and a knowledge of the degree of concentration of the impurities, it is possible to compute impurities in the original sample in the parts-per-million range. The data shown in table 1.2 were obtained by this method. They show the average impurities found in the 402 cylinders analyzed under this program in 1966.

TABLE 1.2.   *Average impurities in Grade-A helium, ppm*

Number cylinders analyzed	H_2O	H_2	Ne	N_2	O_2	A	CO_2	Total ppm
402	2.4	0.1	14.2	2.1	0.4	0.05	0.05	19.3

The moisture content of the shipped helium depends on the internal condition of the shipping container with respect to moisture. As the helium put into the container is completely dry, any moisture in the container, even though it may be only adsorbed moisture on the container's internal surface, will be picked up by the helium until the partial pressure of water vapor in the helium comes into equilibrium with the vapor pressure of the adsorbed water on the container wall surfaces. Analysis for moisture in the helium is made with an electrolytic moisture analyzer [19] mentioned earlier.

Quality Control at Point of Use: In transferring helium from shipping containers or from storage, adequate precautions against its contamination should be taken. All connecting pipelines should be purged with helium. This should be done at low pressure to minimize wastage of helium and to achieve a high lineal velocity of gas flow to aid in blowing dust or scale from the line. Lines should not be left open to the atmosphere after purging. Atmospheric air always contains water vapor, and the dry internal surface of pipe that has been in Grade-A helium service will adsorb water vapor if exposed to air and will release it to the dry helium when the line is returned to helium service.

Care should be taken to avoid backflow of gas from systems to which helium containers are connected because it could cause contamination of the helium and containers. Obviously, where the standards of helium purity are high, it takes only a very small amount of another gas to exceed the allowable impurity level.

1.6.3. Helium Handling and Storage

It is not difficult to handle Grade-A helium without contamination or loss if careful attention is given to procedures and equipment.

Helium Piping, Valves, and Compressors: Despite helium's leakage rate, which is higher than most other gases, through minute cracks or openings, it may be shipped, stored, and handled by distribution lines with negligible loss, provided good equipment and materials are used and reasonable care is taken. Maximum use of welded, brazed, or soldered connections, choice of good quality valves, and systematic and frequent tests for leakage are required. In the past, packless valves have been used on many shipping containers; but with the development of more suitable valve stem packing materials and valve designs, packed stem valves are coming into greater use because they offer advantages of easier operation and lower maintenance costs. Valves having a soft seat serve best where tight close-off is needed. Generally, they are not as serviceable, however, as valves having metal-to-metal plug and seat where throttling from a higher pressure to a lower pressure is involved.

Conventional compressor equipment can be used if choice is made of first class equipment and proper consideration is given to packings and other areas of potential leaks. Because of the necessity of avoiding contamination of high-purity helium, special attention to this matter is required. Oil-lubricated compressors may be used providing adequate cleanup equipment is used after compression. Some users of helium have experienced high-temperature breakdown of compressor oil, which results in hydrocarbon gas contamination of the helium. Such contamination may not be easily and effectively removed by the cleanup equipment; therefore, careful attention should be given this matter. Compressors are available that use Teflon or Kel-F piston rings which need no lubrication. Compressors of the diaphragm-type are used by the Bureau of Mines to compress pure helium. This method of compressing Grade-A helium has been completely satisfactory. Careful maintenance attention is given and effective warning and safety devices are provided to preclude carryover of oil, should there be any rupture of the diaphragms used in the compressors.

Fixed Storage: Storage vessels of seamless pipe, with welded heads and welded connections, and pressure vessels of conventionally welded construction are in common use for helium storage. Most helium storage pressures are in the range of 2000 to 6000 psi. Higher pressures have been used or contemplated at some points of helium distribution or use.

1.6.4. Helium Transportation

Large investment costs for shipping containers and high transportation costs have prompted strong consideration of other methods or improved equipment for helium shipments as possible means of reducing costs. The three most promising methods are (1) shipment in compressed gas containers of greater capacity, (2) shipment of helium as a liquid, and (3) transportation of helium by pipeline. Some significant developments have been made with regard to all three methods and more may be expected in the future.

Three types of containers — railway tank cars, highway tube trailers, and small cylinders — are used for shipping compressed gaseous helium. These are shown in figure 1.13. In 1966, about 80 percent of the helium shipped from Bureau of Mines helium production plants was in railway tank cars. In some instances, the cars are shipped to points where the helium is distributed to users. At these points, helium is transferred

FIGURE 1.13.   *Equipment used in transporting gaseous helium — railway tank car, highway
tube trailer, and standard compressed gas cylinders.*

from the railway cars to tube trailers or cylinders for delivery to individual customers at points where it is used, or is placed in storage
vessels for later use as needed. Shipment of helium from production
plants in tube trailers has some economic advantages when the shipping
points are within about 700 miles of the helium production plants, and
trailers are commonly used for that service. General use of trailers is
growing because they offer advantages of mobility and other convenience at point of use. Small cylinders are used to make deliveries of
helium where the quantities are small or where the use of small cyl-

inders is of advantage to the customer. Most small cylinder shipments are made by motor freight.

Railway Tank Cars: Railway tank cars used for shipping compressed gaseous helium range in capacity from 240,000 to 345,000 cubic feet and have service pressures ranging from 2200 to 4000 psi. In the late 1950's and early 1960's, the capacity of railway tank cars for gaseous helium was increased about 20 to 30 percent by improved design and higher allowable filling pressures. A further increase in capacity of up to 30 percent has been predicted by use of a single large cylinder of welded multilayer construction.

In 1966, the Bureau had 233 railway tank cars in service. Their cost at that time was about $100,000 each. A few are leased to large commercial purchasers of Bureau-produced helium. They use them to ship helium from Bureau of Mines plants to distribution points where the helium is unloaded into highway tube trailers or small compressed gas cylinders for delivery to their customers, or is put into fixed storage for later sale.

Highway Tube Trailers: About 12 percent of the helium sold by the Bureau of Mines in 1966 was delivered in highway tube trailers. The Bureau owned seven trailers, ranging in capacity from 98,000 to 137,000 cubic feet each. The service pressure rating of these trailers is 2640 to 2810 psi. Many helium users also own and use helium tube trailers. The higher capacity trailers became available in the early 1960's as a result of improved design and use of higher strength materials, which allowed higher filling pressures, and of higher permissible weight loads on highways.

Small Compressed Gas Cylinders: In 1966, the Bureau of Mines had approximately 103,000 small standard compressed gas cylinders in Grade-A helium service. A large number of additional cylinders, owned by various helium users and gas distributing companies, were in use for transporting helium. The service pressure rating of the small cylinders ranges from 1800 to 2640 psi. Somewhat more than 8 percent of the helium sold by the Bureau in 1965 was shipped in small cylinders.

Liquid Helium Transportation: The Bureau of Mines has not shipped any helium as a liquid, but some commercial companies liquefy helium and ship it in that form. The new helium plant of the Kansas Refined Helium Company at Otis, Kans., is equipped with a helium liquefier large enough to liquefy the entire product of the plant, about 450,000 cubic feet per day. Most of the helium produced at this plant is shipped as a liquid. The Alamo Chemical Company plant near Elkhart, Kans.,

COST OF HELIUM SHIPMENT

also has a liquefier large enough to liquefy all the helium it produces, and most of the helium will be shipped as a liquid. Further information on liquid helium shipment is given in chapter 5.

Helium Transportation by Pipeline: Relatively small and relatively short pipelines of 2-inch size and up to 90 miles in length have been used by the Bureau of Mines to transport Grade-A helium between some of its helium production facilities. These pipelines are operated at 2500 psi pressure. Economic use of pipelines for transporting large quantities of helium from points of production to markets would be greatly dependent on the stability and continuity of such markets served by the fixed pipeline transportation system, the load factor, and length of amortization period for the investment. The principal artery of such pipeline systems would need to serve strategically located terminals where the helium would be used, or from which further distribution could be made. The cost of such further distribution would need to be added to obtain the overall cost of this form of transporting and delivering helium. Where the aforementioned conditions are favorable, a pipeline system could offer economic benefits in the transportation and marketing of helium.

1.6.5. Cost of Helium Shipment

Helium production plants must be situated where a suitable helium supply is available and cannot, like plants producing oxygen or nitrogen, be arbitrarily located close to the point of use. All of the present helium plants in the United States are situated in the central part of the country, while the largest helium users are on the east and west coasts. The relatively long distances between points of production and markets, together with some other conditions, make shipping time and costs major considerations in helium distribution.

Cost of Gaseous Helium Shipment: Shipment of helium as a compressed gas requires the movement of heavy containers. Railway tank cars weigh about 240,000 pounds each. The shipping charges are based on a lading weight of 40,000 pounds. The cars contain an average of 275,000 standard cubic feet of helium. Highway tube semitrailers are transported on a mileage basis without regard to the weight of the trailer. Their helium-carrying capacity ranges from 98,000 to 137,000 cubic feet. Standard compressed gas cylinders weigh about 130 pounds each and contain 213–242 cubic feet.

TABLE 1.3. *Typical transportation costs in 1966 for transportation of gaseous helium (costs per Mcf of helium shipped in tank cars, tube trailers, and small cylinders to selected destinations from Bureau of Mines plants)*

Destination	Tank cars	Tube trailers	Small cylinders	Approximate round-trip miles
Abilene, Tex................	$1.67	$1.68	$15.55	600
Denver, Colo................	2.15	2.55	14.75	800
Topeka, Kans...............	2.32	2.63	30.32	1,000
New Orleans, La..........	3.73	5.05	33.37	1,750
Chicago, Ill.................	3.80	5.94	15.43	2,000
Huntsville, Ala.............	4.27	6.28	21.63	2,200
Los Angeles, Calif.........	5.94	6.58	25.01	2,250
Knoxville, Tenn............	4.74	6.83	48.19	2,500
Cleveland, Ohio............	4.77	7.62	35.44	2,650
Sacramento, Calif..........	6.17	8.39	25.74	3,000
Cape Kennedy, Fla.........	5.57	8.54	54.90	3,200
Portland, Oreg.............	7.24	9.95	43.29	3,375
Newark, N.J................	6.15	9.90	19.21	3,400
Boston, Mass...............	6.54	11.34	64.66	4,100

NOTE: Capacities of shipping containers assumed to be 275 Mcf for tank cars which was average capacity of cars in use; 125 Mcf for trailers which was representative of late-model trailers in use; and 213 cf for small cylinders. Cylinder quantities are less than truckload. Transportation costs include "use charge" of 11 cents per mile for tank cars and $15 per day for trailers. (M = Roman numeral 1000.)

The shipping costs differ greatly, depending on the type of shipping container used, so the shipping costs per unit volume of helium shipped are greatly different. Table 1.3 gives typical transportation costs in 1966 for transportation of gaseous helium in tank cars, tube trailers, and small cylinders to selected points from Bureau of Mines helium production plants.

Cost of Liquid Helium Shipment: Chapter 5 covers shipment of helium as a liquid. When large volumes of helium are required at a single destination or where the helium can be offloaded at convenient points en route on a particular trip, shipping costs by this method can be lower than by any other means. Where helium is shipped as a liquid only to save on transportation costs, the liquefaction cost has to be taken into consideration. Sometimes additional benefits accrue to help justify this type of transportation.

A study made by the Bureau of Mines on the economics of shipping helium as a liquid showed that where reasonably large quantities of helium were needed and the use rate at a given location was high, savings in shipping costs by this method would more than offset the cost of liquefaction. Confirmation of this is indicated in chapter 5.

1.6.6. Helium Prices and Regulations Governing Sale

Prices paid for helium by the ultimate consumer vary with the users' geographical locations, quantities purchased, and other conditions. In 1966 the delivered price was in the range of $40 to $90 per thousand cubic feet. The prices charged by the Bureau of Mines f.o.b. its production plants from 1955 to 1960, which were based on total cost of production (including amortization and interest), were $15.50 and $19.00 per thousand cubic feet to Federal and non-Federal purchasers, respectively. In 1961, the price to both Federal and non-Federal consumers was increased to $35 per thousand cubic feet in order to provide additional revenue required for long-range financing of the comprehensive helium conservation program that was initiated at that time. This price was still in effect in 1966.

Regulations governing sale of helium by the Bureau of Mines are issued periodically by the Secretary of the Interior. These regulations cover conditions of sale and establish prices for helium, rental rates for shipping containers, and various service charges.

Conversion Table

1 psi $= 6894.8$ newton/meter^2

1 ft$^3 = 0.02832$ meter^3

1 gal $= 0.003785$ meter^3

$$T_K = (T_F + 459.67)/1.8$$

REFERENCES

[1] C. C. Anderson and H. H. Hinson, Helium-bearing natural gases of the United States — Analyses and analytical methods, Bureau of Mines Bull. 486 (1951), 141 pp.

[2] W. J. Boone, Helium-bearing natural gases of the United States — Analyses and analytical methods, Supplement to Bulletin 486, Bureau of Mines Bull. 576 (1958), 119 pp.

[3] R. D. Munnerlyn and R. D. Miller, Helium-bearing natural gases of the United States — Analyses, second Suppl. to Bull. 486, Bureau of Mines Bull. 617 (1963), 93 pp.

[4] R. D. Miller and G. P. Norrell, Analyses of natural gases of the United States, 1961, Bureau of Mines Information Circ. 8221 (1964), 148 pp.

[5] R. D. Miller and G. P. Norrell, Analyses of natural gases of the United States, 1962, Bureau of Mines Information Circ. 8239 (1964), 121 pp.

[6] R. D. Miller and G. P. Norrell, Analyses of natural gases of the United States, 1963, Bureau of Mines Information Circ. 8241 (1965), 102 pp.

[7] B. J. Moore, R. D. Miller, and R. D. Shrewsbury, Analyses of natural gases of the United States, 1964, Bureau of Mines Information Circ. 8302 (1966), 144 pp.

[8] Canadian helium to lose present market in Europe, Oil Week, Nov. 1, 1965, p. 14.

[9] P. K. Smith and H. S. Pylant, Helium plant in commercial operation, Oil and Gas J., Oct. 29, 1962, pp. 136–139.

[10] High on Helium, Chemical Week, May 8, 1965, p. 26.

[11] G. D. Kinney, World's biggest helium plant opens, Oil and Gas J., Sept. 30, 1963, pp. 54–61.

[12] S. Weller and W. A. Steiner, Engineering aspects of separation of gases — Fractional Permeation Through Membranes, Chem. Eng. Prog. 46, 585 (Nov. 1950).

[13] S. A. Stern, T. F. Sinclair, P. J. Garies, N. P. Vahldieck, and P. H. Mohr, Helium recovery by permeation, Ind. Eng. Chem. 57, 49 (Feb. 1965).

[14] D. R. Huffman and R. J. Robinson, Method of separating helium from other constituents of natural gas, U.S. Patent 3,239,996 (Mar. 15, 1966).

[15] E. I. duPont de Nemours & Co., Inc., Private communication (Oct. 31, 1966).

[16] K. B. McAfee, Jr., Bell Labs. Record 38, 354 (1960).

[17] N. Melnyk and H. W. Habgood, Extraction of helium from natural gas. The diffusion-through-glass process, Can. Mining and Metallurgical Bull. (Oct. 1961), pp. 768–774.

[18] David Frazier, Helium separation, U.S. Patent 3,184,899 (May 25, 1965).

[19] F. A. Keidel, Determination of water by direct amperometric measurement, Anal. Chem. 31, No. 12, pp. 2043–2048 (Dec. 1959).

[20] C. G. Kirkland, L. W. Brandt, and W. M. Deaton, Determining trace impurities in grade-A helium, Bureau of Mines Report of Investigations 5644 (1960), 12 pp.

CHAPTER 2

Properties of Helium

D. B. Mann [1]

[1] Cryogenics Division, NBS Institute for Basic Standards, Boulder, Colo. 80302.

Critical analysis of helium refrigeration and liquefaction processes requires an extensive knowledge of the variation of the thermophysical properties. The ideal gas relation, $PV = nRT$, gives a good approximation of physical properties at low pressures and ambient temperatures, but when dealing with processes which extend over broad ranges — as in the case of a cryogenic process, from ambient to near absolute zero — it is necessary to know property values to a high degree of accuracy. Internal consistency of the data is of equal importance to the engineer charged with equipment design and evaluation.

It is the purpose of this chapter to supply the necessary thermo-physical properties over an entire range of temperatures (3 to 300 K) and pressures (0.5 to 100 atmospheres*) useful to a critical description of processes involving liquid helium and liquid helium temperatures. It should be specifically mentioned that this chapter does not deal with superfluid properties. Additional engineering properties such as viscosity and thermal conductivity are included where broad range correlations exist. These data are most useful in support of design calculations of chapters 3 and 4.

---

*Atmosphere (normal = 760 torr) = 1.01325×10^5 N/m².

2.1. PRESSURE-VOLUME-TEMPERATURE SURFACE

2.1.1. Origin of Data and Correlation Methods

The work of Keesom [1][2] assembled and in most cases correlated the experimental property data through 1941. Akin [2], using the Beattie-Bridgeman equation of state and data derived from Keesom, presented thermodynamic properties of helium for temperatures extending from 590 K down to about 12 K and to quite high gas densities.

Lounasmaa [3] provided experimental data which indicated that the virial form of the equation of state used by Keesom was somewhat inadequate in representing the properties for densities greater than the critical density at temperatures below 20 K. Mann and Stewart [4] correlated these data of Lounasmaa with those of Keesom [1], Berman and Mate [5], and Domb and Dugdale [6]. The results of this correlation were presented in graphical form for the temperature region 3 to 20 K.

The work of Edeskuty and Sherman [7] provided experimental data at 4.2 K and below and up to densities in excess of three times the critical density.

Correlation of the applicable data of these more recent investigators with those of Keesom will give a continuous representation of properties extending from 3 to 300 K and pressures to 100 atm.

The following is a list of symbols and definitions used in this chapter:

C_p^* molar specific heat of helium gas at very low pressures. Assumed to be numerically equal to $5/2\ R$ J/g-mol-K.

C_{sat} specific heat of liquid helium at saturation conditions $=$ J/g. mol-K.

ρ mass concentration (density)$=$ g-mol/liter.

H enthalpy $=$ J/g-mol.

H_0 enthalpy value of liquid helium at the conditions $T=0$ K, $P=$ zero.

H_L enthalpy value at the conditions $T=4.2144$ K (normal boiling point, T_{55E}), $P=1$ atm, saturated liquid.

P absolute pressure $=$ atmospheres.

S entropy $=$ J/g-mol-K.

S_0 entropy of liquid helium at the conditions $T=0$ K, and $P=$ zero, assumed to be numerically equal to zero.

---

[2] Figures in brackets indicate the literature references at the end of this chapter.

S_L entropy value at the conditions $T = 4.2144$ K (normal boiling point, T_{55E}), $P = 1$ atm, saturated liquid.

T temperature = degrees Kelvin.

U internal energy = J/g-mol.

V molar volume = liters/g-mol.

Z compressibility factor $= \dfrac{P}{\rho R T}$

The temperature scale is that designated by the symbol T_{55E} [Clement, Logan, and Gaffney [8]]. Molar volumes are used to correlate data and then are converted to units of density. Constants and conversion factors are as follows:

One atmosphere $= 1.013250 \times 10^5$ N/m²
R (gas constant) $= 8.20575 \times 10^{-2}$ liter-atm/g-mol-K
                              (chemical scale)
                            $= 8.31424$ J/g-mol-K
One calorie (thermochemical) $= 4.1840$ J
One liter (old) $= 1.000028 \times 10^{-3}$ m³

The equation of state developed to describe the pressure-density-temperature surface is based on the equation of Benedict-Webb-Rubbin [9] (BWR) as modified for nitrogen by Strobridge [10] and further modified here for helium. With pressure as the dependent variable, the equation is

$$P = R\rho T + \left(Rn_1 T + n_2 + \frac{n_3}{T} + \frac{n_4}{T^2} + \frac{n_5}{T^4} \right)\rho^2 + (Rn_6 T + n_7)\rho^3$$

$$+ n_8\rho^4 + \left(\frac{n_9}{T^2} + \frac{n_{10}}{T^3} + \frac{n_{11}}{T^4} \right)\rho^3 e^{-n_{12}\rho^2/T}$$

$$+ \left(\frac{n_{13}}{T^2} + \frac{n_{14}}{T^3} + \frac{n_{15}}{T^4} \right)\rho^5 e^{-n_{12}\rho^2/T} + n_{16}\rho^5 + n_{17}\rho^6. \qquad (2.1)$$

Values for the constants are as follows:

$R =$ 0.820575 (10^{-1}) $n_4 = -0.1887566673(10^{-1})$
$n_1 =$ 0.1627693557(10^{-1}) $n_5 =$ 0.4792344640(10^{-1})
$n_2 = -0.3700903492(10^{-1})$ $n_6 =$ 0.1560344984(10^{-3})
$n_3 =$ 0.7567259965(10^{-2}) $n_7 =$ 0.9274298542(10^{-3})

$$n_8 = -0.2833997045(10^{-4})$$
$$n_9 = -0.5002871627(10^{-2})$$
$$n_{10} = 0.3451283837(10^{-1})$$
$$n_{11} = 0.1008924438(10^{0})$$
$$n_{12} = 0.65 \quad (10^{-2})$$

$$n_{13} = -0.1851562535(10^{-4})$$
$$n_{14} = 0.4204351888(10^{-4})$$
$$n_{15} = -0.1712445150(10^{-3})$$
$$n_{16} = 0.7739390202(10^{-6})$$
$$n_{17} = -0.2870693948(10^{-8})$$

A least squares method developed by Jones and Gallet [11] and programmed for use on a digital computer was used to determine the values of these constants. Because the constant n_{12} appears in the exponential term, it was necessary to select several values for this constant and solve for the set of constants which gave the minimum in the sum of squares of deviations. The resulting best fit for the data was only slightly affected by changes in the value of the constant n_{12}, but it was found necessary to carry the maximum number of places in the derived constants to assure internal consistency and reproducibility.

Data used for the least squares treatment consisted of 695 pressure, density, and temperature points. These points were taken from the following published works.

Berman and Mate [5]: Thirty-eight data points were used to describe the saturated vapor and saturated liquid conditions. Temperatures range from 2.2 to 5.18 K.

Edeskuty and Sherman [7]: Eighty-eight data points were used to describe the compressed liquid region from 2.2 to 4.2 K. Pressures range from 1 to 140 atm and the highest density values are in excess of three times the critical density.

Hill and Lounasmaa (HL) [12]: A total of 258 experimental data points was used to describe the rather broad temperature and pressure region from about 2.5 to 20 K. Pressures range from 1 to 102 atm with density values extending to three times the critical density.

Keesom [1]: The virial equation of state and the values for the coefficients adopted by Keesom were used to obtain 311 pressure-density-temperature points along 29 isotherms extending from 3.1 to 574 K. Pressure-density-temperature points having densities greater than the critical density were excluded because of the divergence of the equation of state values for pressure from the experimental values of (HL) [12] in the region of the 20 K isotherm.

Except for the two-phase region described by Berman and Mate [5], overlapping of the data regions was extensive.

2.1.2. Pressure-Density Diagram

Figure 2.1 is a plot of pressure versus density for isotherms from 3 to 30 K. The density changes most rapidly in this temperature range. The graph was plotted using eq (2.1).

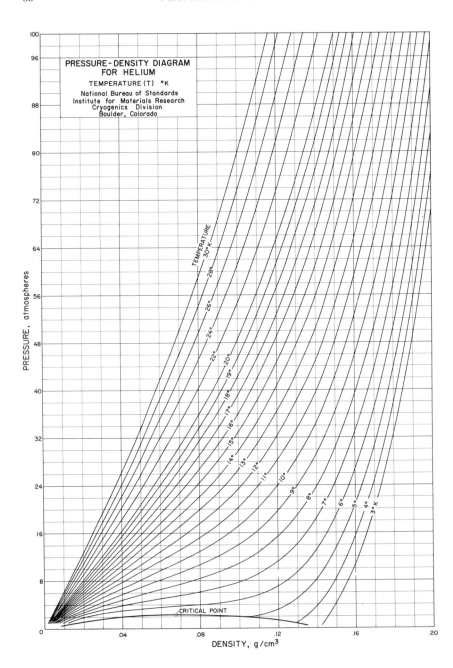

FIGURE 2.1. *Pressure-density diagram.*

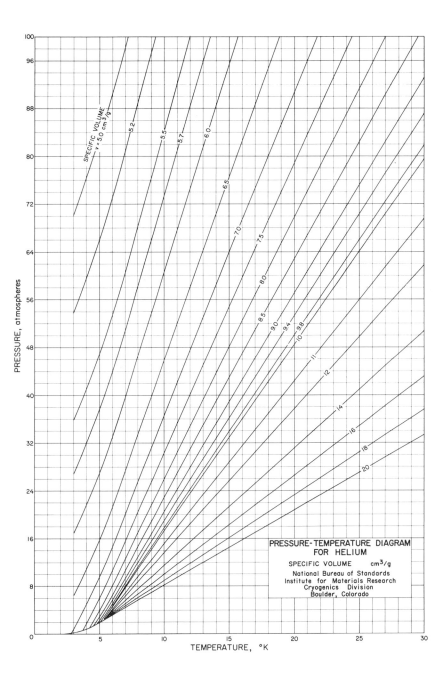

FIGURE 2.2. *Pressure-temperature diagram.*

2.1.3. Pressure-Temperature Diagram

Figure 2.2 is a plot of the data of figure 2.1 on the coordinate system pressure versus temperature. The pressure and temperature data cover the same ranges as figure 2.1 and with specific volume varying from 5 cm³/g to 20 cm³/g. The two-phase liquid-vapor boundary is also indicated.

2.2. THERMODYNAMIC FUNCTIONS

2.2.1. Derived Functions

The property functions of enthalpy, entropy, and internal energy for the single-phase fluid region were calculated using only the equation for the pressure-density-temperature surface, eq (2.1). This procedure was necessary in the absence of specific heat measurements over the entire range of interest. Equations used to calculate these properties are shown below. (For a complete derivation of the equations, the reader is referred to Beattie [13].)

$$H = H_0^\circ + \int_{T=0}^{T} C_p^* dT + (Z-1)RT + \int_0^{\rho} \left[\frac{P}{\rho^2} - \frac{T}{\rho^2} \left(\frac{\partial P}{\partial T} \right)_\rho \right] d\rho \qquad (2.2)$$

$$S = S_0^\circ + \int_{T=0}^{T} \frac{C_p^*}{T} dT - R \ln \frac{P}{Z} + \int_0^{\rho} \left[\frac{R}{\rho} - \frac{1}{\rho^2} \left(\frac{\partial P}{\partial T} \right)_\rho \right] d\rho \qquad (2.3)$$

$$U = H - \frac{P}{\rho}. \qquad (2.4)$$

The values of H_0° (36.5582 J/g-mol) and S_0° (9.2609 J/g-mol-K) are the reference enthalpy and entropy of the ideal gas evaluated at the normal boiling point temperature (4.2144 K) and 1 atm.

The values of enthalpy, entropy, and internal energy of the saturated liquid given in table 2.1 were taken from Mann and Stewart [4]. These values were found by graphically integrating the expressions

$$H - H_0 = \int_{T=0}^{T} C_{\text{sat}} dT + \int_{P=0}^{P} \frac{dP}{\rho}, \qquad (2.5)$$

$$S - S_0 = \int_{T=0}^{T} \frac{C_{\text{sat}}}{T} dT. \qquad (2.6)$$

TABLE 2.1. *Properties of helium, two-phase liquid-vapor region*

Tem-pera-ture	Pres-sure	Saturated vapor				Saturated liquid			
		v	h	u	s	v	h	u	s
K	Atm	cm^3/g	J/g	J/g	$J/gm\text{-}K$	cm^3/g	J/g	J/g	$J/g\text{-}K$
3.00	0.241	224.11	28.96	23.49	10.247	7.0852	5.30	5.13	2.356
3.20	0.320	174.83	29.48	23.81	9.911	7.1849	5.85	5.62	2.527
3.40	0.416	138.70	29.93	24.08	9.606	7.3025	6.47	6.16	2.690
3.60	0.529	111.48	30.34	24.36	9.322	7.4388	7.18	6.78	2.883
3.80	0.661	90.50	30.59	24.53	9.021	7.5965	7.93	7.40	3.059
4.00	0.814	73.86	30.72	24.63	8.736	7.7785	8.81	8.17	3.255
4.20	0.990	60.61	30.79	24.71	8.443	7.9885	9.85	9.05	3.460
4.40	1.190	49.80	30.65 ·	24.65	8.150	8.2305	10.96	9.97	3.674
4.60	1.417	40.72	30.32	24.47	7.845	8.5470	12.33	11.10	3.920
4.80	1.672	32.87	29.49	23.92	7.473	9.0334	13.88	12.35	4.188
5.00	1.959	25.67	28.02	22.92	7.000	9.9404	16.00	14.03	4.598

The specific heat of saturated liquid (C_{sat}) was taken from Hill and Lounasmaa (HL) [14].

Equation (2.1) was developed starting with the work of Lounasmaa [3]. This publication presented the derived constants for the BWR equation of state using the data obtained experimentally by HL [12]. As the data range was extended, the BWR equation was also modified as necessary. The temperature-pressure region 4.8 to 5.8 K and 1.8 to 2.8 atm was less accurately reproduced as this modification proceeded to the form of (2.1). The reasons for this decrease in accuracy was the inability of the developed equation to represent exactly the form of the critical isotherm at or near the critical pressure.

The effect of this problem was twofold. Properties defined by (2.1), (2.2), (2.3), and (2.4) in this temperature and pressure region were found to have substantial errors. In addition, the integration, indicated by (2.2) and (2.3), for the values of derived properties at densities greater than the critical density and at pressures greater than 2.8 atm resulted in substantial errors at temperatures near the critical point.

To eliminate these errors, the properties were derived using (2.1), (2.2), (2.3), and (2.4) for temperatures of 6 K and above for densities greater than critical density and for temperatures approaching the saturated vapor conditions at densities less than the critical density.

Equations (2.2) and (2.3) were then modified so as to substitute for the lower limit of integration the values for the properties along the saturated liquid region. Equations (2.7) and (2.8) indicate this modification and, with (2.4), are the equations used to derive properties at pressures greater than the critical pressure and at temperatures less than 6 K:

$$\Delta S = \int_{\rho_{\text{sat}}}^{\rho} \left[-\frac{1}{\rho^2} \left(\frac{\partial P}{\partial T} \right)_{\rho} \right]_T d\rho \qquad (2.7)$$

$$\Delta H = \frac{P}{\rho} - \left(\frac{P}{\rho_{\text{sat}}} \right) + \int_{\rho_{\text{sat}}}^{\rho} \left[\frac{P}{\rho^2} - \frac{T}{\rho^2} \left(\frac{\partial P}{\partial T} \right)_{\rho} \right]_T d\rho \qquad (2.8)$$

Isobars were then plotted graphically on temperature-entropy and temperature-enthalpy coordinates. The entropy change along the isochore 30.93 g-mole/liter was computed from 4.75 to 10 K using the specific heat data of HL [12] and the expression

$$\Delta S = \int_{T_1}^{T_2} \frac{C_v}{T} dT, \qquad (2.9)$$

where C_v is the specific heat at constant volume. The intersections of the isobars with this isochore given by HL [12] were noted as the temperature was increased.

A correction for the properties along the 5 and 6 K isotherms was determined and the tabulated data were adjusted to be consistent with the above-described specific heat data of HL [12]. In addition, the 2-atm isobar was plotted from HL [12] in the region of the critical values and the tabulated properties obtained directly from this plot.

Values taken from the pressure-density-temperature surface described by (2.1) and the derived properties found from (2.2) through (2.9) are tabulated by Mann [15] as functions of pressure and temperature. Forty isobars are presented covering the range 0.5 to 100 atm. One degree increments of temperature are given except at the two-phase boundaries, and, in general, extend from 3 to 300 K. Values listed in the tables are specific, not molar, quantities. The molecular weight of helium was taken as 4.0028.

It was found that a better representation of the pressure-density-temperature surface could be achieved by considering a number of restricted ranges of temperature and pressure when defining the constants of (2.1), but this procedure would then require the fitting and smoothing of several property surfaces. It was felt that the surface matching would not increase the accuracy of the tabulated values over the entire range of interest by a factor that could justify the extensive data manipulation required.

The pressure-density-temperature surface described by (2.1) fit the original data to varying degrees of accuracy depending on the temperature and pressure region considered. In general, the ability of (2.1) to reproduce the original data is less accurate in the regions of phase change, and in particular, in the region of the critical point. As mentioned above, the liquid-vapor region was handled graphically in an attempt to reduce the error in this region.

In the temperature region 10 to 300 K the accuracy of the values of pressure, density, enthalpy, and entropy is estimated to be within 3 percent while internal energy values may vary somewhat more.

Below 10 K and at low pressures the properties of enthalpy, entropy, internal energy, and pressure are accurate to an estimated error of 3 percent, while density may have an uncertainty of as much as 5 percent. At higher pressures the density is defined to within the estimated 3 percent, but the pressures may be in error as much as 5 percent.

Values for the specific heats of helium derived from the graphs are estimated to be within 5 percent in the temperature range 10 to 300 K. It is not recommended that specific heats be extracted from the graphs at temperature levels below 10 K.

2.2.2. Temperature-Entropy Diagram

Figures 2.3 and 2.4 are plots of the physical and thermodynamic properties of helium on temperature-entropy coordinates. Two charts are used to give clarity in presentation of the data below 25 degrees. The charts are overlapping in temperature between 25 and 15 K. It will be noted that the area in the region of the critical has not been defined. This is caused by the lack of data in this region and the inability of (2.1) to predict properties in this pressure temperature region.

2.2.3. Enthalpy-Entropy Diagram

The enthalpy-entropy diagram of figure 2.5 will aid in the design of equipment operating below 25 K. Where the temperature-entropy diagram of figures 2.3 and 2.4 aid in describing thermodynamic cycles, the design parameters for the critical low-temperature heat exchangers can best be found using the enthalpy-entropy plot.

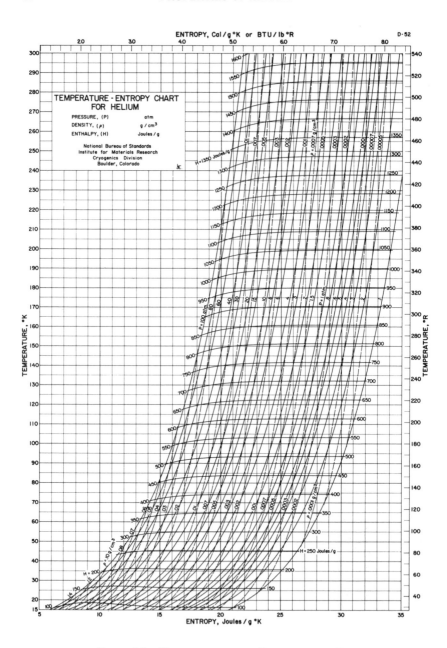

FIGURE 2.3.   *Temperature-entropy diagram, 15–300 K.*

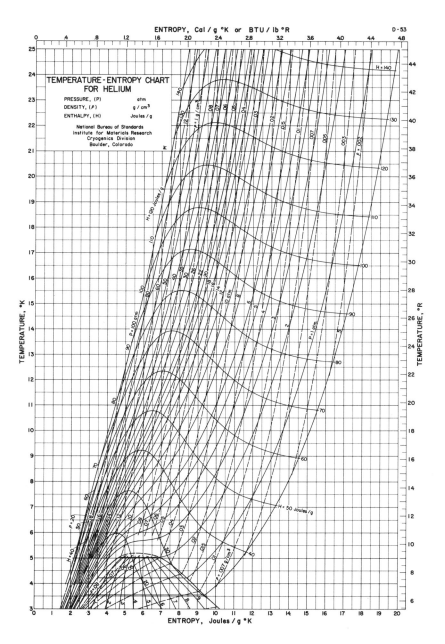

FIGURE 2.4.   *Temperature-entropy diagram, 3–25 K.*

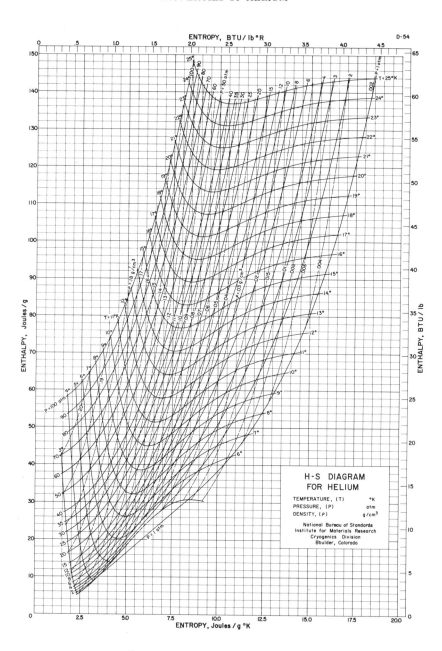

FIGURE 2.5. *Enthalpy-entropy diagram.*

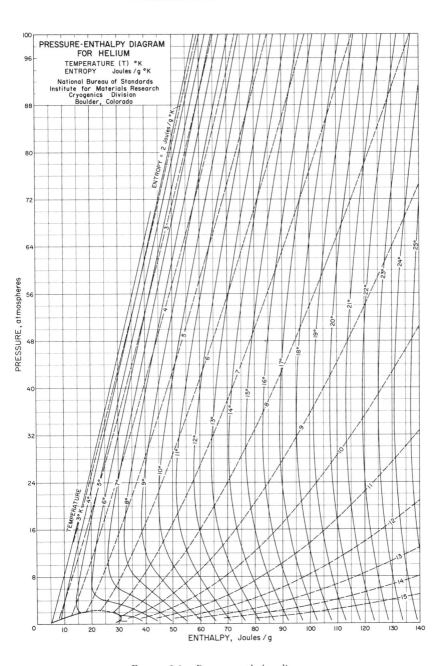

FIGURE 2.6.   *Pressure-enthalpy diagram.*

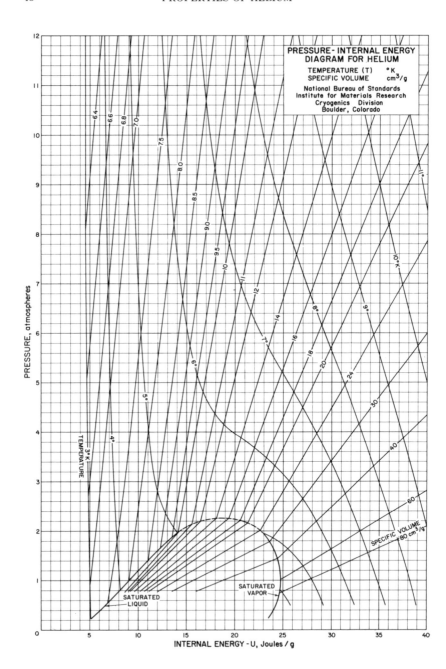

FIGURE 2.7. *Pressure-internal energy diagram.*

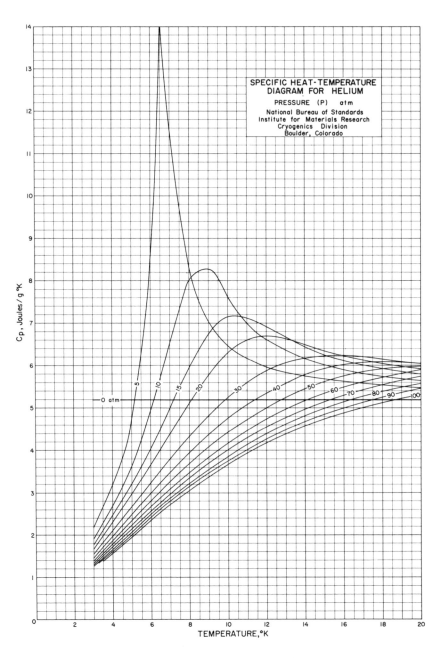

FIGURE 2.8.   *Specific heat-temperature diagram.*

2.2.4. Pressure-Enthalpy Diagram

A third cross plot of the physical and thermodynamic properties of helium is shown in figure 2.6. These data are also derived from the original equation and are of aid to the engineer and designer of heat exchanger equipment for helium service.

2.2.5. Pressure-Internal Energy Diagram

The properties charted in figure 2.7 are especially useful in describing the process of constant volume heat addition. Such processes occur in storage and transport of liquid helium where the storage vessel is sealed and a pressure rise caused by heat leak into the vessel is desired as a function of time. The internal energy function is defined by eq (2.4).

2.2.6. Specific Heat-Temperature Diagram

This diagram (fig. 2.8) describes the specific heat function as it relates to pressure and temperature changes near the critical point. These data are taken directly from HL [12], as the state equation is not capable of showing specific heat variations in the region near the critical point.

TABLE 2.2. *Dynamic viscosity of gaseous helium* [1]

T	μ (micropoises)	T	μ (micropoises)
300	201.2	100	98.8
280	192.4	80	85.6
260	183.4	70	78.5
240	174.2	60	71.0
220	164.6	50	63.1
200	154.8	40	54.6
180	144.6	30	45.4
160	134.0	20	34.9
140	122.9	10	22.3
120	111.2	5	14.2

2.3. TRANSPORT PROPERTIES

2.3.1. Viscosity

It can be shown [1] that viscosity is a very weak function of pressure at temperatures near room temperature. As the temperature is lowered to near the two-phase liquid-vapor region, viscosity becomes a strong function of pressure. At the present time, no correlation of a continuous nature has been performed on viscosity of gaseous or liquid helium. The engineer and designer are therefore forced to use the functional relationship derived by Keesom [1] for viscosities of helium gas at low pressure. This relationship is

$$\mu = 5.023 T^{0.647}. \tag{2.10}$$

Viscosity (μ) is given in micropoises. Selected values of viscosity are given in table 2.2.

2.3.2. Thermal Conductivity

The situation in regard to data on thermal conductivity of helium gas is similar to that of viscosity. Thermal conductivity is also a weak function of pressure near ambient temperature conditions. As the temperature is lowered to the region near the two-phase liquid-vapor boundary, thermal conductivity becomes a strong function of pressure. Again correlations of a continuous nature are not available. The engineer is again forced to rely on the data of Keesom [1] for thermal conductivity. These data are presented in table 2.3.

TABLE 2.3.   *Thermal conductivity of gaseous helium* [1]

T (K)	k (Watts/cm-K) $\times 10^3$
273	1.44
260	1.39
220	1.24
180	1.08
140	0.90
100	0.70
60	0.48
20	0.21

2.4. DISCUSSION

The compilation and correlation of the thermophysical properties of helium presented in this chapter are only one in a series of such presentations begun by Keesom, Bijl, and Monte [16]. As investigative and measurement techniques improve, so do the data necessary to revise the correlations. Zelmanov [17] published data which affected properties correlations below 20 K. This information was the basis for a revision to the original Keesom, Bijl, and Monte [16] data and was published by Scott [18]. New experimental measurements by Lounasmaa [3] for the temperature region 3 to 20 K and the correlations of this information by Mann and Stewart [4] pointed up the need for a revision of the properties charts over the entire temperature range of 300 K.

The widespread use of the digital computer has aided significantly in the task of correlating experimental data. Numerical methods, previously found impractical, could be applied to the development of a correlating function or equation of state. McCarty and Stewart [19] applied these techniques to the temperature region 20 to 300 K. Mann [15] using the work of Strobridge [10] developed the modified BWR equation (with 18 constants) that was used in this chapter. As indicated previously, this state correlating function met the requirements of the process engineer interested in equipment and process design over the temperature range 3 to 300 degrees. This equation does have a number of disadvantages. To name two, it is impractical to use without the aid of the digital computer and it becomes quite inaccurate for helium near its critical point.

Additional experimental data and correlations will certainly follow to improve the precision and accuracy of helium property data. Glassford and Smith [20] have already extended the experimental data to 1300 atm below 20 deg. It is the opinion of this author that the experimentalist should not neglect the region near the critical point of helium. Lounasmaa [3] did provide some experimental data in this extremely difficult region, but more data are necessary. It is also suggested that a new approach to a correlating function should be made; one that takes into account quantum effects of helium at these low temperatures.

With additional development of high-precision measurement techniques as well as the progress in computer technology, additional advances in correlating methods will lead to even more accurate and precise property representations.

REFERENCES

[1] W. H. Keesom, Helium (Elsevier Publ. Co., Amsterdam, The Netherlands, 1942).

[2] S. W. Akin, The thermodynamic properties of helium, ASME Trans. **72**, 751 (1950).

[3] O. V. Lounasmaa, Specific heats at low temperatures, Thesis submitted for degree of Doctor of Philosophy, University of Oxford, Great Britain (1958).

[4] D. B. Mann and R. B. Stewart, Thermodynamic properties of helium at low temperatures and high pressures, NBS Tech. Note 8 (1959).

[5] R. Berman and C. F. Mate, Some thermal properties of helium and their relation to the temperature scale, Phil. Mag. **3A**, 461 (1958).

[6] C. Domb and J. S. Dugdale, Solid helium, Progress in Low Temperature Physics (ed. C. J. Gorter, North Holland Publ. Co., Amsterdam, The Netherlands, 1957), Vol. **II**, p. 338.

[7] F. J. Edeskuty and R. H. Sherman, PVT relations of liquid He³ and He⁴, J ᴖw Temperature Physics and Chemistry (ed. J. R. Dillinger, Univ. of Wisconsin Press, Madison, Wisc., 1958), p. 102.

[8] J. R. Clement, J. K. Logan, and J. Gaffney, Liquid helium vapor and pressure-temperature scale, Phys. Rev. **100**, 743 (1955).

[9] M. Benedict, G. B. Webb, and L. C. Rubin, An empirical equation for the thermodynamic properties of light hydrocarbons and their mixtures, J. Chem. Phys. **8**, 334 (1940).

[10] T. R. Strobridge, The thermodynamic properties of nitrogen from 64 to 300 K between 0.1 and 200 atmospheres, NBS Tech. Note 129 (1962).

[11] W. B. Jones and R. M. Gallet, The representation of diurnal and geographic variations of ionospheric data by numerical methods, Telecomm. J. No. 5, 29 (1962).

[12] R. W. Hill and O. V. Lounasmaa, The thermodynamic properties of fluid helium, Phil. Trans. Roy. Soc. (London) **252A**, 357 (1960).

[13] J. A. Beattie, Thermodynamic properties of real gases and mixtures of real gases, Thermodynamics and Physics of Matter (ed. F. D. Rossini, Princeton Univ. Press, Princeton, N.J., 1955), p. 240.

[14] R. W. Hill and O. V. Lounasmaa, The specific heat of liquid helium, Phil. Mag. **2A**, 143 (1957).

[15] D. B. Mann, The thermodynamic properties of helium from 3 to 300 K and from 0.5 atmospheres to 100 atmospheres, NBS Tech. Note 154 (1962).

[16] W. H. Keesom, A. Bijl, and L. A. J. Monte, Le diagramme log T, S de l'helium, Appl. Sci. Res. **A4**, 25 (1953).

[17] J. Zelmanov, The entropy diagram for helium at low temperatures, J. Phys. (USSR) **8**, (1944).

[18] Russell B. Scott, Cryogenic Engineering (D. Van Nostrand Company, Inc., Princeton, N.J., 1959).

[19] R. D. McCarty and R. B. Stewart, An equation of state for calculating the thermodynamic properties of helium at low temperatures, Progress in International Research on Thermodynamic and Transport Properties (ASME, New York, N.Y., 1962), p. 107.

[20] A. P. M. Glassford and J. L. Smith, Jr., Pressure-volume-temperature and internal energy data for helium from 4.2 to 20 K between 100 and 1300 atmospheres, Proc. International Institute of Refrigeration, Commission 1, Boulder, Colo. (1966), p. 343.

CHAPTER 3

Liquefaction Techniques

Samuel C. Collins [1]

[1] Village Hill Road, Belmont, Mass. 02178.

3.1. PRINCIPLES OF REFRIGERATION

3.1.1. Joule-Thomson Effect

The specific heat of real gases is a function of the pressure. Over a wide range of temperature and pressure, the specific heat increases with the pressure. The Joule-Thomson coefficient, $\left(\dfrac{\partial T}{\partial p}\right)_h$, will, therefore, increase in magnitude as the temperature falls, passing from negative values at higher temperatures to zero at the inversion temperature and, finally, to positive values at lower temperatures. This property is illustrated in the enthalpy-temperature diagram of figure 3.1.

Isothermal compression, state 5 to state 1, is attended by a substantial decrease in specific enthalpy. If the compressed gas undergoes isenthalpic expansion, 1 to 1′, there is a significant drop in temperature, a positive Joule-Thomson effect. If the compressed gas is led through one channel of a counterflow heat exchanger before expansion and the colder expanded gas is returned through a second channel of the heat exchanger, the colder gas will absorb heat from the incoming high-pressure stream, with the result that the latter will arrive at the expansion valve

---

EDITORS' NOTE: The contributions to helium liquefaction and refrigeration made by Samuel C. Collins have resulted in widespread impact on technology. In 1958, on the fiftieth anniversary of the first liquefaction of helium, he was awarded the Kamerlingh-Onnes Gold Medal for his development of the Collins Helium Cryostat. In 1951 he was awarded the John Price Wetherill Medal of The Franklin Institute and in 1965 was the first recipient of the highest award given by the Cryogenic Engineering Conference, The Samuel C. Collins Award.

This chapter was prepared by Prof. Collins, at the request of the editors, to present his views on liquefaction techniques for liquefaction of helium. Our decision to separate liquefiers and refrigerators into two chapters is not unique, since all liquefiers are refrigerators but all refrigerators are not necessarily liquefiers. Recent industrial practice, however, has prompted dividing the subject into two parts.

at a progressively lower temperature until the liquid phase appears. Referring to the diagram of figure 3.1, the state of the high-pressure gas changes from 1 to 2 in the heat exchanger. After expansion at 2, there are two phases: liquid at 3, and saturated vapor at 4. The low-pressure stream is warmed from 4 to 5 by heat received from the high-pressure stream during its passage through the heat exchanger. It has been assumed that the heat exchanger is well insulated and highly efficient. Otherwise, the temperature at 5 would be appreciably lower than that at 1.

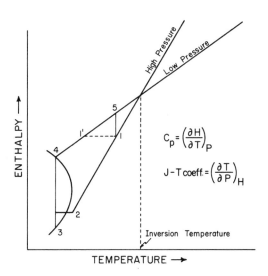

FIGURE 3.1. *Joule-Thomson refrigeration process.*

Assuming no leakage of heat from the surroundings and no work done by the gas, the fraction, ϵ, of the stream which remains as liquid is given by the relation:

$$\epsilon = \frac{h_5 - h_1}{h_5 - h_3}. \tag{3.1}$$

If there is no accumulation of liquid, the maximum refrigerative effect,

Q, is expressed by the equation:

$$Q = h_5 - h_1. \qquad (3.2)$$

Note that the amount of refrigeration available from this simple system is independent of the temperature level at which it is applied so long as that level is chosen to lie between the boiling point of the liquid phase at the lower pressure and the temperature of the warm end of the heat exchanger. The amount of refrigeration is greatly affected by the temperature level at the warm end of the heat exchanger or, more specifically, the temperature of the compressed gas entering the warm end of the heat exchanger. The lower this temperature, the greater will be the magnitude of Q in eq (3.2) and of ϵ in eq (3.1).

The usefulness of the Joule-Thomson effect as a means of liquefying gases depends upon the possibility of starting with compressed gas at a temperature well below the inversion point. In the case of helium, this implies a temperature well below 30 K. Actually, for useful yields of liquid, temperatures in the range of 8 to 15 K are necessary. There are two accepted methods of precooling helium to the desired level; one by the use of liquid hydrogen which goes down to 14 K under reduced pressure, and the other by expanding a part of the helium stream in an external-work machine. More elaborate counterflow heat exchangers are required for the application of these coolants.

3.1.2. Liquid Hydrogen Cooling

A liquid hydrogen bath is placed in the high-pressure flow stream just prior to the inlet of the Joule-Thomson heat exchanger. The temperature of this bath is lowered by pumping to a pressure near the triple point of the liquid hydrogen (14 K). Provision must be made for recovering the refrigerative value of the effluent helium, which leaves the warm end of the Joule-Thomson heat exchanger at about 15 K on its way to the compressor operating at room temperature. This can be done easily in a second heat exchanger for cooling the high-pressure stream by transferring its heat to the outgoing gas. Partial use of the hydrogen vapor can be made.

Because of the fire and explosion hazard introduced by the presence of liquid hydrogen, its use in the liquefaction of helium is lagging.

3.1.3. External Work Machines

When a compressed gas expands adiabatically in an engine, the temperature decreases chiefly because of the decrease of internal energy. The work is expressed by the relation:

$$W = RT_0 \frac{k}{k-1} \left[1 - r^{\left(\frac{k-1}{k}\right)} \right], \tag{3.3}$$

where T_0 is the temperature of the gas entering the engine, r is the ratio of final to initial pressure, and k is the ratio of specific heats, $\frac{c_p}{c_v}$. The refrigeration generated by the expansion resides in the cold gas discharged by the engine. It is usefully applied by allowing the cold gas to absorb heat from the material which is to be cooled; in this case, a stream of helium. Whereas the work done by the engine equals the decrease in the enthalpy of the gas, the available refrigeration is the product $-C_p\Delta T$ where C_p is the specific heat at constant pressure and ΔT is the change in temperature of the gas as a result of the expansion. The work is exactly equivalent to the available refrigeration only at the inversion temperature for the pressure range involved. Note that the work done is directly proportional to the temperature of the gas entering the engine. It is desirable, therefore, to perform the expansion at the highest temperature at which the resultant refrigeration can be used.

A cold stream of expanded helium is preferred to an evaporating liquid for cooling a stream of compressed helium. Assuming the transfer of heat to take place in a counterflow heat exchanger, the loss of entropy by the stream being cooled is more nearly equal to the gain of entropy by the fluid being heated and the process is, therefore, more nearly reversible.

3.1.4. The Stirling Cycle

A special variety of the external work machine which is sometimes used to cool helium to the 15 K level or lower for partial liquefaction in a Joule-Thomson process is the reversed heat engine of Stirling. In this machine the refrigerative effect is produced by the adiabatic expansion of compressed helium just as in the ordinary expansion engine. Instead of the counterflow heat exchanger with its pair of channels for high- and low-pressure streams respectively, however, the Stirling system employs a regenerator, a cylindrical vessel filled with porous material of substantial heat capacity and extensive surface. Compressed helium flows momentarily through the regenerator into the expansion chamber. Expansion occurs and, thereafter, the cold expanded helium returns through the regenerator. A thermal gradient is

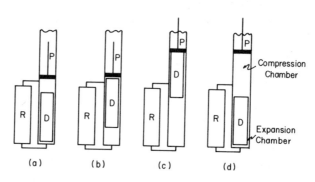

FIGURE 3.2. *The Stirling cycle.*

soon established in the regenerator with the result that each new charge of compressed helium arrives at the expansion chamber with a relatively low temperature. After expansion, the temperature is lower still. The principle of operation is illustrated by the four sketches of figure 3.2. At *a*, the charge of helium has been compressed but it still resides in the compression chamber—the displacer D being in its lowest position. At *b*, the displacer has been moved upward, thereby forcing the helium to flow through the regenerator R into the expansion chamber. At *c*, both piston P and displacer have moved upward to create a larger volume in the expansion chamber. The pressure and temperature of the helium fall to the minimum level. At *d*, the expanded gas has been forced to return to the compression chamber by way of the regenerator. Provision is made for the absorption of heat by the cold helium along the path between the expansion chamber and the regenerator.

The advantages of the Stirling cycle over the conventional expansion engine-counterflow heat exchanger assembly are the relative simplicity of both the regenerator and displacement apparatus, the absence of valves, and a greater tolerance for impurities. The disadvantages are the large clearance volume presented by the voids in the packing of the regenerator and the difficulty of providing adequate heat capacity, since the specific heat of all solid substances approaches zero at very low temperatures.

3.1.5. Simon Expansion Liquefier

No summary of means for liquefying helium would be complete without mention of Simon's expansion liquefier. In this liquefier, gaseous helium is pumped into a metal container which can be cooled to the temperature of liquid or solid hydrogen. When the container, together with its charge of helium, now at a pressure of 100 to 150 atm, has attained the desired temperature, it is thermally isolated from the surroundings. The pressure is then reduced slowly by valving the helium to an external gas holder. At any stage of the expansion, the helium left in the vessel will have expanded reversibly. It does work on the gas being pushed out. The overall expansion is rather efficient and the amount of liquid left in the container when the pressure has returned to 1 atm is approximately 60 percent of the quantity possible with a completely reversible expansion. If the pressure and temperature are 150 atm and 11 K respectively at the beginning of the expansion, the container will be about four-fifths full of liquid when the expansion is complete.

An all-important factor contributing to the success of the Simon expansion liquefier is the vanishingly small heat capacity of the vessel into which the helium is compressed. Substantially none of the liquid formed is evaporated in cooling the container from the starting temperature to 4.2 K.

The charging half of the cycle of the Simon liquefier is relatively wasteful of liquid hydrogen. The heat absorbed by the hydrogen bath is the sum of the decrease of the internal energy of the helium after it enters the container and the flow work of compression. The latter term is Σmpv where m is the mass of a small quantity of entering gas, p the pressure, and v its specific volume. If all of the gas enters at the same temperature, T_1, the total flow work is NRT, where N is the number of moles of helium entering the vessel and R is the gas constant. The amount of liquid hydrogen required to absorb the heat produced by the flow work may actually exceed that needed to bring about the reduction of the internal energy of the helium. It is a case of comparing the magnitudes of two products; namely, RT_1 and $C(T_1 - T_2)$, where T_2 is the final temperature before expansion.

3.2. COMMON HELIUM LIQUEFIERS

3.2.1. Helium Liquefaction Cycle

Nearly all of the liquid helium produced at the present time is made in liquefiers which utilize liquid nitrogen for all of the help it can give and, in addition, expansion engines at one or more temperature levels. In figure 3.3, a liquefaction cycle with nitrogen cooling and adiabatic expansion of a portion of the helium at each of two temperatures with isenthalpic expansion of the remainder is shown. The counterflow heat exchanger is made up of six sections, although fewer sections are often used. It is possible to construct a helium liquefaction cycle with adiabatic expansion at only one temperature level when liquid nitrogen is used, but the yield of liquid per mole of helium circulated is greater with multiple level expansion. Ideally, the number of thermal stages of expansion should be such that the entire temperature interval between 300 K and 4.2 K is spanned by the engines, just as sections 3 and 5 of the heat exchanger of figure 3.3 are bracketed by engines E_1 and E_2, respectively. The fraction of the total stream of helium which is to be

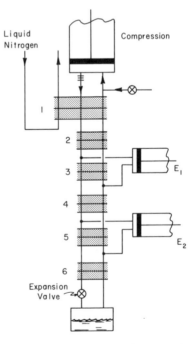

FIGURE 3.3. *Helium liquefaction cycle.*

liquefied could then be cooled all the way from 300 K with the highest thermodynamic efficiency.

Referring again to the cycle of figure 3.3, liquid nitrogen cooling may be supplanted by a third expansion cylinder. Sometimes liquid nitrogen is not readily available, or is expensive, or requires too much attention. In such circumstances, moderate efficiency can be attained with adiabatic expansion at only two levels and high efficiency with expansion at three temperature levels.

3.2.2. Management of the Heat Exchanger

Broadly the function of the heat exchanger is to shuttle the refrigerant to and fro between the compressor—which does work at room temperature—and the engine and throttle valve, which operate at very low temperatures. This process should be performed with minimum loss of refrigeration. The heat exchanger tends to be large and costly. It is sometimes desirable to accept certain deficiencies on the part of the heat exchangers in order to conserve space, shorten cooldown time, or save capital outlay. It is often desirable to squander liquid nitrogen or expanded helium at higher temperature levels in order to conserve refrigeration generated at lower temperatures.

Consider, for instance, section 1 of the heat exchanger of figure 3.3. It carries the major part of the heat load of the entire heat exchanger system. Note the effect of liquid nitrogen, generously applied, upon the performance of this section. Without liquid nitrogen, the incoming stream of compressed helium must be cooled by the outgoing stream, whose mass rate of flow is probably no more than 92 percent of that of the incoming stream. Even if the heat exchanger is highly efficient, the temperature difference between streams at the cold end will be at least 20 K. Although little or no refrigeration is being discarded to the surroundings, the 20 K deficit at the cold end of section 1 must now be made good by refrigeration generated at a lower temperature. By the use of either liquid nitrogen or expanded helium from an engine operating at an elevated temperature, the mass rate of flow of outgoing fluid can be made to exceed that of the incoming gas, and the temperature "pinch" (minimum temperature difference between high and low pressure stream) can thereby be shifted from the warm end to the cold end of section 1 so as to trade inexpensive high-level refrigeration for the more expensive low-level variety.

In section 2, the temperature difference must grow larger toward the cold end because of the unbalanced flow, but nothing can be done about it. In section 3, however, the opportunity recurs to change the balance of flow by adjusting the portion of the high-pressure stream which passes through engine E_1. The temperature of the compressed helium entering section 4 can, therefore, be brought very close to that of the expanded helium leaving the warm end of that section. In section 5, the provision for optimum flow through section 6, the Joule-Thomson heat exchanger, automatically shifts the balance of flow heavily in favor of the outgoing low-pressure stream so that the ΔT at the end of section 5 is very small.

When refrigeration rather than liquid helium is the desired service, the mass rate of flow of the outgoing stream of helium is greater, and the requirement for liquid nitrogen and/or expanded helium is greatly reduced.

3.2.3. The Joule-Thomson Heat Exchanger

For any chosen temperature at the warm end of the Joule-Thomson exchanger, there is an optimum pressure. Reference is made to the temperature-entropy diagrams, figures 2.3 and 2.4 of Chapter 2. Note that the lines of constant enthalpy are curves having maxima at pressures ranging from 35 atm at 20 K to 3 atm at 4.5 K. Isothermal compression at lower pressures is attended by a decrease of enthalpy and at higher pressures by an increase of enthalpy. At any given temperature there is a pressure at which the enthalpy is a minimum. At 8 K, for instance, the minimum comes at 15 atm. If helium in this state is processed in a heat exchanger and throttle valve, the maximum fraction liquefiable, as computed by eq (3.1) with data taken from figure 2.3, is 0.5, and the maximum refrigeration by eq (3.2) is 21.97 J/g. Had the pressure been either higher or lower, the results would have been less favorable. It should be observed at this point that in order to secure the performance indicated above the pressure of the incoming stream cannot remain at 15 atm. It must be reduced to a lower value (4 to 6 atm) partway along the Joule-Thomson heat exchanger. Otherwise the temperature difference between high- and low-pressure streams becomes zero, and heat transfer stops before the enthalpy of the high-pressure stream reaches the required value. The enthalpy of 15 atm helium at 4.5 K is approximately 17 J/g, whereas at 4 atm and 4.5 K the enthalpy is only 11 J/g. In general, it can be said that continuous adjustment of the pressure of the stream of compressed helium, so as to maintain the condition of minimum enthalpy at every temperature level, will provide a maximum ΔT throughout the length of the heat exchanger for driving heat from one stream to the other. This is especially important when refrigeration at 4.2 K is wanted. In practice, continuous adjustment of the pressure is not feasible, but two or three expansion valves in series will accomplish essentially the same result.

The lower the temperature at the warm end of the Joule-Thomson heat exchanger, the greater is the fraction of the J-T stream liquefied, or the greater is the refrigerative effect at 4.2 K if there is no accumulation of liquid. This does not mean, however, that the lower engine, E_2, should be operated at the lowest possible temperature for the sake of more intense precooling of the J-T stream. It must be remembered that the refrigerative power of the gas expanded in the engine decreases linearly with the temperature at which the expansion begins. Optimum conditions are reached by due consideration of the two effects discussed above, as well as the interaction with the remainder of the heat exchange system. Precooling of the Joule-Thomson stream is rarely carried below 8 K and may stop at a level several degrees higher.

3.2.4. Expansion Machines

There are many varieties of reciprocating expansion engines in use. The most significant differences relate to the piston, its construction, and the material of which it is made. The piston may be equipped with conventional nonmetallic piston rings which seal against leakage and prevent contact between the metallic part of the piston and the cylinder wall. The piston may be encased in a plastic sheath which is so closely fitted to the cylinder that leakage is acceptably low. The piston and cylinder may be made of alloy steel of great hardness. The piston rod is very slender and is made to operate in tension so as to avoid sidewise forces on the piston.

Another type of piston which shows considerable promise is an elongated plastic plunger of uniform diameter, one end cold, the other at room temperature. The cylinder is longer than the piston and of uniform bore. Sealing is accomplished by a single O-ring at the warm end. There is no leakage and little danger of seizure. There is, however, appreciable clearance volume.

Turbines for expanding helium have been developed, and they are now being used in a few installations. It is expected that they will find extensive use in large liquefiers and refrigerators. The following sections describe large-scale helium liquefiers. Not all manufacturers are represented here, but the installations are typical of the state of the art in this rapidly expanding field.

3.3. HELIUM LIQUEFACTION FACILITIES

3.3.1. Otis, Kans. Helium Liquefier (Ch. Trepp, Sulzer Brothers, Ltd., Winterthur, Switzerland)

It may be shown that it is more economical to transport helium in liquid form than as compressed gas in high-pressure cylinders. For large delivered quantities (e.g., in trailers of up to 30 m³ capacity) the ratio of packing weight to contents is more favorable with liquid than with gas transports. For this reason, a liquefier processing helium was added to a new helium extraction plant at Otis, Kans. The nominal liquefaction capacity of this unit is 800 l/hr.

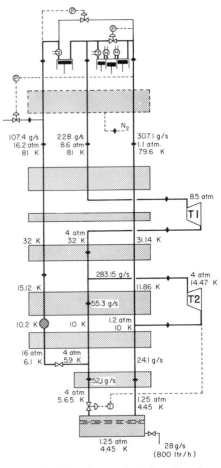

FIGURE 3.4. *Flow diagram for helium liquefaction.*

The flow diagram for the helium liquefaction process is shown schematically in figure 3.4. The liquefaction process can be split into three temperature ranges corresponding to the different methods employed for cooling.

First range: 300−80 K: precooling with liquid nitrogen.

Second range: 80−10 K: cooling with work performing expansion. A medium-pressure stream flows through two series-connected cold helium gas turbines which operate at different temperatures.

Third range: 10−4.45 K: Joule-Thomson stage, double throttling of liquefaction stream. The advantages of double compared with single throttling result in smaller, more efficient low-temperature heat exchanges.

In the design of a liquefaction cycle incorporating turbines, a difference must be made between losses incurred through dissipation of mechanical work performed and those due to non-isentropic expansion. The latter assume increasing importance as the temperature becomes lower. In the case of heat exchanger design, an attempt was made to differentiate between the exchanger losses and the transfer losses. An exact separation is not possible. The former are caused by the finite size of the heat exchanger surfaces, the latter by the difference in the products of the mass rate and specific heat of the heat-exchange streams.

The sum of all individual losses is equal to the difference between the effective and the theoretical performance. If effective performance is expressed as 100, we obtained for this liquefaction cycle losses equal to 74 percent and a thermodynamic efficiency of 26 percent.

Since in this plant the feed gas is admitted at 80 K and 16 kg/cm^2, the above efficiency cannot be equated with that of a plant taking in helium gas under ambient conditions. A comparison has been made by including the losses and thermodynamic efficiency of a process of isothermal compression at 310 K and isobaric cooling from 310 to 80 K. It may be shown that plant efficiencies of 35 percent may be obtained assuming isothermal compression.

The plant may be regarded as a closed cycle since it is not connected with a gas holder on the low-pressure side. In normal operation the large liquid helium vessel does, in fact, have a similar influence on the cycle as a gas holder.

The low pressure (liquefaction pressure) is maintained constant with suitable control arrangements. Reduction of the feed rate would result in a decrease in the low pressure, and for this reason the discharge rate of the medium-pressure compressor is regulated with bypasses

FIGURE 3.5.   *View of the Otis plant.*

FIGURE 3.6.   *Turbines for the Otis plant.*

according to the liquefaction pressure. The regulating valve in the feed line remains fully open.

At nominal load the compressor bypass valve is fully closed. Any increase in the feed rate beyond nominal load capacity would result in the liquefaction pressure rising. In this case, the feed rate is reduced and the excess gas let off to storage vessels. Constant pressure is maintained in the high-pressure stream by the bypass of the fourth compressor stage.

A photograph of the plant structure is shown in figure 3.5. All components below 80 K are enclosed in one evacuated cold box. Heat exchangers are of the plate fin type.

A photograph of the cold gas turbines is shown in figure 3.6. Oil-lubricated high-speed centripetal turbines are employed. In air tests, efficiencies of 85 percent have been attained. Wheel diameters are 50 and 45 mm. Maximum speed is 100,000 rpm.

3.3.2. 500 Incorporated (S. C. Collins and Arthur Post)

The first helium liquefier to be manufactured in quantity was produced by Arthur D. Little, Inc. The original model of this machine, as developed by Collins in 1946, had a capacity of about 2 l/hr. Numerous modifications have led to much higher rates of liquefaction. A later model, illustrated in figure 3.7, liquefies at the rate of 9 l/hr with virtually no operator attention. A large external dewar is employed, and the

FIGURE 3.7. *Collins helium liquefier.*

helium is liquefied within the dewar by means of a remote expansion valve. This system is made by 500 Incorporated, a subsidiary of ADL. Helium refrigerators based on a Stirling-type cycle developed by McMahon and Gifford [1] [2] are also manufactured by 500 Incorporated. These machines are designed for long periods of unattended operation and are used for cooling masers, superconducting magnets, etc., as well as for liquefying helium.

3.3.3. Union Carbide, Linde Division (A. J. Westbrock)

In 1962–63 the Linde Division of Union Carbide Corporation installed what were then the largest helium liquefiers in the world [2]. These units were of the same basic design. Two installations were made under contract with NASA at the Lewis Research Center, Cleveland, Ohio, while the third was placed in commercial operation by Linde at Amarillo, Tex. Capacity of these machines exceeded 100 l/hr measured in 7000-l storage dewars which were installed with each unit.

Liquid production is accomplished by means of a Claude process as illustrated in figure 3.8. The Grade-A helium feed gas is compressed from slightly above atmospheric pressure to 270 psig in three stages of compression.

The gas then flows through a water-cooled aftercooler into the liquefier cold box, where the high-pressure gas is cooled to approximately 80 K against recycle helium gas and nitrogen vapor from the nitrogen forecooler. The gas then flows through the nitrogen forecooler, after which it passes through a silica gel adsorption trap which removes trace impurities, principally nitrogen, from the helium feed gas. The gas is then further cooled to a temperature of approximately 24 K against low-pressure helium return gas. Next the gas is divided into two streams; one fraction is expanded in the expansion engine to 13 K while the other, still at high pressure, is cooled further against expanded gas and then to approximately 6.0 K by heat exchange against the low-pressure recycle stream. This very-low-temperature, high-pressure gas is then expanded through a Joule-Thomson throttle valve to about 4.5 psig with resultant liquefaction of approximately 15 percent of the expanded stream. The liquid yield and non-liquefied gas are separated in a phase separator. The liquid made is transferred to the storage dewar, while the low-pressure gas is passed countercurrent to the high-pressure

---

[2] Figures in brackets indicate the literature references at the end of this chapter.

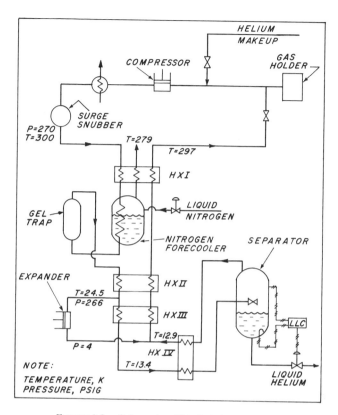

FIGURE 3.8. *Schematic of Linde helium liquefier.*

helium gas progressively through each of the heat exchangers from the cold end to the warm end, with the exception of the forecooler. This recycle stream is joined by makeup helium and flows to the inlet of the compressor first stage. A gas holder floats on the suction side.

Both oil-lubricated and dry-lubricated three-stage reciprocating compressors have been used in these installations. With the oil-lubricated machine, the system also incorporates an effective oil-removal trap at the warm end. All of the compressors have special oil-pressurized packing gland seals to reduce helium loss to about 0.1 percent of helium feed flow.

The cold boxes are of double wall dewar type construction using evacuated perlite insulation between walls. Heat leak is absorbed by the use of liquid nitrogen coils on the inner vessel wall, on the gel trap, and in the forecooler. Heat leak by conduction was minimized by the use of stainless steel in the inner vessel, piping, and supports.

Heat exchangers in the cold box are of the brazed aluminum plate and fin type. These provide maximum surface with minimum space requirements and desirable physical properties at the extremely low temperatures encountered.

The low-temperature expanders are reciprocating units of high efficiency. Thermal efficiencies in excess of 70 percent were obtained. The expanders are insulated by double-walled permanent vacuum perlite insulated bell jar type vessels that can be easily removed for routine maintenance of the expander cylinder and valves. Connection between the liquefier cold box and the expanders is by means of super-insulated piping.

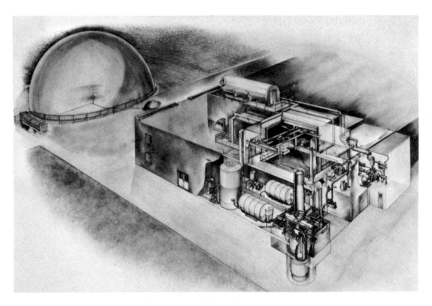

FIGURE 3.9.   *Linde helium liquefier installation at NASA-Lewis Research Center.*

Liquid helium produced in the separators within the cold boxes is transferred automatically by liquid level control through super-insulated piping into the 7000 liter super-insulated liquid helium dewars. The normal evaporation rate is approximately 0.3 percent/day. To reduce conductive heat leak to these dewars, their design incorporates a number of design features, including re-entrant load rods, re-entrant piping, helium-vapor-cooled radiation shields, in addition to the super insulation.

The Linde liquefier at Amarillo, Tex., is used for the commercial production of liquid helium which is shipped throughout the country. Demand for liquid helium increased to the extent by 1965 that the Amarillo unit was modified in that year to utilize liquid hydrogen fore-cooling in order to increase production. This change has upgraded production from the unit to more than 250 l/hr.

The liquefiers installed at the NASA Lewis Research Center are used in conjunction with a nominal 6-ft diam by 12-ft high space simulator also built by Linde. The installation is shown in figure 3.9. Space simulation is accomplished within the chamber, which is maintained at a vacuum of 10^{-11} torr through diffusion pumping and cryopumping. The test object radiates to high emissivity walls maintained at liquid helium temperature.

Helium vaporized during testing is warmed to ambient temperature and flows to the 92-ft-diam helium recovery gas bag shown to the left in the picture. Recovered helium is reprocessed through the liquefier and stored in the dewars which are a part of the system.

An additional use of these helium liquefiers by NASA has been the production of liquid helium for distribution to other NASA installations throughout the country.

FIGURE 3.10   *Air Products liquefier.*

3.3.4. Air Products and Chemicals, Incorporated (W. A. Snow, A. R. Winters, R. B. Currie)

In 1958 Air Products and Chemicals, Incorporated, under contract to the U.S. Navy, produced a portable helium liquefier for installation at the Naval Air Station at Lakehurst, N.J. This liquefier was part of a program supported by the U.S. Navy to reduce costs in the servicing of the blimp fleet stationed at Lakehurst. The liquefier was capable of delivering to storage an equivalent of 35,000 scf per day (59 l/hr). The liquefier is shown in figure 3.10 together with a Navy blimp it was to service.

A multipurpose helium refrigerator-liquefier was developed and built by Air Products under contract with the RCA Service Company for NASA Langley Research Center. The system was designed to meet the following requirements:

FIGURE 3.11. *Multipurpose liquefier-refrigerator.*

1. Provide 1.32 kW of refrigeration below 5 K to a helium cryopanel located inside a high-vacuum space chamber.
2. Maintain the cryopanel below 88 K in the presence of a 3 kW heat load inside the chamber.
3. Produce 140 net l/hr of helium when operating as a liquefier.

A photograph of the apparatus is shown in figure 3.11. The process cycle is quite complex and reflects the dual requirements of the refrigerator liquefier system. A complete description is given by Snow, Winters, and Currie [3].

FIGURE 3.12.   *CVI, Incorporated, add-on liquefier.*

3.3.5. CVI Corporation, Helium Add-on Liquefier (C. B. Hood)

The CVI Add-On Liquefier was developed to provide an in-house liquefaction capability to laboratories already operating refrigeration equipment at the 20 K level. The design capacity is 34 l/hr when operating with a refrigerator providing 1.2 kW of refrigeration at 20 K. Helium at 20 atm, precooled to 80 K, is cooled in three successive steps by the 20 K load stream and low-pressure flash gas before it is expanded into a collection tank. The warmed flash gas is recompressed in an auxiliary compressor and returned to the refrigerator low side at 2.6 atm. The heat exchanger and collection tank assembly is suspended in an evacuated vertical cylinder. The exchanger assembly is shown in figure 3.12 with the control panel/skid assembly shown beside it.

REFERENCES

[1] H. O. McMahon and W. E. Gifford, A new low-temperature gas-expansion cycle, Parts I and II, Advances in Cryogenic Engineering (ed. K. D. Timmerhaus, Plenum Press, New York, N.Y., 1960), Vol. 5, p. 354.

[2] J. L. Aberle and A. J. Westbrock, Liquid helium and nitrogen supply systems for space simulators, Advances in Cryogenic Engineering (ed. K. D. Timmerhaus, Plenum Press, New York, N.Y., 1963), Vol. 8, p. 190.

[3] W. A. Snow, A. R. Winters, and R. B. Currie, A multi-purpose high capacity helium refrigerator-liquefier, Proc. Institute of Environmental Sciences, April 21–23, 1965; A. R. Winters and W. A. Snow, Capacity and economic performance of a large 5 K helium refrigerator, Advances in Cryogenic Engineering (ed. K. D. Timmerhaus, Plenum Press, New York, N.Y., 1966), Vol. 11, p. 116.

CHAPTER 4

Refrigeration

T. R. Strobridge [1]

[1] Cryogenics Division, NBS Institute for Basic Standards, Boulder, Colo. 80302.

4.1. INTRODUCTION

Much early low-temperature research was devoted to condensing the more stubborn of the normally gaseous elements. Liquefaction of the lowest temperature species, helium, was finally accomplished by H. Kamerlingh Onnes on July 10, 1908 [1].[2] For this contribution to the technology, Onnes was awarded the Nobel prize. Many of the succeeding experiments concerned the behavior of helium itself and led to the discovery of the lambda transition and the unique, interesting properties of liquid helium II. Investigations rapidly branched out to other materials and superconductivity was observed in mercury by Onnes in April of 1911 [2]. It is interesting to note that in the short communication reporting the evident disappearance of resistance, Onnes remarked on the advantages of having superconducting "films of molecular thickness," although he had in mind applications different than those encountered today. Many of the unique properties of materials at helium temperatures are currently being utilized for technological applications. Thus pulsed or steady-state refrigeration is required simply to maintain the low-temperature environment. Refrigerators are differentiated from liquefiers because in the latter, the desired effect is the removal of energy from the helium itself so that it will condense, while the refrigerator absorbs energy at low temperatures from heat sources external to the working fluid.

This chapter is devoted to refrigeration methods encountered today—evaporating liquid helium baths, the Simon process, the Joule-Thomson, Brayton, Claude, Stirling, and Gifford-McMahon cycles. The very special He^3-He^4 dilution refrigerators are excluded. Examples of analysis techniques using the appropriate thermodynamics are given for some of the cycles along with descriptions of typical modern refrigerators and their components. Finally, data are presented on existing closed-cycle refrigerators which allow prediction of the weight, volume, and power requirements of 4 K refrigerators of various capacities.

---

[2] Figures in brackets indicate the literature references at the end of this chapter.

4.2. THERMODYNAMIC RELATIONSHIPS

4.2.1. First Law of Thermodynamics

The first law of thermodynamics relates the mass and energy fluxes which occur in natural events. Thereby it is used to predict the outcome of processes, providing a tool for the analysis of the performance of refrigerators and their components. Derivation of the first law has been made in detail many times over and once more would serve no useful purpose. The nomenclature for the thermodynamic relations in this chapter has been adapted from Van Wylen and Sonntag [3], and the reader is referred to their treatise for a thorough modern treatment of classical thermodynamics. A control volume is defined as a volume enclosed by a control surface which surrounds the material to be studied. Mass, work, heat, and momentum can flow across the control surface into and out of the control volume. If attention is to be focused on a fixed quantity of mass, the imaginary boundaries drawn about that mass define a thermodynamic system. Work and heat may cross the boundary of a system, but mass may not. Referring to figure 4.1, the first law for uniform state, uniform flow processes is

$$Q_{c.v.} + \sum m_i \left(h_i + \frac{V_i^2}{2g_c} + Z_i \frac{g}{g_c} \right) = W_{c.v.} + \sum m_e \left(h_e + \frac{V_e^2}{2g_c} + Z_e \frac{g}{g_c} \right)$$

$$+ \left[m_2 \left(u_2 + \frac{V_2^2}{2g_c} + Z_2 \frac{g}{g_c} \right) - m_1 \left(u_1 + \frac{V_1^2}{2g_c} + Z_1 \frac{g}{g_c} \right) \right]_{c.v.} \tag{4.1}$$

where $Q_{c.v.}$ and $W_{c.v.}$ are the heat and work crossing the control surface, m is mass, h is specific enthalpy, u is specific internal energy, V is velocity, and Z is vertical position. The subscripts i and e refer to the incoming and exiting flows and 1 and 2 refer to states 1 and 2 in the con-

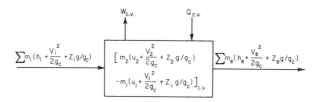

FIGURE 4.1.   *Pictorial description of first law of thermodynamics for uniform state, uniform flow process.*

trol volume indicated by the subscript c.v. The proportionality constant that relates force, mass, time, and length in Newton's second law is g_c and the local acceleration of gravity is g. (In the SI system,

$$g_c = 1 \text{ kg-m/N-s}^2.)$$

The convention is adopted that heat transferred to the system is considered positive, as is work done by the system. The terms uniform state, uniform flow mean that:

"1. The control volume remains constant relative to the coordinate system.
2. The state of the mass crossing the control surface is constant with time and uniform over the various areas of the control surface where the flow occurs.
3. The state of the mass within the control volume may change with time but at any instant of time the state is uniform over the entire control volume (or over several identifiable regions that make up the entire control volume)." [3]

Equation (4.1) is an especially useful form of the first law. For example, if there is no mass flow across the control surface, then the control volume becomes the system and eq (4.1) reduces to

$$_1Q_2 = {}_1W_2 + m \left[(u_2 - u_1) + \frac{V_2^2 - V_1^2}{2g_c} + (Z_2 - Z_1) \frac{g}{g_c} \right]. \qquad (4.2)$$

For a system undergoing a process from state 1 to state 2, eq (4.2) simply shows that in the absence of mass transfer, the difference between the heat transfer and the work done on or by the system is equal to the change in internal, potential, and kinetic energies associated with the mass within the system. When both the amount and the state of the mass within the control volume remain constant with time, eq (4.1) becomes

$$Q_{\text{c.v.}} + \sum m_i \left(h_i + \frac{V_i^2}{2g_c} + Z_i \frac{g}{g_c} \right) = W_{\text{c.v.}} + \sum m_e \left(h_e + \frac{V_e^2}{2g_c} + Z_e \frac{g}{g_c} \right). \qquad (4.3)$$

Such a process is commonly referred to as a steady flow process where $\sum m_i = \sum m_e$. If we imagine now that the control volume surrounds a stationary vessel that is to be filled by a pipe that passes through the control surface, the appropriate form of eq (4.1) is

$$Q_{c.v.} + m_i \left(h_i + \frac{V_i^2}{2g_c} \right) = W_{c.v.} + [m_2 u_2 - m_1 u_1]_{c.v.} \qquad (4.4)$$

where the heat transfer, velocity, and work terms may or may not be negligible. In many instances the velocity terms in the relations given above will indeed be negligible. When those terms are included, all velocities must be relative to the same coordinate system. Care must be taken to make the necessary incremental solutions if any of the terms vary with time. An example of this situation is the cooldown of a low-temperature refrigerator wherein temperatures throughout the entire refrigerator do indeed vary with time until steady-state operation is reached. During cooldown, primary contributions to the internal energy terms, contained within the brackets describing the contents of the control volume, come from the material in the piping, heat exchangers, and other low-temperature apparatus in the refrigerator, and not from the working fluid itself. Applications of the first law of thermodynamics to various refrigerator components will be given in later sections of this chapter.

4.2.2. The Second Law of Thermodynamics

The second law of thermodynamics leads to the definition of entropy and is the basis for the concepts of the thermodynamic temperature scale, the Carnot cycle, reversibility, and irreversibility. As stated, the first law predicts the outcome of an assumed process. However, the first law holds equally well for the process proceeding in the reverse direction. The permissible directions for processes are given by the second law. A corollary of the second law is that during a process, the total entropy change of a system or control volume and the surroundings (the universe) must always be greater than or equal to zero. A reversible process will cause zero entropy change of the universe while there will be a net entropy increase as a result of an irreversible process. An assumed process can occur only if the net entropy change is zero or positive.

According to Van Wylen [3], "A reversible process for a system is defined as a process which once having taken place can be reversed and in so doing leaves no change in either the system or the surroundings." Reversible processes and cycles are ideals to which actual processes and cycles can be compared to measure their performance. The thermal efficiency of an actual refrigerator is compared to that of a Carnot refrigerator operating between the same temperature levels. The ratio of the amount of power required by a Carnot machine to the refrigeration produced is given by

$$\frac{W_n}{Q_{\text{Carnot}}} = \frac{T_0 - T}{T} \tag{4.5}$$

where W_n is the net power, Q is the refrigeration produced, T is the temperature, on the thermodynamic temperature scale, at which the cycle is producing refrigeration, while T_0 is the temperature at which heat is being rejected by the machine — usually about 300 K, the nominal temperature of the earth's atmosphere or cooling water supply. Thus, for a helium temperature refrigerator operating between 4.2 and 300 K the best performance that could be achieved is 70.4 units of power required per unit of refrigeration. As will be shown in section 4.5, it is not unusual for an actual machine to consume 100 times the Carnot power per unit of usable refrigeration. The efficiencies of various processes are also calculated by comparing them with appropriate, assumed, reversible processes.

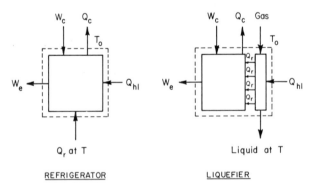

FIGURE 4.2. *Comparison of energy and mass transfers across control volume for a refrigerator and a liquefier.*

4.3. REFRIGERATION CYCLES AND METHODS

4.3.1. The Relationship of Refrigerators and Liquefiers

In 1967 during the Eleventh International Congress of Refrigeration in Madrid, Spain, Professor Kurti of the Clarendon Laboratories at Oxford University made some very interesting remarks about the subject at hand. He noted that although there are many natural spontaneously occurring events which result in temperatures above that of the surroundings, the creation of temperatures below that of the surroundings requires the intervention of man. Very low temperatures are produced both in helium refrigerators and helium liquefiers. Although the terms refrigerator and liquefier bring to mind devices that are dissimilar in nature, a slightly closer examination reveals that in many ways they are much alike. Figure 4.2 illustrates the energy and mass transfers across the control surfaces around a refrigerator and a liquefier operating at steady state. The effect desired from a refrigerator is the ability to absorb energy at low temperatures. This refrigeration effect is shown as Q_r in figure 4.2. The other energy transfers across the control surface are the work, W_c, that is necessary to produce the cooling; the work, W_e, that is produced by expansion engines if any, heat leak through the insulation to the low-temperature portions of the refrigerator, Q_{hl}; and the heat rejected to the atmosphere, Q_c, which is the algebraic sum of all of the other energy transfers. Here it is indicated that the refrigeration effect, Q_r, is produced at a single temperature, T. A liquefier can be thought of as a refrigerator and an independent side stream of gas which is to be cooled from ambient temperature to its liquefaction temperature. One essential difference between the two cooling devices is that in the liquefier, cooling for the side stream must be produced at all intermediate temperatures from ambient to the liquid temperature. In practice liquid is indeed produced internally in many helium refrigerators. The material to be cooled is then attached to a vessel within the refrigerator which contains the liquid helium. Any energy evolved by the refrigerated material itself or transferred to it from the ambient surroundings tends to raise its temperature. The energy is transferred to the then colder liquid helium, a portion of which evaporates, and the cold gas is returned to the refrigerator for recycling. If the object to be cooled cannot be placed within the refrigerator cold box itself, the liquid can be piped to a remote location through insulated channels and the cold gas returned to the refrigerator. In either case, there is no mass transfer into or out of the control surface. As the control surface is drawn around the liquefier in figure 4.2, there is mass transfer across that surface. A different situation could be imagined wherein the liquid is drawn out of a reservoir in the liquefier, used to cool some object, and warm, room-temperature gas returned to the liquefier. The control surface could be drawn around the entire system and there would be no mass transfer across the control surface. The essential difference is, however, that warm gas is returned to be cooled and reliquefied.

There is one more point to be made about the situation described by figure 4.2. There are no intermediate temperature thermal shields indicated between ambient temperature and the lowest temperature parts of the apparatus. In that situation, any heat leak into the cold box reduces the useful refrigeration at the refrigeration temperature by an equivalent amount or, in the case of the liquefier, reduces the liquefaction rate.

4.3.2. Liquid Helium Baths

By far the most common method of providing cooling at 4.2 K is by using liquid helium, supplied from a remote liquefier, as the heat sink. The material which requires this low-temperature environment is placed in thermal contact with the liquid helium bath either by immersing it in the liquid or attaching it to the container. The heat load imposed upon the low-temperature sink consists of the energy evolved, if any, by the cold object and heat leaks to the low-temperature apparatus via support structures, through insulations, and by radiation. As soon as a temperature difference providing the driving potential is established, energy will be transferred to the colder liquid. If the vessel containing the liquid is maintained at a constant pressure, i.e., allowed to vent, the liquid will evaporate at a rate sufficient to maintain equilibrium temperature at that pressure. The cold saturated helium vapor leaving the vessel has a refrigeration potential and in some instances the vent pipe is attached to intermediate temperature shields which reduce the amount of heat transfer from the surroundings to the low-temperature space, thus decreasing the liquid evaporation rate.

The heat of vaporization of liquid helium (see chapter 2) is 0.725 W-hr/l at 1 atm. The rate of liquid evaporation is found by dividing the total heat load (supplied to the liquid) by the heat of vaporization of the liquid. Thus a 1-W heat load will evaporate 1.38 l of liquid per hour and large heat loads require substantial amounts of the relatively expensive liquid. Each new cooling requirement forces a choice between refrigerating with bulk liquid helium or with a closed cycle refrigerator. Winters and Snow [4] describe an economic analysis of providing refrigeration at liquid helium temperatures for large heat loads. The analysis takes into account the capital and operating costs, both direct and indirect, for various duty cycles. Their results show that for a 100-W heat load, unless the system is to be operated in excess of 95 hr per year over a 10-year period, it is economically favorable to provide the refrigeration with bulk liquid helium. At higher heat loads the economic break-even number of operating hours per year becomes smaller.

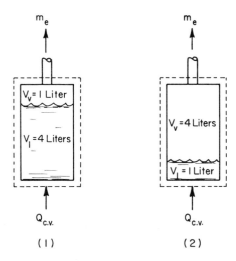

FIGURE 4.3. *Liquid helium bath used for example calculation of the heat transferred to the liquid in an insulated enclosure.*

Since the heat leak to insulated low-temperature liquid containers is often estimated by measuring the amount of gas that is evolved, let us examine the 5-l liquid helium vessel in figure 4.3. Initially the vessel is shown to contain 4 l of saturated liquid helium at 1 atm pressure with a 1-l ullage volume filled with saturated vapor. In addition to heat transfer across the control surface there is mass transfer at the vent. After a period of time, 3 l of liquid have evaporated because of the heat influx, leaving 1 l of saturated liquid and 4 l of saturated vapor. The remainder of the helium has passed out through the vent. Data from chapter 2 show

that 7827.7 J are required to effect a phase change for 3 l of liquid helium
and that 374.5 g of liquid will evaporate. Misinterpretation of the situation seems to occur often enough that it is worthwhile to point out the
errors which can be made. The proper form of eq (4.1) for the container is

$$Q_{c.v.} = m_e h_e + m_{l_2} u_{l_2} + m_{v_2} u_{v_2} - m_{l_1} u_{l_1} - m_{v_1} u_{v_1}. \qquad (4.6)$$

In order to evaluate eq (4.6), two types of dynamic measurements,
the mass flow out of the vessel and the liquid level, must be made and
the container geometry must be well known. Obviously, eq (4.6) is not
the most convenient approach for determining the heat transfer, since
if the change in liquid level is known, the mass of liquid evaporated can
be determined from the vessel geometry and the product of the heat
of vaporization, and the mass of liquid which has changed phase gives
the heat transfer. Often it is more convenient to measure the mass flow,
m_e, than it is to monitor the liquid level. All too often it is assumed that
the internal energy-mass products in eq (4.6) are negligible and $Q_{c.v.}$
is equated to $m_e h_e$. If this is done for the example in figure 4.3, the calculated heat leak is 28 percent too high. The product $m_e L_v$, where L_v
is the heat of vaporization, which is sometimes used for an approximate
calculation, leads to a computed heat input that is 13.3 percent too low
for the example, because only 86.7 percent of the mass that changes
phase passes through the vent. Equation (4.7),

$$Q_{c.v.} = \frac{m_e L_v}{(1 - v_l/v_v)}, \qquad (4.7)$$

where v_l and v_v are the specific volumes of the saturated liquid and
vapor, takes into account the amount of mass that changes from liquid
to vapor but is retained in the vessel and is the most convenient path to
correct results providing the assumption that the liquid and vapor are
saturated is valid for the situation in question. If there is temperature
stratification in the liquid or vapor, the measurement of m_e will not be
sufficient to determine the heat load to the liquid.

4.3.3. The Simon Process — Adiabatic Expansion

Before the development of the Collins liquefier, the Simon process
was often used to batch-produce small amounts of liquid helium. When
a high-pressure gas is allowed to vent, the fluid in the thick-walled con-

tainer expands isentropically and its temperature decreases as the pressure is lowered. Although the expansion process is isentropic, as the fluid cools there will be heat transferred to it from the warmer walls of the vessel, resulting in an entropy increase of the fluid. Fortunately at liquid helium temperatures the specific heat of most container materials is very low and such entropy contributions may be negligible.

In practice, liquid helium is produced by the Simon process in the following manner. The apparatus is designed so that the high-pressure vessel can be either thermally isolated from its surroundings or brought into contact with one of two heat sinks, usually liquid nitrogen and liquid hydrogen. The vessel is filled with helium, usually at a pressure in excess of 100 atm, and that pressure is maintained by introducing more helium as the vessel and the helium are cooled to liquid nitrogen temperature. Then liquid hydrogen is used to cool the apparatus to about 20 K. The liquid helium yield is increased substantially if the pressure over the hydrogen is reduced so that the temperature of the vessel approaches 10 K. As soon as the lowest temperature has been attained, the high-pressure vessel is isolated from the surroundings and the expansion process is carried out by relieving the pressure in the cold vessel.

The amount of liquid helium produced depends upon the state of the fluid prior to the expansion process. The technique is described by Simon [5, 6], and Pickard and Simon [7]. Scott [8] develops the correct relationship for predicting the liquid yield when using this technique.

Primarily because of economic advantages, the Simon process has been used recently by Taylor [9] to intermittently refrigerate sodium magnet coils at approximately 7 K. The system produces 15 kW of refrigeration for a period of 1 min and is capable of repeating that duty every 6 hr. The high-pressure helium and the vessel are first cooled to 12 K by a closed-cycle helium gas refrigerator. The flow path conducts the fluid from the vessel to the sodium magnet coils and then through thermal regenerators into ambient temperature low pressure helium storage. Just prior to refrigerating the magnet coils, the helium in the vessel is at 12 K and about 160 atm. Since the coils must be maintained at about 7 K during operation, the vessel must be blown down to about 70 atm in order to reduce the temperature prior to the experiment and that helium is used to precool the magnet coils and the regenerators. The thermal regenerators are used to cool the helium gas as the vessel is being recharged in preparation for another refrigeration cycle, thus minimizing the loss of cooling capacity.

4.3.4. The Joule-Thomson Process

The lowest temperature stage in virtually all liquid-helium-temperature refrigerators consists of a counterflow heat exchanger, an expansion valve, and an evaporator. The expansion process through the valve is irreversible and the fluid performs no external work, although prior to passage through the restriction it has the potential for doing so by virtue of its elevated pressure. In section 4.3.1, the energy balance around an entire refrigerator showed that the refrigeration capacity would increase if the work produced by expansion machines were extracted from the control volume. Therefore, if the pressure reduction of the fluid occurred in a work-producing expander, rather than irreversibly through a valve, the cycle efficiency would increase. In most instances, the valve has been chosen over a mechanical expander because the increased cost and complexity of the expander were judged to overshadow the benefits to cycle performance.

The Joule-Thomson process is defined as the adiabatic isenthalpic reduction in pressure of a fluid flowing through a restriction in a passage. Although this process takes place only in the expansion valve, the additional energy transferred in the heat exchanger and evaporator will

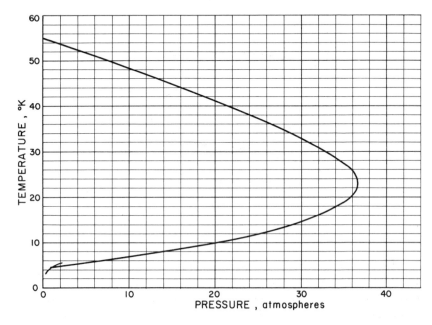

FIGURE 4.4. *Helium inversion curve.*

also be considered. The Joule-Thomson process has been extensively analyzed by Dean and Mann [10] and much of the material in this section is from that work. Because the Joule-Thomson process is used so extensively in liquid-helium-temperature refrigerators, the differences between the refrigerators can be thought of as primarily the various methods used for precooling the fluid before entering the Joule-Thomson exchanger.

The temperature change as a result of an adiabatic isenthalpic process depends upon the properties of the fluid, the inlet pressure and temperature, and the final pressure. The Joule-Thomson coefficient is

$$\mu = \left(\frac{\partial T}{\partial p}\right)_h . \tag{4.8}$$

This coefficient may be positive, negative, or zero and the locus of points where the Joule-Thomson coefficient is zero is called the inversion curve and is shown on temperature-pressure coordinates in figure 4.4. The vapor pressure curve for helium appears in the lower lefthand corner of that figure.

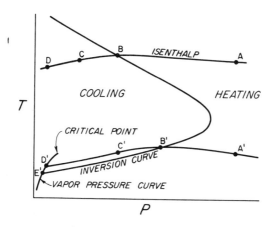

FIGURE 4.5. *Joule-Thomson expansion process.*

Regions of heating and cooling upon expansion are shown in figure 4.5. A Joule-Thomson expansion process which has initial and end states within the inversion curve envelope where μ is positive will lower the temperature of the fluid, while such a process occurring outside the envelope will raise the temperature of the fluid. Expansion from a temperature above the maximum inversion temperature will always result in heating. If the fluid is expanded from state A to state B, the temperature of the fluid will rise. Further expansion to state C results in cooling to the original temperature and an end state of D will lower the temperature below the initial temperature. Since the same net temperature drop is obtained by expanding the gas from either states C or A to state D, there is no reason for expending the energy required to compress the fluid to any pressure higher than the pressure at C.

Lowering the initial temperature results in operation in the portion of the temperature-pressure plane where the slopes of the isenthalps are greater and eventually where the isenthalps intersect the vapor pressure curve. This intersection is the extension of the isenthalps into the two-phase liquid-vapor region and means that a fraction of the gas expanded into this region is liquefied.

State D' is the intersection of an isenthalp with the two-phase liquid-vapor region and E' is the intersection of the isenthalp with the isobar corresponding to the exit pressure of the expansion valve. The choice of the final pressure corresponding to E' establishes the temperature of the liquid following the expansion process. The pressures at D' and E' should be as low as possible if maximum temperature drop is desired.

The Joule-Thomson refrigeration system is a counterflow regenerative heat exchanger connected in series with an expansion valve and an evaporator as shown schematically in figure 4.6. The compressor for the system operates at ambient temperature while the heat exchanger in figure 4.6 operates generally in the cryogenic temperature range. Intermediate heat exchangers and expansion engines are not considered as part of the thermodynamic system.

In order to cool the system down to the refrigeration temperature, an outside source of refrigeration must be used to precool the helium at station 1 to about 55 K and preferably much lower. With the system at the uniform precooling temperature, the refrigeration process is started by supplying a quantity of compressed cold gas to station 1. The refrigeration made available by the expansion process is used to cool the mass of metal of the evaporator and the return stream side of the heat exchanger. The external heat load is withheld in order to expedite cooling. Cooling the heat exchanger return stream side, between stations 4 and 5, results in cooling the inlet gas stream between stations 1 and 2. For the ideal heat exchanger considered here, stations 1 and 5 remain at the initial temperature while the temperature of stations 2, 3, and 4 is depressed. As the

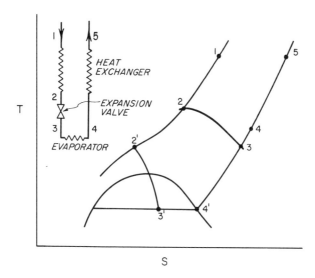

FIGURE 4.6. *Schematic of a Joule-Thomson refrigeration system.*

temperature of station 2 is depressed, the temperature of stations 3 and 4 also becomes colder due to the Joule-Thomson effect. Thus the refrigeration process is self-perpetuating until an equilibrium condition is reached.

The stable equilibrium condition at which a Joule-Thomson refrigerator is normally operated is shown by stations 1, 2′, 3′, 4′, and 5 on the temperature-entropy surface of figure 4.6. Temperature depression at the expansion valve continues until liquid is condensed into the evaporator. Refrigeration is obtained isothermally by the evaporation of the liquid. A prerequisite for this type of operation is that the return stream pressure be less than critical pressure, since the temperature at which the evaporator will operate is fixed by the vapor pressure of the refrigerant.

This type of operation tends to be stable in temperature due to the presence of liquid and the magnitude of the heat of vaporization. Mass flow through the evaporator must be matched to the heat load for continuous stable operation, as an excessive heat load will result in reducing the quantity of liquid rather than in changing the system temperature. If corrective action is not taken, such as increasing the compressor flow rate, the evaporator will eventually go dry, forcing the evaporator temperature to increase into the non-isothermal operating region. In contrast, insufficient heat load will result in flooding of any type of evaporator. Thus, the refrigeration process must be controlled in either mode, but the case of isothermal operation is easier to control.

Dean and Mann [10] made extensive calculations to obtain the characteristics of the Joule-Thomson system. If the coefficient of performance method of rating refrigerators is applied to cryogenic systems, the results are performance figures less than unity. Here the performance has been rated using the reciprocal of the coefficient of performance and is the compression power requirement divided by the refrigeration absorbed. The power required for the compressor was assumed to be equal to the power required to compress an ideal gas isothermally between the same states:

$$W_c = -\dot{m}\,\frac{RT_{amb}}{M}\ln\,(P_1/P_5),\qquad(4.9)$$

where W_c is the compressor power requirement, $\dot{m}$ is the mass flow rate of the fluid, R is the universal gas constant, T_{amb} is the compression temperature, M is the molecular weight, and P_1 and P_5 are the compressor discharge and suction pressure. To obtain realistic refrigeration power requirements, the power term as calculated by eq (4.9) must be divided by the isothermal compression efficiency—a figure of 50 to 60 percent is common for reciprocating compressors using piston rings. The useful refrigeration Q, absorbed at 4.2 K, was calculated from a first law energy balance. Performance is rated by the ratio W_c/Q, the dimensionless figure of merit. In order to put the calculations on a common basis, division by the isothermal efficiency has not been performed and is left to the reader who must consider the merits of his compressor. When a refrigeration system is considered that utilizes other energy sources, such as an auxiliary refrigerator, that power term must be added to the numerator to obtain an overall performance figure.

Application of the first law of thermodynamics to the refrigeration system of figure 4.6 where frictional losses due to velocity effects are negligible yields the following energy balance:

$$\dot{Q} = \dot{m}(h_5 - h_1)\qquad(4.10)$$

where $\dot{Q}$ is the refrigeration power. The externally useful refrigeration is equal to the difference in the total enthalpy of the refrigerant entering and leaving the system at the top of the heat exchanger stations 1 and 5. The figure of merit, W_c/Q, is found by forming the ratio of eqs (4.9) and (4.10).

Calculations were made for a wide range of parameters consisting of the heat exchanger operating pressures, precooling temperature, and temperature difference at the top of the heat exchanger. The majority of the calculations were made with a return stream pressure of 1 atm, allowing isothermal refrigeration at the normal boiling point temperature. Inlet stream pressure and precooling temperature were varied from near the critical to near the maximum inversion pressure and temperature. The temperature difference at the top of the heat exchanger was varied by reducing the temperature at station 5. The figure of merit and the flow rate in gram moles per second required to produce 1 W of useful refrigeration were calculated for each set of parameters.

Temperature differences between heat exchanger refrigerant streams introduce irreversibilities, but they are necessary to effect heat transfer. Consider the equations which describe the heat transfer between the two gas streams of the heat exchanger.

$$\text{heat exchanger load} = \dot{m} \int_{T_1}^{a} C_{p_{1-a}} dT = \dot{m} \int_{T_5}^{b} C_{p_{5-b}} dT \qquad (4.11)$$

where a and b are intermediate temperatures of the high and low pressure gas streams (see fig. 4.7), and C_p is specific heat at constant pressure. The temperature and pressure dependency of the specific heat allows

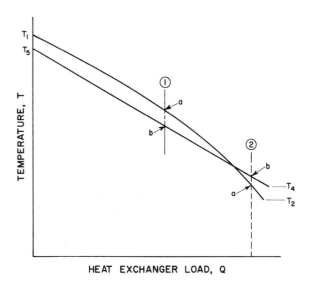

FIGURE 4.7. *Heat exchanger cooling curve — general case.*

the possibility that $b > a$ for small values of $T_1 - T_5$. Since b represents the temperature of the available refrigeration of the low-pressure stream, the condition $b > a$ is not consistent with the second law concept of heat energy flow and is therefore indicative of an invalid choice of operating parameters. Either $T_1 - T_5$ must be increased or other operating pressures and precooling temperatures must be chosen. Increasing $T_1 - T_5$ without changing the precoolant temperature will always increase W_c/Q because of the temperature dependence of the term $(h_5 - h_1)$ in eq (4.10). The designer should investigate the temperature distribution within the heat exchanger for both gas streams using eq (4.11). Even though a minimal temperature difference occurs within or at the cold end $(T_2 - T_4)$ of the exchanger, the temperature difference $T_1 - T_5$ may be used as a parameter to indicate heat exchanger energy losses. Once this temperature difference is fixed, then the internal temperature differences become a function of the properties of the gas.

It is desirable to determine the combination of parameters that gives both the maximum obtainable refrigeration for a given compressor size and the most economical operation. However, no practical single set of parameters satisfies both requirements.

An examination of figure 4.5 shows that the maximum refrigeration is obtained by an expansion process when the initial state of the gas before expansion is on the inversion curve. The effect of inserting an evaporator and a heat exchanger in the system is not so easily seen. Consider eq (4.10). The pressure, temperature, and mass flow rate at station 5 and the temperature and flow rate at station 1 may be considered constant for an equilibrium condition. Thus, the only variable is $h_1 = f(P)$, and the condition for maximum refrigeration becomes $\left(\dfrac{\partial h_1}{\partial P}\right)_T = 0$. This may be restated as

$$\left(\frac{\partial h_1}{\partial T}\right)_P \left(\frac{\partial T}{\partial P}\right)_h = 0 \qquad (4.12)$$

or

$$C_p \cdot \mu = 0.$$

The Joule-Thomson coefficient must be zero in order to satisfy eq (4.12), as C_p is never zero through the operating range of the Joule-Thomson process. Thus, to obtain maximum refrigeration for a fixed mass

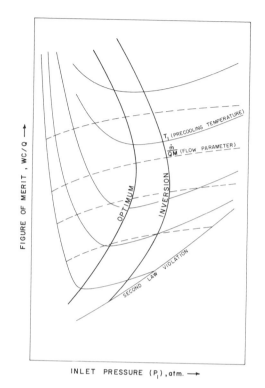

FIGURE 4.8. *Generalized performance surface for a Joule-Thomson refrigeration system.*

flow rate and precooling temperature, the inlet stream pressure must lie on the inversion curve.

Figure 4.8 is an unscaled representation of the performance surface for a Joule-Thomson refrigeration system giving the figure of merit and flow rate as a function of inlet pressure for values of $T_1 - T_5$ with $P_5 = 1$ atm. Continuous curves of W_c/Q are shown for each precooling temperature (T_1) from near the normal boiling temperature to near the maximum inversion temperature. The locus of the minimum W_c/Q is marked "optimum," indicating the best operating pressures from the standpoint of power requirement. The inversion curve has been superimposed on the performance curve to indicate the states where maximum refrigeration is achieved as a function of mass flow.

Flow rate information, $\dfrac{\dot{m}}{QM}$, where M is molecular weight, included with the performance curves by dashed lines, gives the flow in gram moles per second required to produce 1 W of refrigeration. Since this is a flow rate divided by an energy rate, the time units cancel causing the flow information to have units of gm-mole/J. Multiplying these values by 47.5 converts the flow information to cubic feet per minute (standard of 1 atm and 0 C) per watt of refrigeration—convenient units when dealing with American compressor manufacturers.

Results of eq (4.11) are given by a line marked "second law violation," indicating a limit to the range of possible operating parameters. Calculations of heat exchanger operation on or below this line result in $T_4 > T_2$ for isothermal refrigeration. Attempts to operate in this region result in $T_1 - T_5$ becoming larger than the designer anticipates with a

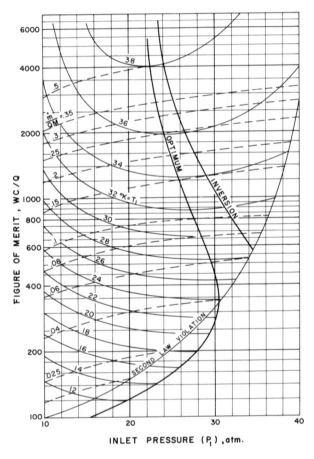

FIGURE 4.9.   *Joule-Thomson refrigerator performance* $-(T_1 - T_3) = 0.25$ *K.*

corresponding reduction of performance—possibly to a point where no useful refrigeration is obtainable. One exception to this statement may be made if the refrigeration system is modified by inserting another heat exchanger and expansion valve in series as discussed later in connection with the Claude cycle.

Figures 4.9 and 4.10 are representative of the results of the calculations for two different heat exchanger temperature differences and show the effect of the irreversibilities in the exchanger. For example, at a precool temperature of 26 K, the optimum power required per unit of refrigeration increases by 32 percent as the heat exchanger temperature difference $(T_1 - T_5)$ spreads from 0.25 to 0.50 K.

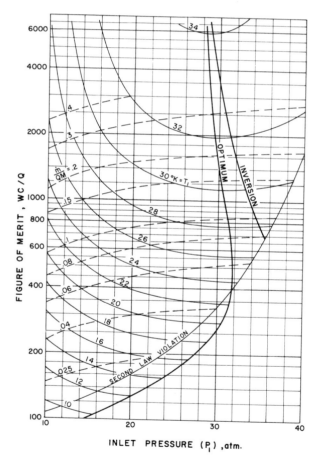

FIGURE 4.10. *Joule-Thomson refrigerator performance* — $(T_1 - T_5) = 0.50 K.$

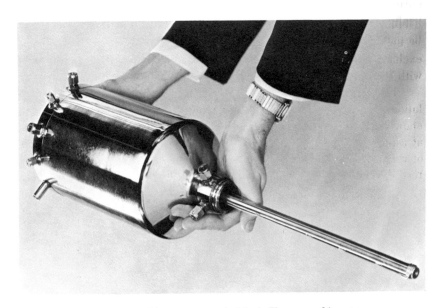

FIGURE 4.11. *Miniature cascaded Joule-Thomson refrigerator.*

This 0.5-W, 4 K refrigerator consumes about 0.5 l/hr of liquid nitrogen, 0.92 scfm of gaseous hydrogen at 58 atm, and 1.4 scfm of gaseous helium at 34 atm.

(Photo courtesy of Air Products and Chemicals, Inc.)

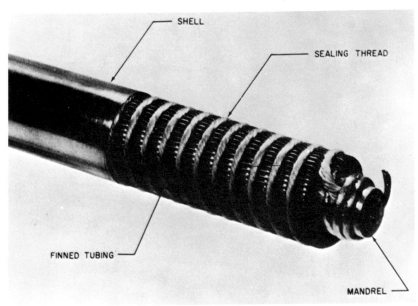

FIGURE 4.12. *Section of finned-tube heat exchanger.*

(Courtesy of Air Products and Chemicals, Inc.)

Dean and Mann [10] present the results of similar calculations for parahydrogen and for nitrogen. Thus, information is available which permits the study of a cascaded Joule-Thomson helium refrigerator where the helium stream is precooled by a parahydrogen Joule-Thomson system which is in turn precooled by a nitrogen Joule-Thomson circuit. Just such a refrigerator is shown in figure 4.11. This small unit provides 0.5 W of refrigeration at 4.4 K and can be supplied with vacuum shrouds which are suitable for experiments in spectroscopy, x-ray diffraction Mössbauer effects and other current research. The compressed gases may be supplied to the unit either from high-pressure storage cylinders, in which case the low-pressure gases are vented to the atmosphere in an open cycle mode of operation, or the gases may be recirculated by a compressor in a closed cycle mode. One of the miniature heat exchangers from this refrigerator is shown in figure 4.12.

4.3.5. The Brayton Cycle

The hydrogen and nitrogen precooling circuits in the cascaded Joule-Thomson helium refrigerator remove energy from the helium as it is progressively cooled from room temperature to the inlet of the final heat exchanger. The same energy removal is often accomplished by utilizing the refrigeration produced by one or more mechanical expanders of either the reciprocating or turbo-machinery varieties described later. In 1873 a Boston engineer, George Brayton, conceived an ideal heat engine combining constant pressure and constant entropy processes. During the past several years the Brayton cycle, operating as an open cycle refrigerator, has been used extensively in aircraft cooling, and the cycle is being considered for space power systems. The low-temperature refrigeration performance of the cycle has been studied by Muhlenhaupt and Strobridge [11] with nitrogen, parahydrogen, and helium as the working fluids.

A schematic flow diagram of the modified Brayton refrigeration cycle is shown in figure 4.13, and the process paths are illustrated on temperature-entropy coordinates in figure 4.14. The processes are isobaric cooling in the high-pressure side of the heat exchanger between stations 1 and 2, adiabatic expansion between 2 and 3, isobaric heat absorption of the refrigeration load between 3 and 4, isobaric heating between 4 and 5, and isothermal compression at T_1 between the high and low pressures. The process path shown in figure 4.14 between stations 5 and 1 is not isothermal because a finite temperature difference will

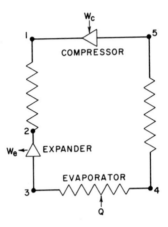

FIGURE 4.13.   *Schematic of modified Brayton cycle refrigerator.*

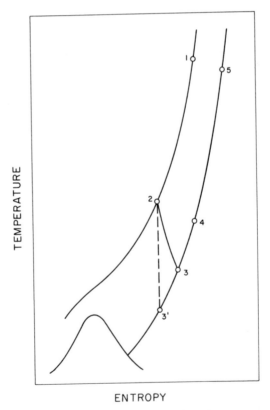

FIGURE 4.14.   *Process paths of modified Brayton cycle refrigerator.*

exist in the heat exchanger of any refrigerator. It is assumed that the temperature of the fluid at the inlet to the compressor will be T_1 due to heat transfer with the surroundings through the interconnecting piping. The modification to Brayton's original cycle is the assumed isothermal rather than the isentropic compression. The compression power required will be calculated from the same relationship used for the Joule-Thomson cycle discussed in the previous section. The figure of merit, W_c/Q, is given by

$$W_c/Q = \frac{RT_1 \ln \dfrac{P_1}{P_5}}{M(h_4 - h_3)}. \tag{4.13}$$

The expansion device does produce a certain amount of power which presumably could be routed back to the compressor drive, reducing the amount of power required from outside sources. In actual practice, the amount of power produced by the expander is very small compared to that required by the compressor, and is not recovered. Therefore, the expander power is not reflected in eq (4.13). The Brayton cycle does not produce refrigeration at a single temperature as does the Joule-

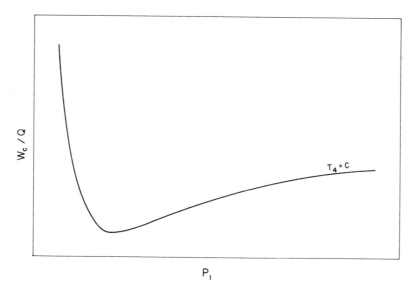

FIGURE 4.15. *General performance of Brayton cycle refrigerator as a function of compressor exhaust pressure for a constant temperature differential and expander efficiency.*

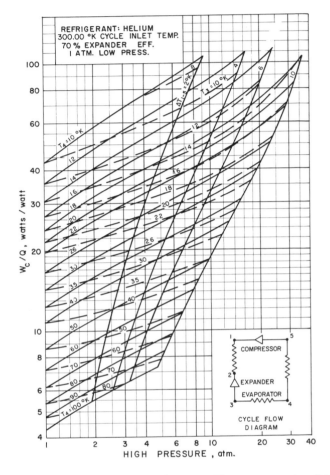

FIGURE 4.16.   *Brayton refrigerator performance — 70 percent expander efficiency.*

Thomson process; rather, the heat sink temperatures vary from T_3 up to T_4, which will be referred to as the refrigeration temperature for this cycle since it is the highest at which heat is absorbed from the load. In order to see how the heat exchanger and expander efficiencies affect the figure of merit, assume that the compression temperature, the pressures, and the refrigeration temperatures are fixed. Neglecting for the moment any heat leak to the heat exchanger, eq (4.1) yields the following

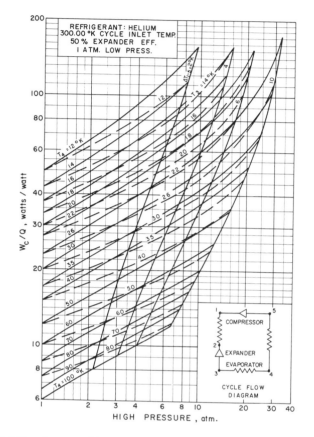

FIGURE 4.17. *Brayton refrigerator performance—50 percent expander efficiency.*

enthalpy balance for the heat exchanger:

$$h_1 + h_4 = h_5 + h_2. \tag{4.14}$$

The assumptions have fixed the enthalpies at stations 1 and 4. Any losses in the exchanger will depress the temperature and hence the enthalpy at 5, forcing an enthalpy and temperature rise at 2. Even though the compressor power requirement stays constant, any inefficiencies in the heat exchanger raise the operating temperature of the expander and therefore decrease the enthalpy change across the evaporator as h_3 becomes larger. The isentropic efficiency of the expander is defined

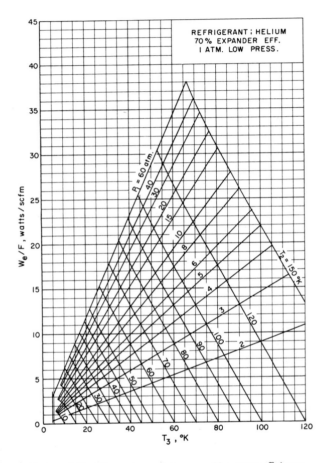

FIGURE 4.18. *Expander performance — 70 percent efficiency.*

as

$$\eta_e = \frac{h_2 - h_3}{h_2 - h_3'} \tag{4.15}$$

where the prime indicates the enthalpy following an isentropic expansion
from the inlet to the expander. Losses in the expander have the same
effect as those in the heat exchanger, since the temperature at station 3
is increased and the amount of useful refrigeration depends on the enthalpy at the outlet of the expander.

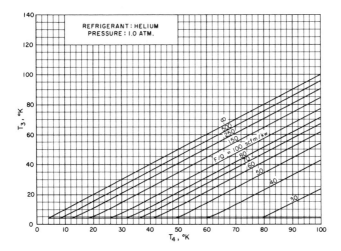

FIGURE 4.19. *Brayton cycle helium flow requirement per unit of refrigeration as a function of the evaporator inlet and outlet temperatures.*

If the refrigeration temperature and the expander and heat exchanger efficiencies are selected, assuming ambient temperature compression and 1-atm low pressure, the power required to produce a unit of refrigeration is a function of the high pressure. Figure 4.15 shows a typical plot of eq (4.13) evaluated at various high pressures for a given refrigeration temperature, heat exchanger temperature difference, and expander efficiency. This curve shows that under the assumed conditions, there is in fact an optimum compressor discharge pressure at which the cycle should be operated if maximum thermal efficiency is desired. Fixing the expander and heat exchanger efficiencies and repeating the calculations for other refrigeration temperatures will produce a family of curves similar to that in figure 4.15. The locus of the minima in those curves then gives the optimum operating pressures for that particular expander efficiency and heat exchanger temperature difference over a range of refrigeration temperatures. Going one step further; and finding the locus of the optimum pressures at other heat exchanger temperature differences, then produces the charts shown in figures 4.16 and 4.17, which are for 70 percent and 50 percent expander efficiencies, respectively. Performance charts such as these quickly show the effect of component efficiencies upon the power required to produce the refrigeration. For example, at a refrigeration temperature of 20 K and a 70 percent expander efficiency, increasing the heat exchanger temperature difference from 2 to 4 K would require a 27 percent increase in compressor power to produce the same amount of refrigeration. At a 4 K heat exchanger temperature difference, a change in the expander efficiency from 50 to 70 percent would divide the power requirement in half. Other information needed for preliminary design work, such as the expander power output, the expander inlet temperature, and the flow rate, is given in figures 4.18 and 4.19. It should be noted that the minima in the curves illustrated in figure 4.15 are quite wide, so that within reasonable limits, the Brayton cycle refrigerator can be operated at nonoptimum pressures without suffering a severe loss of efficiency. The further effects of precooling, pressure drop, and reheat are discussed in the reference given.

4.3.6. The Claude Cycle

The Claude cycle, as it has become known after the Frenchman who constructed one of the first really successful low-temperature expansion engines, has been used for many years in air liquefaction and separation plants. This thermodynamic cycle has also found use in other applications at lower temperatures and has been incorporated in several different liquid helium temperature refrigerators. The cycle can be thought of as a Joule-Thomson system precooled by a Brayton cycle refrigerator. In practice, however, the cycles are superimposed and share the same warm heat exchangers and compressor, as shown in figure 4.20 and companion figure 4.21.

The compressor circulates the helium at mass flow rate $\dot{m}_1$. As the high-pressure stream passes through the warmest of the counterflow heat exchangers HX I, it is cooled by the low-pressure stream to temperature T_2. At that point, some of the fluid is diverted through the expansion engine at rate $\dot{m}_2$. The remainder of a flow, $\dot{m}_1 - \dot{m}_2$, is further cooled in HX II to below the inversion temperature by both the low-pressure stream returning from the load and by the cold exhaust of the expansion engine, and then passes through the final heat exchanger before entering the Joule-Thomson valve. A portion of the stream is liquefied during the expansion process, and this liquid is evaporated as the stream passes through the heat absorber. The vapor then returns through the low pressure side of the heat exchanger.

Figure 4.20 shows two expansion valves, one of which splits the Joule-Thomson heat exchanger into two sections. At times, intermediate valves are necessary to produce the proper temperature profiles in the Joule-Thomson heat exchanger and, in fact, three valves are used in a 300-W, 1.85 K refrigerator which will cool a superconducting linear accelerator at Stanford University [12].

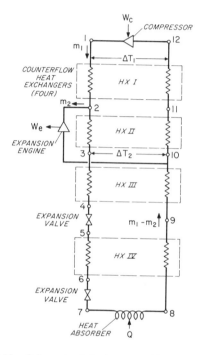

FIGURE 4.20.   *Schematic of single-engine Claude refrigerator.*
The presence of an expansion valve between 4 and 5 will change cycle to the curve 5–6'.

Steady-state conditions are assumed throughout for analysis. Potential and kinetic energy contributions to the fluid energy are negligible. With these considerations, application of the first law of thermodynamics to the various components of the system yields the following equations:

For the upper heat exchanger HX I,

$$h_1 - h_2 = h_{12} - h_{11}. \tag{4.16}$$

For heat exchanger HX II,

$$(\dot{m}_1 - \dot{m}_2)(h_2 - h_3) = \dot{m}_1(h_{11} - h_{10}). \tag{4.17}$$

For heat exchanger HX III,

$$h_3 - h_4 = h_{10} - h_9. \tag{4.18}$$

For the lower heat exchangers HX III and HX IV,

$$h_3 - h_6 = h_{10} - h_8. \tag{4.19}$$

For the expansion valve,

$$h_7 = h_6. \tag{4.20}$$

For the heat absorber evaporator,

$$Q = (\dot{m}_1 - \dot{m}_2)(h_8 - h_7). \tag{4.21}$$

The figure of merit is

$$W_c/Q = \frac{m_1 R T_1 \ln(P_1/P_{12})}{M(\dot{m}_1 - \dot{m}_2)(h_8 - h_7)}. \tag{4.22}$$

Rearranging eq (4.17) and substituting equalities gives the expression for percent of total mass flow through the expander

$$\frac{\dot{m}_2}{\dot{m}_1} = \left(\frac{h_1 - h_{12} + h_{10} - h_3}{h_2 - h_3}\right) \times 100. \tag{4.23}$$

Using the above equations and the expression for isothermal compression work, Muhlenhaupt and Strobridge [13] have made calculations which assist in obtaining the most efficient performance from the

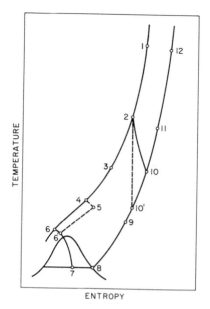

FIGURE 4.21. *Process paths of single-engine Claude refrigerator.*

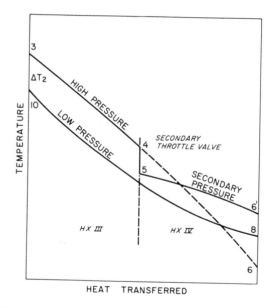

FIGURE 4.22. *Cooling curve for heat exchanger with secondary valve as shown in figure 4.21.*

Claude cycle refrigerator. For a given set of heat exchanger and expander efficiencies and a high pressure, there is, in terms of the amount of power required per unit of refrigeration, an optimum engine inlet temperature. Equation (4.23) shows that the flow distribution is a function of the engine inlet temperature. The Joule-Thomson portion of the cycle becomes more efficient as the inlet temperature of the exchanger (governed by the inlet temperature of the expansion machine and its efficiency) is lowered. However, at lower temperatures the precooling refrigeration from the expander decreases so the expander flow rate must increase and more compressor power for precooling is required. The optimum engine inlet temperature occurs at a balance between these two opposing effects. For each set of conditions, the best value of T_2 was found to within 0.05 K and the curves in figures 4.23 through 4.26 are all for optimum T_2.

It is possible to select numerous sets of independent parameters which are invalid for a single expansion-valve refrigerator due to implied violations of the second law of thermodynamics in the Joule-Thomson heat exchanger as discussed in section 4.3.4. The fluid entering the low-pressure side of that heat exchanger is assumed to be saturated vapor at 1 atm, station 8, figure 4.20 and state 8, figure 4.21. Optimization of T_2 determines state 10, selection of ΔT_2 gives state 3, and solution of eq (4.19) determines state 6. All these manipulations are straightforward applications of the first law of thermodynamics. However, because the specific heats of the high- and low-pressure streams are different, it may be that under the assumed conditions, the calculated temperature at state 6 is lower than at state 8. This impossible situation is illustrated schematically in figure 4.22 where the temperatures of the high- and low-pressure streams are plotted as a function of the heat transferred between them. This cooling curve shows, with the dashed high-pressure line, the invalid temperature profile in the heat exchanger calculated from the first law of thermodynamics for a single-valve arrangement. The effect of a secondary valve between 4 and 5 is to lower the pressure to some intermediate level where the specific heat of the fluid will give a positive temperature difference throughout the exchanger. The heat balance below the expansion machine is not affected by the second valve. During the computations, if a negative temperature difference was found between 6 and 8, a second valve was included in an attempt to correct the situation. The region where such valves are required is indicated on the performance charts.

Typical results of the performance characteristic calculations of the single-engine Claude-cycle refrigerator at 4.2 K are shown in figures 4.23 through 4.26. Figure 4.23 shows the compression power per unit of refrigeration W_c/Q as a function of high-pressure P_1 for various values of expander inlet temperature T_2 and upper heat exchanger inlet temperature (low-pressure side) T_{11}. The values on the charts represent the conditions for which the expander inlet temperature T_2 is at an optimum level and the cycle inlet temperature T_1 is at a temperature of 300 K. The solid line marked "two valves" indicates the limit to the range of possible operating pressures for the single-valve refrigerator. Hence, an additional valve must be included in the system before higher pressures are valid. The power requirement per unit of refrigeration reaches a minimum value; and the cycle can be optimized for high pressure as well as for expander inlet temperature. Figure 4.24 gives expander power per unit of refrigeration at 4.2 K, W_e/Q, as a function of high-pressure P_1 for various values of expander flow $\dot{m}_2$. Notice the relatively small power output of the expander compared to the power input to the compressor.

Figure 4.25 shows the expansion engine outlet temperature T_{out} as a function of the expander inlet temperature T_{in} for several values of helium inlet pressure P_{in}, while figure 4.26 shows total volumetric flow F_t as a straight-line function of the compression work per unit of refrigeration W_c/Q for several values of high-pressure P_1.

The shapes of the curves in figures 4.23 and 4.24 reflect the characteristics of the Brayton cycle and the Joule-Thomson process, which in turn depend upon the thermodynamic properties of the working fluid. For illustration, at a ΔT_2 of 1.0 K, the minimum W_c/Q occurs at about 25 atm high pressure with an engine inlet temperature of about 27 K. The outlet temperature of a 70 percent efficient expander with an inlet at 27 K will be $\sim$ 12 K (see fig. 4.25). Since ΔT_2 is 1.0 K, the inlet to the Joule-Thomson heat exchanger will be at 13 K. From figure 12 of Dean and Mann [10], the optimum high pressure for the Joule-Thomson process, with the inlet at 13 K and a 1 K temperature difference, is $\sim$ 23 atm with the performance decreasing as the high pressure is decreased. The optimum high pressure for a Brayton cycle with the discharge of the expander at 12 K is greater than 23 atm for an ambient temperature difference in the heat exchanger of 10 K. Therefore, the best high pressure for the combination of the cycles falls somewhere in between — in this case $\sim$ 25 atm.

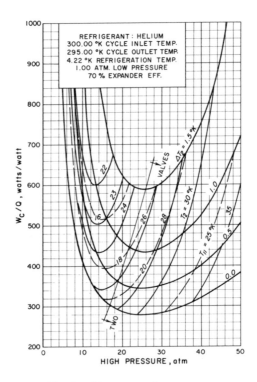

FIGURE 4.23.   *Claude refrigerator, performance — compressor power.*

Consider now the effect of changing the value of ΔT_2 while holding the high pressure constant at ~ 25 atm. The performance of the cycle increases as ΔT_2 becomes smaller because the Joule-Thomson process efficiency increases. The optimum engine inlet temperature rises slightly, since the most favorable inlet temperature for the Joule-Thomson process varies in the same way. Helium behaves almost as an ideal gas at moderate pressures and down to fairly low temperatures. This means that the temperature difference at the cold end of HX I will be about the same as at the warm end, and the curves for constant values of T_{11} will roughly parallel, or at least have the same general characteristics as, those for constant T_2.

At lower pressures, the performance of both cycles becomes progressively unfavorable and the power requirement per unit of refrigeration increases rapidly. There is still a general trend of increasing

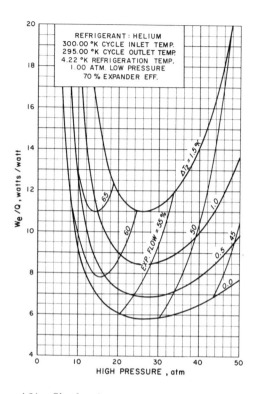

FIGURE 4.24.   *Claude refrigerator performance – expander power.*

optimum engine inlet temperature with better Joule-Thomson heat exchanger performance at constant pressure (see the curve for $T_2 = 22$ K) in figure 4.23.

In figure 4.24 the expansion engine power output, i.e., the amount of precooling performed by the expander, is given as a function of pressure for several values of ΔT_2. At low pressures, two effects are evident. The relative amount of flow through the expander increases as does the amount of energy removed from the cycle per unit of refrigeration. The total flow rate is proportional to W_c/Q, so the amount of precooling required is also proportional to W_c/Q as reflected by the shape of the curves in figure 4.24. The relative flow through the expander decreases at higher pressures where a greater amount of work is produced per unit flow.

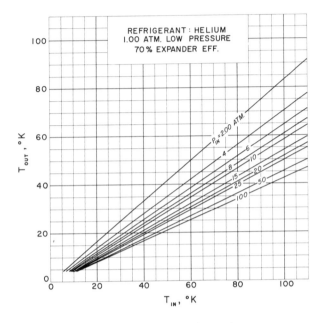

FIGURE 4.25. *Expansion engine performance.*

For discussion purposes, consider a set of realistic component efficiencies (i.e., realistic in the sense that no advance in technology would be required to design and fabricate such components today). Depending on the mass flow rate, expander efficiencies between 50 and 80 percent can be achieved. The temperature difference at the warm end of HX I could be between 5 and 10 K, while ΔT_2 across HX III could be less than 1 K, with 0.5 K considered to be a reasonable value. Choosing ΔT_1 as 5 K, ΔT_2 as 0.5 K and η_e as 70 percent, figure 4.23 shows a power requirement of about 345 W/W for a 100 percent efficient compressor and no pressure drop. Typical isothermal compressor efficiencies are about 60 percent. Estimates can be made of the effect of fluid pressure losses. For example, if the pressure drop were 10 percent of total pressure in both the high- and low-pressure streams, the intake and discharge at the compressor would be 0.9 and 27.5 atm, respectively, for optimum conditions. Ideally, this would raise W_c/Q to about 365. If the compressor efficiency is included, W_c/Q would be about 610. In addition,

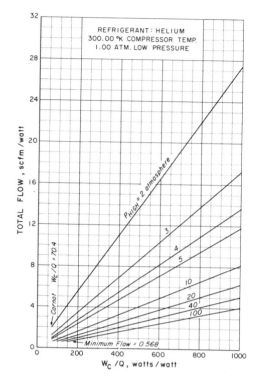

FIGURE 4.26. *Claude refrigerator helium flow rate requirement.*

there are other losses, such as heat leak to the low-temperature space, which become critical in smaller capacity refrigerators and which should be considered when translating the information given here to real situations.

Inspection of the performance charts shows the possible improvement in thermal efficiency if the components could be slightly upgraded. Consider making the following changes in efficiencies given in the example.

1. Decrease ΔT_2 from 0.5 K to 0.25 K,
2. Increase η_e from 70 to 80 percent, and
3. Increase η_c from 60 to 70 percent while holding ΔT_1 constant at 5 K.

From Muhlenhaupt and Strobridge [13], W_c/Q is about 245. The assumed pressure drop increases that value to about 260, and the compressor efficiency increases it still further to a final value of 371, which is a considerable improvement.

About the same improvement in performance as in the previous example is available by precooling the cycle with liquid nitrogen. Precooling involves depressing T_1 to the temperature of an evaporating liquid-nitrogen bath and providing an additional heat exchanger to communicate with the ambient temperature compressor. The liquid nitrogen consumption is determined by the efficiency of the warmest heat exchanger. The cooling provided by the liquid can be converted into an equivalent power requirement to be added to the compressor power. In most instances it is estimated that the increase in W_c/Q would not exceed 10 percent and is considered to be negligible. Inclusion of the equivalent power required for precooling would involve additional parametric studies beyond the scope of this work. Typical conditions could be:

$T_1 = 77.36$ K,

$\Delta T_1 = 2.0$ K,

$\Delta T_2 = 1.0$ K,

$\eta_e = 70$ percent,

$\eta_c = 100$ percent, and

$W_c/Q = 243$ at a high pressure of 19 atm with no pressure drop. Many existing Claude cycle refrigerators are liquid nitrogen precooled, but only the largest of these approach the power requirement of 468 W/W of refrigeration (see section 4.5) which comes from adjusting the above conditions for 10 percent pressure drop and 60 percent compressor efficiency.

4.3.7. The Stirling Cycle

The operating principles of the Stirling cycle have previously been discussed in Chapter 3. This periodic flow cycle, incorporating one or more regenerators, lends itself to compact construction with one piston serving for both compression and expansion in a single-stage unit.

A two-stage Stirling cycle refrigerator is shown in figure 4.27. The top flange is the coldest of the heat sinks. The slightly larger flange is the intermediate temperature station and the bottom flange is the attachment point for the insulating enclosure. This particular refrigerator will absorb about 80 W at 20 K.

FIGURE 4.27. *Two-stage Stirling cycle refrigerator which can simultaneously provide about 80 W of refrigeration at 20 K and 250 W at 75 K.*

The power consumption at 12 K, the lowest temperature which can be attained, is 11.5 kW or 15.4 hp. (Photo courtesy of North American Phillips Co.)

    Stirling cycle refrigerators are not in themselves suitable for re-
frigeration at liquid helium temperatures because of the rapidly dis-
appearing specific heat of the regenerator materials at low temperatures.
The lowest temperatures reported for pure Stirling cycle two-stage
refrigerators are about 12 K. However, helium Joule-Thomson circuits
are effectively precooled by this type of refrigerator. The precooling
stations at two separate temperature levels are shown in figure 4.28,
which is a schematic of such a refrigerator suggested by Rietdijk [14].

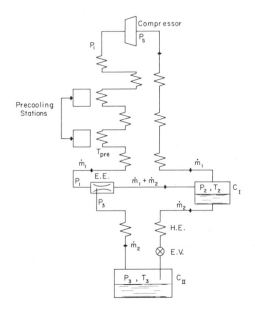

FIGURE 4.28.   *Schematic of Stirling precooled refrigerator with an expansion ejector.*
(Courtesy of Philips Research Laboratories.)

Energy is transferred from the helium to the Stirling cycle refrigerator
through heat exchangers attached to the cold heads of the cooler. The
configuration shown is analogous to a two-expander Claude cycle. After
leaving the lowest temperature precooling station at about 15 K, the helium enters the high-pressure side of the Joule-Thomson heat exchanger.
An expansion valve and evaporator at the low-temperature end of that
exchanger would complete the cycle and provide refrigeration at about
4 K if the compressor suction pressure were at 1 atm. A rather more
elegant arrangement is shown in figure 4.28 which allows the compressor

suction pressure to be above the vapor pressure of the helium at the refrigeration temperature. The refrigerant is held at three different pressure levels by an expansion ejector. At the highest pressure, full compressor flow enters the nozzle of the ejector where it is accelerated to high velocities with a corresponding decrease in pressure. This region of low pressure induces flow, $\dot{m}_2$, from the low-temperature evaporator through the low-pressure side of the final heat exchanger. The two flow streams mix and, as the velocity is decreased, experience a rise in pressure to P_2. A fraction of the fluid emerging from the ejector may be liquefied. The stream is divided with $\dot{m}_1$ returning to the compressor through the low-pressure side of the heat exchangers and $\dot{m}_2$ is diverted through the high-pressure side of the lowest temperature heat exchanger to an expansion valve and the evaporator. As mentioned in section 4.3.4, the cooling capacity of a Joule-Thomson system depends only upon the mass flow rate and enthalpy difference at the warm end of the Joule-Thomson heat exchanger and is independent of the refrigeration temperature. Therefore, the expansion ejector can offer advantages in two ways. First, lower refrigeration temperatures can be achieved without any decrease in compressor suction pressure; second, cooling may be produced at 4 K with a compressor suction pressure in excess of 2 atm. Savings in compressor and heat exchanger size are made in either case. Haisma and Roozendal [15] report refrigeration temperatures as low as 1.75 K with P_1 at 31 atm and P_2 at 1.15 atm. A production model of this type of refrigerator is not ready as yet, but a 10-l/hr helium liquefier featuring a noncontaminating rolling-diaphragm sealed-compressor, heat exchangers laminated from metal gauze, paper, and resin, and an expansion ejector which permits a 2.5 atm compressor suction pressure has been marketed in Europe [16]. It should be noted that several thousand Stirling cycle refrigerators are in the field in the United States today for cooling electronic equipment at temperatures higher than liquid helium.

4.3.8. The Gifford-McMahon Cycle

By itself the Gifford-McMahon refrigeration cycle has about the same low-temperature limit as the Stirling cycle, since there is periodic reversing flow through one or more regenerators. Since this cycle lends itself very readily to staging, refrigerators precooled at three different

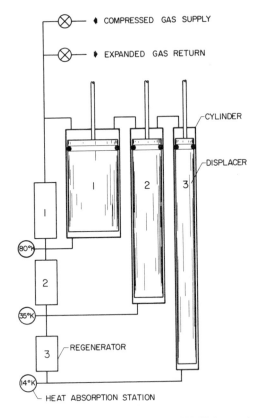

FIGURE 4.29.   *Schematic of Gifford-McMahon cycle.*

temperature levels have been built for liquid helium temperature service. Figure 4.29 schematically shows a three-stage unit. The three cylinders are made of low-conductivity material and are fitted with displacers, sealed against the cylinders at the top, whose movements are
controlled from outside the cryostat. The three thermal regenerators
are indicated as are the three heat-absorption stations at 14, 35, and
80 K. The regenerators are packed with a material such as metal screens
to produce the desirable characteristics of high heat capacity per unit
volume, low pressure drop, small void volume, and low axial thermal
conductivity. Imagine now that all three displacers are in their lowest
position and that steady-state operating conditions have been reached
so that the proper thermal gradient exists in the regenerator material

from room temperature to 80 K in the first regenerator. The compressed gas supply valve is opened, and helium enters the system, raising the pressure in the volume at the top of the cylinders above the displacers. When the pressure in the regenerators and the volume above the displacers reach the maximum pressure, the displacers are all moved to the upper position, forcing the gas above them through the regenerators and into the volumes which now appear below the displacers. The gas is cooled as it gives up heat to the cold regenerators and the decrease in specific volume allows more fluid to enter the system from the compressed gas supply. The supply valve is closed and the exhaust valve is slowly opened. Refrigeration is now produced as each of the elements of fluid do work on preceding elements as they pass out of the system. The fluid is warmed as it passes through the regenerators and through the heat absorption stations. When the pressure in the system reaches its lowest level, the displacers are moved to the lower position, forcing the remaining cold gas out through the regenerators and to the compressor suction. At this time the temperature distribution in the regenerators has returned to its original profile. This refrigerator inherently has several mechanical advantages. Most of the low-temperature apparatus is passive except the displacers, which are shown as sealed at room temperature. Later models have displacer seals at low temperatures, but the problem is not serious since the pressure difference across the seals is only that

FIGURE 4.30. *Internal components of Gifford-McMahon refrigerator.*
(Courtesy of 500 Inc.)

which is required to induce flow through the regenerators. The displacers are operated at low speed, typically less than 100 rpm, and the light duty drive mechanism is used to operate the room-temperature inlet and exhaust valves. Difficulties encountered with contaminants in the refrigerant are alleviated somewhat, since the exhaust phase of the cycle tends to flush impurities back out of the system.

The nonmetallic displacer piston and small piston rod are in the upper left-hand corner of figure 4.30, which shows the internal components of a prototype for a Gifford-McMahon helium refrigerator. In order, to the right of the displacer, are the cylinder assembly, small regenerator matrixes and spacers, the internal shell of the Joule-Thomson heat exchanger, other regenerator matrixes, the external shell of the Joule-Thomson heat exchanger, a radiation shield, and the mounting flange. Refinements of this design are incorporated in a 2 W liquid helium temperature refrigerator described by Stuart et al. [17]. In this unit the regenerators are inside the nonmetallic displacers, and the internally finned tubing which constitutes the high-pressure side of the Joule-Thomson heat exchanger is wrapped on a larger diameter tube which is filled with perforated disks and spacers. Very close temperature regulation, ± 0.01 K at about 4 K, is reported.

4.4. COMPONENTS AND PRESENT-DAY REFRIGERATORS

4.4.1. Compressors

Gas compression equipment is required for all helium refrigerators. The compressors directly affect the performance of the refrigerator in several different ways. In many applications, reliability and continuous operation of the refrigerator are of paramount importance. There are other components in refrigerators whose partial failure or degradation of performance may be overcome. There is no way, however, that the operation can continue in the event of a compressor failure unless standby compressors are available or perhaps high-pressure gas storage has been provided. The compression equipment is usually the most expensive single component of a helium refrigerator, at times accounting for about one-third of the capital cost. In addition to being expensive, the compression equipment is often responsible for the major portion of the inefficiencies of low-temperature refrigerators.

Conventional oil-lubricated reciprocating compressors are often used for helium refrigerators. Although the design of oil-lubricated reciprocating compressors has been established through many years of experience and a wide variety of capacities is available, such compressors do present the problem of oil contamination of the refrigerant. It is entirely possible to remove the oil contaminants from the refrigerant stream, but this involves additional capital and operating expense, and can be bothersome, to say the least. The oil can be removed from the helium as shown in figure 4.31. First the high-pressure stream from

FIGURE 4.31.   *Removal of oil contaminants from refrigerant stream.*

the compressor is passed through a separator which removes large droplets entrained in the stream. Next, a filter is used to remove smaller-sized droplets before the stream enters the absorbent bed. The filter might consist of the container packed with glass wool. The absorbent bed, if properly sized and designed, will remove essentially all of the oil vapor from the stream. Care must be taken that microscopic droplets in the range from 0.01 to 3 μm in diameter do not enter the absorbent bed. Particles in that size range may pass directly through the absorbent bed because they do not possess enough Brownian motion to insure contact with the absorbent. Usual absorbents are silica gel or activated charcoal. There can be other associated problems. For example, when one hydrogen temperature refrigerator was put on stream some years ago, the low-temperature heat exchangers periodically became plugged by frozen contaminants. It was found that while all of the oil was being removed from the refrigerant, the contaminant was air, which had been dissolved in the oil and was carried into the system.

There are several types of compressors which are used to avoid oil contamination. Figure 4.32 shows a diaphragm compressor, and figure 4.33 is an internal view. Here the refrigerant is completely separated from any possible oil contamination except in the event of diaphragm failure. The diaphragm is moved back and forth by, a column of oil which is driven by a reciprocating piston. Although long life has been

FIGURE 4.32. *Two-stage diaphragm compressor rated for 15 scfm at 245-atm discharge pressure with 1-atm suction pressure and a 11.2-kW drive motor.*
(Photo courtesy of American Instrument Co., Inc.)

reported for the diaphragms, it is generally recommended by the manufacturers that routine replacement of the diaphragm be scheduled at 1500 to 2000 hr of operation. A diaphragm failure is commonly detected in two ways; the first of these is a photoelectric device sensitive to naphthalene quinoline, which is present in most lubricating oils or can be added if necessary. The detector is located in the high-pressure discharge of the compressor and is sensitive to two parts per million of oil contaminants. If oil is detected, the device puts out an electrical signal which can be used to activate the soleniod valves, switches, or alarms so that appropriate action can be taken. The other method of detecting diaphragm failure is to sense the pressure in between the triple diaphragms which are used in these compressors. Pressure-activated switches then produce the needed electrical signals.

Other reciprocating compressors do not provide any lubrication in the cylinder and separate the cylinder from the crankcase oils by

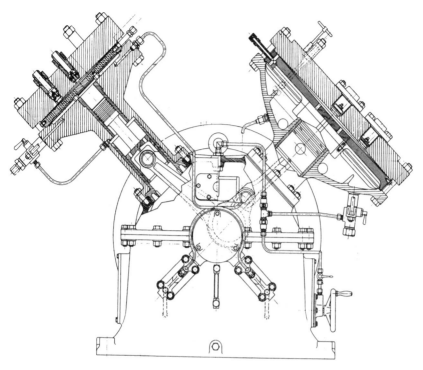

FIGURE 4.33. *Section view of diaphragm compressor.*
(Courtesy of American Instrument Co., Inc.)

specially designed distance pieces. The sealing of the piston in the cylinder is accomplished with either Teflon-filled rings or by using a special labyrinth seal in which there is no contact between the piston and the cylinder (see fig. 4.34). These labyrinth-sealed pistons are usually run at high rpm. Since there is not a positive seal between the two members, there is some leakage past the piston, decreasing slightly the efficiency of the machine. Tests have shown (Zürcher and Meier [18]) that little is gained by putting plastic piston rings in a labyrinth-sealed compressor. While there are leakage losses incurred in the labyrinth-sealed compressor, the additional friction losses caused by the plastic rings rubbing on the cylinder walls result in about the same compressor efficiency, especially at higher pressure ratings. The higher cylinder wall temperatures encountered when using the plastic piston rings also tend to decrease the efficiency. Notice in figure 4.34 the oil wiper rings situated above the cross head and the nonlubricated piston

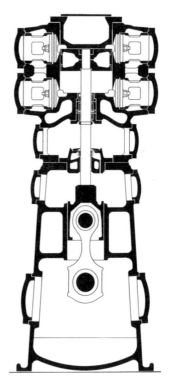

FIGURE 4.34.   *Section view of labyrinth piston compressor.*
(Courtesy of Sulzer Brothers, Ltd.)

rod packing at the lower end of the cylinder. Oil can be prevented from
creeping up the connecting rod into the packing in several ways. First,
the distance between the oil wiper rings and the packing can be made
greater than the piston stroke so that the wetted area never enters the
packing. Second, a baffle plate installed on the piston rod in the space
between the wiper mechanism and the packing helps to prevent oil
from moving up the rod. Some plastic piston ring designs use a broad
rider ring which supports the piston in the cylinder, accompanied by
one or more compression rings which are spring-loaded against the
cylinder wall. An interesting combination of two types of nonlubricated
reciprocating compression devices is shown in figure 4.35. The volume
displacement of diaphragm compressors is limited to about 110 cfm
because of the large diaphragm diameters needed at low pressures. In

FIGURE 4.35. *Combination of plastic piston ring and diaphragm compression stages.*
A 94-kW drive motor is required for this 140 scfm helium compressor with 245-atm discharge pressure and 1-atm suction pressure.
(Photo courtesy of American Instrument Co., Inc.)

figure 4.35 the first three stages of the compression are accomplished by plastic-ringed pistons and the final compression is via a diaphragm stage.

In comparison to reciprocating devices, turbomachinery has the reputation for high reliability. This factor, in addition to the possibility of alleviating the oil contamination problem through the use of gas-lubricated bearings, has prompted the development of turbomachinery for miniature helium refrigerators. In these refrigerators the small turbocompressor rotors (see figs. 4.36 and 4.37) are supported on bearings lubricated by the refrigerant gas itself. Theoretically, these very high-speed compressors should have indefinite life since there is no metal-to-metal contact and hence no rubbing wear. The development of these compressors presented a formidable task, since turbomachinery is best suited to high flow rates. At the low flow rates required by the refrigerators for which these compressors were developed, very high rotational speeds are necessary to achieve reasonable efficiencies. Since speeds approaching 120,000 rpm are common, gas-lubricated bearings become mandatory because conventional types of bearings are not suit-

FIGURE 4.36. *Miniature centrifugal helium compressor.*
This two-stage compressor is rated at 35 scfm (3.02 g/s) with 0.82-atm inlet and 1.29-atm discharge. The power consumption of the 16-kg compressor is 1.43 kW at 85,000 rpm.   (Photo courtesy of Airesearch Manufacturing Co.)

able. Further complication arises because, in general, more stages of compression are required to obtain the same pressure ratio with turbo-compressors as compared to positive-displacement compressors. The development of suitable power supplies to drive the compressor motor, which is integral with the rotor shaft; the design of the motor itself with the associated heat-dissipation problems; the establishment of bearing designs which allow startup, the acceleration through critical shaft speeds, and the shutdown—all add to the difficulties in these development programs.

Separate approaches have been taken in the design of the compressors shown in figures 4.36 and 4.37. The centrifugal compressor shown in figure 4.36 is supported on foil-type gas-lubricated bearings. Both the thrust and journal bearings consist of alternating foils of Teflon and spring steel. Further details about the compressor and bearings may be found in Wapato [19].

Tilting-pad journal bearings support the shaft of the four-stage regenerative compressor shown in figure 4.37. These journal bearings and the stepped-thrust bearings are self-acting, as are the foil-type bearings. This particular 4-hp compressor has a pressure ratio of 1.75

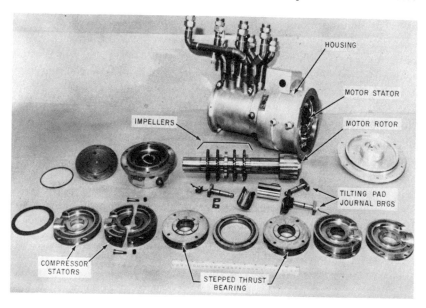

FIGURE 4.37. *Regenerative helium compressor.*
A 3-kW induction motor drives shaft at 47.500 rpm. The compressor pressure ratio is 1.75 at a flow of 22.9 cfm.
(Photo courtesy of General Electric Co.)

and operates at 47,500 rpm (Colyer and Gessner [20]). The two compressors both suffer from the losses characteristic of turbomachinery. These are electrical inefficiencies in the drive motor, windage losses at the wheels, aerodynamic losses in the flow passages, pressure drop in the intercoolers, and friction losses at the bearings. All these inefficiencies require additional input power to accomplish the required purpose.

The power required for compression of the refrigerant can be conveniently estimated as follows. First assume that the refrigerant is an ideal gas and that it will be compressed isothermally. Given the flow rate and the inlet and outlet pressures, calculate the ideal power required from eq (4.8). The next step is to apply a correction factor which relates the performance of real compressors to that predicted by eq (4.8). Experience has shown that W_c as calculated from eq (4.8) should be divided by a factor somewhere between 0.5 and 0.6 for conventional reciprocating compressors. That correction factor is somewhat lower for the miniature turbomachinery just described.

4.4.2. Heat Exchangers

The importance of highly efficient counterflow heat exchangers was seen in earlier sections, where the effect of the heat exchanger performance upon cycle efficiency was demonstrated. The first law of thermodynamics, applied to counterflow heat exchangers, neglecting heat transfer from the surroundings, states simply that the total enthalpy change of the warm streams must equal the total enthalpy change of the cold streams. The second law tells us that in order to minimize the entropy increase associated with the operation of the heat exchanger, the temperature difference between streams must be as small as possible. In principle, at least, temperature differences can be made smaller and smaller by increasing the length of the fluid flow paths. However, this means that the pressure drop in the fluid streams will increase and hence more compressor power will be required to move the fluid through the system. The choice of an optimum heat exchanger for a particular refrigerator depends upon the opposing effects of the heat transfer and pressure drop characteristics of the exchanger in addition to the cost and the volume of the exchanger. The simplest type of counterflow heat exchanger consists of two concentric tubes. The high-pressure stream flows in one direction in the inner tube and the low-pressure fluid moves in the opposite direction in the annulus between the inner and outer tubes. Modern heat exchangers are much more complicated and fall into two broad groups—the shell-tube, and the plate fin. In general, the shell-tube type exchanger can be used at higher pressures while the plate fin exchanger has the characteristic of a large amount of heat transfer surface per unit volume.

Equation (4.24) gives the heat transferred from the warm fluid to the cold fluid across a differential area

$$dQ = U\Delta T dA \qquad (4.24)$$

where U is the overall heat transfer coefficient and ΔT is the temperature difference between the fluids. It can be seen that an increase in either the heat transfer coefficient or the area will result in the same heat transfer at a smaller ΔT, which is desirable from the viewpoint of overall cycle efficiency. Efforts to improve heat exchanger performance have led to a proliferation of different designs. Tubes finned both inside and out are extensively used to increase the effective heat transfer surface, as are the extended surfaces employed in plate fin exchangers. Accurate

FIGURE 4.38. *Hampson type heat exchanger being wound.*
(Courtesy of Air Products and Chemicals, Inc.)

prediction of the characteristics of a new heat exchanger design is very difficult and usually heat-transfer coefficients and pressure-drop friction factors are determined from test models. Experimental correlations for 88 different surface configurations are given by Kays and London [21]. Treatments of the basic principles involved are contained in McAdams [22] and Jakob [23].

The Hampson type of shell-tube exchanger consists of a number of helices of small tubing through which the high-pressure stream flows. Cylindrical members both inside and outside of the helices form an annular space for the low-pressure stream. One of the difficulties that may be encountered with this highly efficient exchanger is the fact that several parallel paths (see fig. 4.38) are used for the high-pressure stream and even flow distribution is difficult to achieve. On the low-pressure side improper spacing of the high-pressure tubes will cause flow channeling, and again, uneven distribution. For maximum efficiency each of the high-pressure streams should transfer the same amount of heat over the same temperature difference to the low-pressure stream. Nonuniform flow distribution and its effect on heat exchanger performance are treated by Fleming [24].

The arrangement of the miniature counterflow coaxial tube heat exchanger in figure 4.39 is one way to reduce the flow channeling problems. Each of the high-pressure tubes is contained in its own low-pressure channel, assuring a constant hydraulic diameter for the fluid flowing in the annuli. Another highly effective, lightweight miniature heat exchanger of the plate fin variety is shown in figure 4.40. The fins in the core of this exchanger, which is brazed in a hydrogen atmosphere, are 0.051 cm high and 0.00254 cm thick and are spaced 0.063 cm apart. The design flow rate is 2.16 g/s of helium with a 3 percent pressure drop in both the high- and low-pressure sides. At the inlet of the exchanger, about 63.8 K, the design temperature difference between the high-pressure and low-pressure streams is about 1.10 K and the effectiveness of the 5-kg exchanger is 0.978, where the effectiveness is defined as the ratio of the heat actually transferred to the cold stream in the exchanger to the maximum amount that could be transferred consistent with the second law of thermodynamics.

4.4.3. Expanders

Even though counterflow heat exchangers are used to conserve the cooling capacity of the low-pressure stream, additional cooling is re-

FIGURE 4.39. *Miniature coaxial tube counterflow heat exchanger.*
(Courtesy of General Electric Co.)

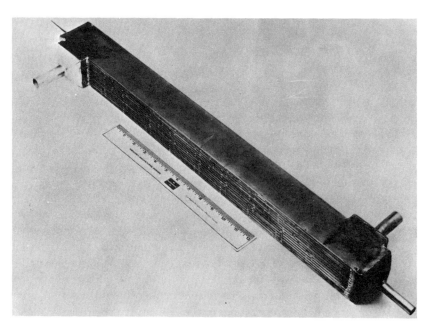

FIGURE 4.40. *Miniature plate fin heat exchanger.*
Flow rate is 2.16 g/s and a temperature difference of 1.1 K at the warm end of the heat exchanger leads to an effectiveness of 0.978. The exchanger mass is about 5 kg.   (Courtesy of Airesearch Manufacturing Co.)

FIGURE 4.41.   *Two-cylinder reciprocating expander which operates at about 20 K with 72 percent efficiency.*
Speed is between 150 and 450 rpm and the unit produces 1.7 kW of refrigeration.   (Courtesy of CVI, Inc.)

quired in refrigerators using the Joule-Thomson process. This additional refrigeration, called precooling, is often supplied by work-producing expansion machines. A portion, or all, of the high-pressure refrigerant is passed through a mechanical expander where its potential for doing work is exploited. The temperature of the fluid decreases as it gives up energy in the form of mechanical power. The low-temperature, low-pressure exhaust stream of the expander is then used to cool other refrigerant streams as they pass to lower temperature portions of the refrigerator. As seen in figure 4.2, the cooling capacity of a refrigerator depends directly upon the amount of work produced by the expansion device. If the amount of energy crossing the control surface can be made greater because of an increase in the output of the expansion machine, the refrigeration capacity is enlarged by an equivalent amount. An expansion machine operating between two given pressure levels will produce the greatest amount of work and the lowest exhaust temperature if the expansion process is isentropic, that is, adiabatic and reversible. Any losses incurred in the expansion machine will decrease

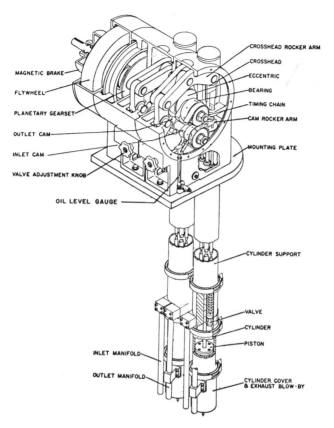

FIGURE 4.42. *Sectional view of reciprocating expander.*
(Courtesy of Air Products and Chemicals, Inc.)

its refrigeration capacity and increase the exhaust temperature. The efficiency of expansion machines is defined as the ratio of the actual enthalpy change of the fluid as it passes through the machine to the enthalpy change which would occur if the gas were expanded in an isentropic process starting at the same initial conditions and ending at the same final pressure. Typical expander efficiencies lie between 50 and 80 percent.

Since these mechanical expanders operate at depressed temperatures, unique problems are encountered. Ordinary lubricants are prohibited, and a means must be provided for transmitting the power produced by the expander to the room temperature surroundings without producing excessive heat leaks. In the reciprocating expansion machine described in chapter 3, heat leak to the low-temperature expansion cylinder is minimized by operating the piston and valves with long, slender rods in tension. The self-centering piston is lubricated by a thin film of gas leaking past it. Distance pieces of up to 6 ft can be used to isolate the low-temperature cylinders from the crankcase in the expander shown in figure 4.41. This two-cylinder unit will produce about 1.7 kW of refrigeration at 20 K, and operates between 150 and 450 rpm. The measured isentropic expansion efficiency at about 20 K is 72 percent (Hood [25]). A larger reciprocating expander described by Snow et al. [26], and shown in figure 4.42, uses wax-impregnated leather for piston rings. In this expander the room-temperature crosshead assembly and the low-temperature cylinders are separated by 8-ft distances pieces. The exhaust of the warmer expansion cylinder is normally about 12 K, while the cold cylinder is about 6 K.

In recent years much attention has been devoted to the development of turboexpanders, and a 100,000-rpm oil-lubricated centrifugal turbine

FIGURE 4.43.   *Miniature gas-lubricated turboexpander.*
About 225 W of refrigeration were produced by this turbine operating between 20 and 1 atm. An efficiency of about 40 percent was measured with the inlet temperature at 30 K and a flow of 60 scfm. Improvements at lower pressure ratios are mentioned in the text.

was shown in figure 3.6 of chapter 3. The theory of the externally pressurized gas-lubricated bearings which were used to support the turbine shown in figure 4.43 is presented by Sixsmith and Wilson [27]. This miniature turboexpander revolving in excess of 500,000 rpm dissipates the energy extracted from the refrigerant in a helium brake circuit via the impeller located at the opposite end of the 0.794-cm-diam titanium shaft. Titanium was chosen for the shaft material because of its high strength to weight ratio, and low thermal conductivity. When assembled, the 30 K turbine wheel is only about 1.27 cm from the nearest room-temperature gas-lubricated bearing, so a low conductivity shaft is essential. At a pressure ratio of about 4.9 to 1, the turbine efficiency was 65 percent, and improvements to later versions yielded efficiencies approaching 80 percent. Self-acting tilting-pad journal and gimbaled spiral-grooved thrust bearings aline the shaft of the 77 K turboexpander shown in figure 4.44. As can be seen, the nozzle is bladed for partial admission to the 1.59-cm-diam impulse turbine wheel. A three-phase

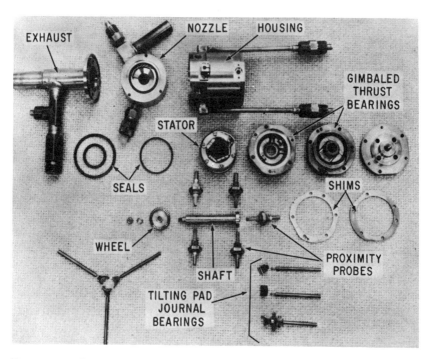

FIGURE 4.44. *Disassembled miniature turboexpander which produces about 80 W of power at 200,000 rpm operating at 77 K.*

(Courtesy of General Electric Co.)

permanent magnet alternator converts the mechanical energy to electrical energy for dissipation outside the low-temperature environment. For further design and performance details see Colyer [20].

A third helium turboexpander is shown disassembled in figure 4.45. The nominal inlet temperature to this expander is reported by Wapato [19] as 22 K. A full-admission nozzle directs the fluid to the shrouded impulse turbine driving the alternator. The rotating assembly is supported by self-acting conical foil bearings which absorb both radial and thrust loads at the operating speed of 196,000 rpm.

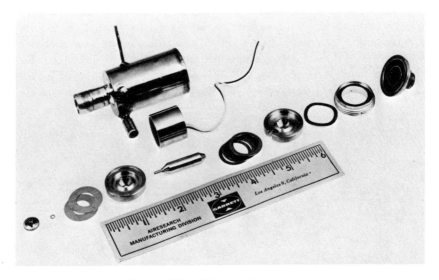

FIGURE 4.45. *Helium turbo-alternator.*
Electrical power output – 13.1 W. Overall efficiency – 32.4 percent.   (Courtesy of Airesearch Manufacturing Co.)

4.4.4. Modern Refrigerators

A number of liquid helium temperature refrigerators are in operation today. Refrigerators with capacities as small as about 1 W and very large units (capacity in excess of a kilowatt) are on stream. A photograph of a Gifford-McMahon cycle refrigerator during assembly is shown in figure 4.46. The unit is inverted in this view with the low-temperature section extending upward. The displacer drive mechanism is seen at the bottom. Several refrigerators of this type are currently being used to cool low-noise maser amplifiers in satellite communication ground sta-

FIGURE 4.46.   *Gifford-McMahon cycle refrigerator during assembly.*
(Courtesy of 500 Inc.)

tions. This particular unit produces about 1 W of refrigeration at 4.2 K. The refrigeration temperatures spanned by Claude cycle refrigerators range from 1.85 K up to near the critical temperature of helium. Components of two lightweight Claude cycle refrigerators being developed for the U.S. Air Force were shown in previous sections. The space application for these small refrigerators demands lightweight, reliability, and low power input. Gas-lubricated turbomachinery was selected to enhance the reliability even though it is difficult to obtain the highest efficiency at low flow rates with this class of machinery. In contrast to alternators which generate electrical power that is dissipated in a load resistor outside the cryostat, the energy abstracted from the re-

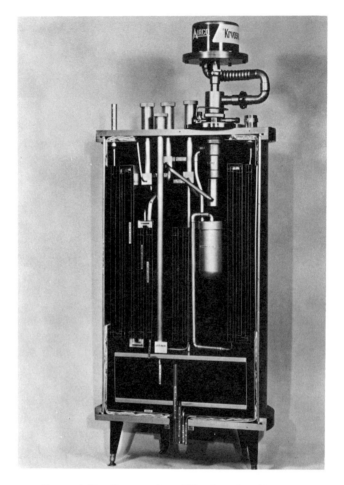

FIGURE 4.47.   *Cutaway view of Claude cycle refrigerator.*
Forty-watt capacity will be used to cool a superconducting quadripole magnet.   (Courtesy of AIRCO Co.)

frigerant as it passes through the turboexpander shown in figure 4.47 is dissipated in a separate helium brake circuit. The brake circuit piping and the helium-water heat exchanger are seen at the very top of figure 4.47, which shows a mockup of the 40-W refrigerator which will be delivered to Brookhaven National Laboratories. The turboexpander is located directly beneath the brake assembly in the cryostat. The canister just below the expander is a filter, which points out the necessity of insuring that particulate matter does not enter the small passages in the nozzle and turbine blading. The cylindrical heat exchangers and low-temperature apparatus are protected from the surroundings by laminar insulation and a gas-cooled thermal shield at an intermediate temperature. A 2-W, two expander Claude cycle refrigerator has been designed for cooling electronic equipment [28]. One of the features of this small-capacity unit is that, although the valves in the expansion engine are operated by bellows-sealed tension rods, the piston is sealed by carbon-filled PFE rings and operates the piston rod, which is made of stainless steel tubing, in compression. The crosshead and motor-generator assembly are hermetically sealed. The heat exchangers are constructed by laminating a series of metal disks with epoxy. The disks lie in a plane perpendicular to the direction of flow, and are separated by a thin film of epoxy. Heat is conducted from the warm to the cold stream via the metallic members, yet the axial conduction is reduced because of the relatively low thermal conductivity of the epoxy. Multilayer insulation occupies the vacuum space of the double-walled cold box and the refrigerator can operate with helium at atmospheric pressure in the inner vessel.

All of the equipment, including the compressors, gas holder, cold box with control console and expander assembly, gas supply manifolding and liquid helium collection dewar, comprising a liquefier-refrigerator, are seen in figure 3.7 of chapter 3. This 10-l/hr liquefier, using the two 15-hp 35-scfm compressors, can deliver 35 W of refrigeration at 4.5 K. In addition to the two expansion engines exhausting at approximately 60 K and 15 K, liquid nitrogen precooling can be used to produce maximum cycle efficiency. Larger capacity units are available, producing up to 400 W of refrigeration at 4.5 K precooled by liquid nitrogen and slowly operating expansion engines with pistons made of a plastic material sealed at room temperature.

The 800-l/hr helium liquefier at Otis, Kans., discussed by Trepp in the chapter on liquefaction, is the largest capacity liquid helium temperature facility at this time. Since that facility is not designed to function as a refrigerator, the 1.4-kW helium refrigerator (see Snow et al. [26]) designed for the NASA Langley Research Center, Materials Research Space Chamber, is the largest capacity liquid helium temperature refrigerator in service. Both plate fin and shell-tube heat exchangers are used in this two expansion engine Claude cycle refrigerator. Figure 3.11 of chapter 3 is a photograph of the cold box containing the heat exchangers and expanders. Depending upon the operating mode selected, this refrigerator will provide cooling at 4.5, 20, or 80 K, and has a liquefaction capacity in excess of 150 l/hr with 600 installed horsepower.

Two Claude cycle refrigerators are in operation at temperatures below the normal boiling point of helium. The 80-cm helium bubble chamber at the Rutherford High Energy Laboratory, England, is cooled by a refrigerator which will absorb 73 W at 3 K in addition to a 500-W 80 K load arising from the bubble chamber and cryostat heat shield. The plant features dry-lubricated compressors with carbon PTFE piston rings, aluminum plate fin heat exchangers, and externally gas lubricated high-speed turboexpanders. The design and fabrication of this refrigerator are fully described by Firth et al. [29]. As mentioned, a 300-W 1.85 K refrigerator to cool a superconducting electron linear accelerator has been delivered to Stanford University. Here, precooling is accomplished by the use of liquid nitrogen and two reciprocating expansion engines. The Joule-Thomson heat exchanger in this unit has three expansion valves in order to maintain the proper temperature profiles, but the situation is further complicated by the very low pressure in the return stream and by the problems of film creep and superleaks presented by the superfluid helium.

4.5. EFFICIENCY, WEIGHT, AND VOLUME OF 4.2 K REFRIGERATORS

The size and power requirements of liquid helium temperature refrigerators were determined in a survey by Strobridge and Chelton [30]. These characteristics are important because in practice they may limit the applicability and operating time of the equipment. Although the data acquired through the survey show considerable scatter, the expected trends can be developed and attempts were made to establish guides by which the weight, volume, and power requirements may be predicted. The data on liquid helium temperature refrigerators available at that time are given in table 1. The first 13 of the 26 units existed and, presumably, the performance data given were measured. The remaining refrigerators were under development or were proposed and the values shown may be subject to change. Capacities range from less than 1 W up to several kilowatts. Liquid nitrogen requirements are shown for the precooled refrigerators. The additional power necessary to provide the precooling in lieu of liquid nitrogen was not added to the values of W_c/Q for lack of a common basis for comparison. However, it is estimated that the average increase in total input power would be less than 10 percent.

Study of figures 4.48, 4.49, 4.51, and 4.52 shows that the functions that have been defined are subject to arbitration because of data varia-

TABLE 1. *Physical characteristics, liquid helium temperature refrigerators*

ID	Temp. (K)	Capacity (W)	Power (kW)	Weight (kg)	Volume (m³)	W_c/Q (kW/W)	% Carnot	Sp. Wt. (kg/W)	Sp. Vol. (m³/W)	Cycle	Liq. N_2 Req. (l/hr)
1	4.2	4.	7.46	390	0.68	1.865	3.8	98	0.17	Gifford†	
2	4.2	0.75	2.24	124	0.11	2.987	2.4	165	0.15	Gifford†	
3	4.5	1400.	600.			0.429	15.3			Claude	130.
4	4.5	2.1	3.40	438	1.54	1.619	4.1	209	0.73	Claude	
5	4.2	0.75	3.00	358	0.73	4.000	1.8	477	0.97	Gifford†	
6	4.5	10.	8.00	1700		0.800	8.2	170		Claude	1.0
7	4.5	7.	8.00	1700		1.143	5.7	243		Claude	
8	4.4	1.25	7.46		0.082	5.968	1.1			Cascade JT	
9	2.5	0.2	1.58	136		7.890	1.5	680	0.41	Claude	
10	4.4	350.	340.			0.971	6.9			Claude	
11	4.3	3.	5.00	590	1.77	1.667	4.1	197	0.59	Gifford†	3.5
12	4.3	35.	26.	2245	5.89	0.743	9.3	64	0.17	Claude	10.
13	4.3	200.	75.	8620	17.7	0.375	18.3	43	0.088	Claude	25.
14	2.5	0.25	7.00	204	0.11	28.00	0.43	816	0.44	*Claude	
15	4.2	0.50	5.58	424	0.99	11.16	0.63	848	1.98	*Gifford†	
16	3.6	2.	9.00	40	0.056	4.50	1.8	20	0.028	*Claude	
17	3.6	1.	3.75	30	0.062	3.75	2.2	30	0.062	*Claude	
18	4.2	1.	4.00	41	0.037	4.00	1.8	41	0.037	*Claude	
19	4.2	5.	5.00	227	0.19	1.00	7.0	45	0.038	*Solvay	
20	4.2	1.	2.30	45	0.25	2.30	3.1	45	0.25	*Claude	
21	4.2	0.70	8.40	68	0.045	12.0	0.59	97	0.064	*Cascade JT	
22	4.4	0.75	7.50	2310	4.13	10.0	0.67	3080	5.51	*Claude	
23	4.5	50.	51.	5990	23.7	1.02	6.4	120	0.47	*Claude	19.
24	4.5	170.	105.	7940	39.9	0.618	10.6	47	0.23	*Claude	38.
25	4.5	1000.	584.	38600	210.	0.584	11.2	39	0.21	*Claude	152.
26	4.5	5000.	2020.	93000	428.	0.404	16.3	19	0.086	*Claude	495.

*Under development or proposed.
†Gifford-McMahon cycle.

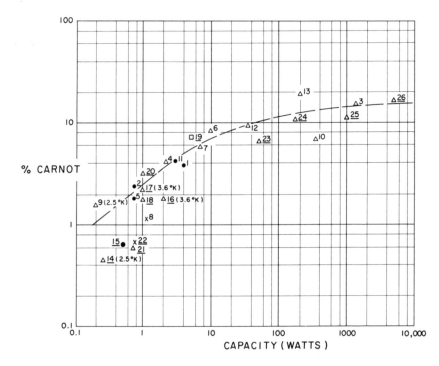

FIGURE 4.48. *Efficiency of liquid helium temperature refrigerators as a function of refrigeration capacity.*

tion. The dashed lines shown in the figures were established through the authors' best judgment and were substantiated by simple least squares treatment. Clearly, extrapolations of the dashed lines should be avoided or made with extreme care, especially for lower refrigeration capacities. The general shape of the curves can be predicted from a knowledge of the performance of low-temperature machinery. However, since the data are minimal, it is difficult to define the curves quantitatively.

The power required per unit of refrigeration for a Carnot refrigerator was given by eq (4.5), and it is informative to form the ratio

$$\text{Percent Carnot} = \frac{\left(\dfrac{W_c}{Q}\right)_{\text{Carnot}}}{\left(\dfrac{W_c}{Q}\right)_{\text{Actual}}} \times 100. \tag{4.25}$$

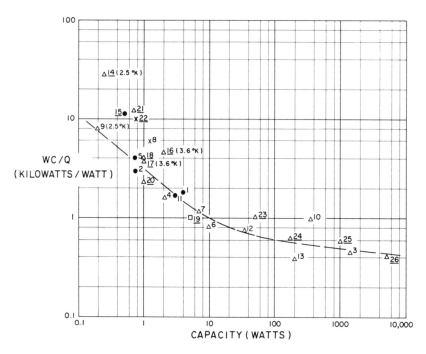

FIGURE 4.49.   *Specific power requirements of liquid helium temperature refrigerators as a function of refrigeration capacity.*

This ratio indicates the extent to which the real refrigerator deviates from ideal performance and is given in table 1 and plotted in figure 4.48 as a function of refrigeration capacity. Since the coordinates of the plot are logarithmic, the scatter in the points shown amounts to considerable deviation in the values. The units under development have been differentiated from those which have been constructed and tested by underlining the point numbers which refer to the entries in table 1.

The dashed line in figure 4.48 was established using the data for existing refrigerators only for capacities of 10 W or less, and all of the data for the larger units. This line was then used as the basis for all other curves relating to efficiency.

There does not appear to be any significant difference, within the scatter of the data, in the performance of the refrigerators using the different cycles. The efficiencies of the Claude and the Gifford-McMahon refrigerators seem to be comparable although the majority of the experimental units are of the Claude type. The performance of both cascade

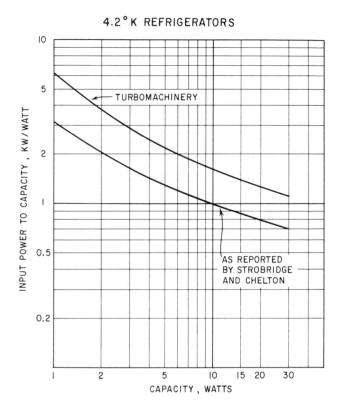

FIGURE 4.50.   *Comparison of turbomachinery power requirements to figure 4.51.*
(Courtesy of General Electric Co.)

Joule-Thomson refrigerators is lower than the general trend, as is expected.

The adverse effects of miniaturization are apparent from figure 4.48. The heat leak to the low-temperature regions of the smaller units will be proportionally higher than in the larger ones and the net refrigeration potential is decreased. In addition, it is more difficult to construct highly efficient components in the small sizes, and certain other losses do not decrease in direct proportion to refrigeration capacity.

The input power required per unit of refrigeration is shown as a function of refrigerating capacity in figure 4.49. This graph shows the same information as figure 4.48, but the required specific power can be read directly. It should be noted that all of the input energy and the energy from the refrigerated load must be dissipated at ambient temperature. In both figures 4.48 and 4.49 it is apparent that the majority of the small-capacity proposed refrigerators are expected to have poorer thermal performance than that of the existing ones. An examination of the weight and volume data shows that, in general, the low-capacity proposed refrigerators are smaller and lighter than the existing ones. Some sacrifice in efficiency has been necessary to effect these gains. Indeed, Colyer [31] subsequently presented the data for low-capacity lightweight turbomachine refrigerators in figure 4.50, which gives specific power requirements 1.5 to 2 times higher than figure 4.49.

Figure 4.51 shows that weight reductions of nearly a factor of 10 are expected for some of the low-capacity refrigerators. Two possible reasons for this significant potential gain are: First, it is probable that minimum weight was not a design criterion, since low mass is not of primary importance in a number of applications. Secondly, optimistic estimates may have been made for the weights of the proposed units. However, it is reported that the weights and volumes of two of the experimental units will not vary significantly from the original estimates. The dashed line was fitted only to the data for existing refrigerators and is a good representation even for the points at higher capacities (23 through 26). The low-capacity proposed Claude cycle units are generally lighter than those of the other types. Since the majority of the data for the proposed refrigerators are for a capacity of about 1 W, it would not be expedient to make general conclusions about the weight advantage of the Claude cycle for all refrigeration capacities.

The dashed line shown in figure 4.52 was established in a similar fashion to those for refrigerator performance and weight. This line is a reasonable representation of the volume characteristics which may be expected from present-day designs. The large-capacity refrigerators are intended to operate at a permanent installation and no effort was made to reduce significantly the weight and volume. The conclusions which may be drawn from an inspection of figure 4.52 are that the potential for significant volume reduction is great and that the proposed lower capacity Claude refrigerators again appear to be attractive.

The data for the efficiencies of the various refrigerators are more consistent than for their weights and volumes. This indicates that efforts have been made to utilize highly efficient components and it is not likely that major improvements in the performance of the cycles will be forthcoming. The efficiency of low-temperature refrigerators will slowly improve as the components are refined. It is not unreasonable to expect

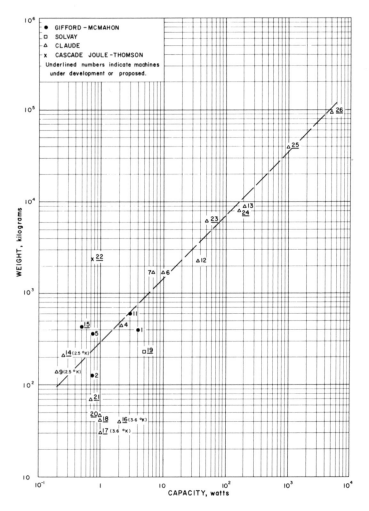

FIGURE 4.51.   *Weight of liquid helium temperature refrigerators as a function of capacity.*

that significant improvements can be made over the weights of existing units through careful design and, indeed, the majority of the proposed refrigerators are expected to be considerably lighter. Substantial reductions in volume are predicted for the machines under development.

Based upon the trends established for the existing refrigerators, it appears that a 4.2 K unit with a capacity of 10 to 50 W would require 700 to 1000 W of input power per watt of refrigeration. Such a unit would

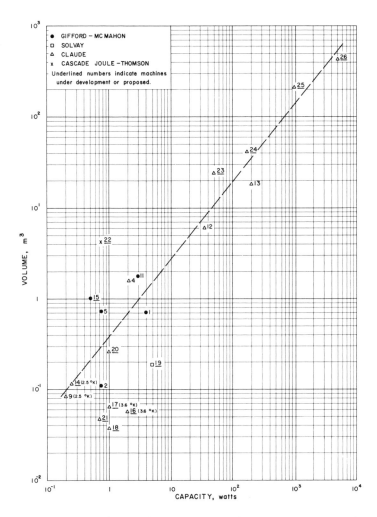

FIGURE 4.52. *Volume of liquid helium temperature refrigerators as a function of capacity.*

weigh about 87 to 130 kg/W of refrigeration and occupy a volume of about 0.28 m³/W of refrigeration. If these figures are biased by the values given for the proposed refrigerators in the 1 to 5-W range, the power requirement would be about 1000 to 1500 W/W of refrigeration. Assuming that the weights and volumes can be cut to one-half of that given by the present estimates through further development, then the specific weights and volumes become 43 to 65 kg/W and 0.14 m³, respectively.

REFERENCES

[1] H. Kamerlingh Onnes, The liquefaction of helium, Commun. Phys. Lab., Univ. Leiden, No. 108 (1908).

[2] H. Kamerlingh Onnes, V. The disappearance of the resistance of mercury, Commun. Phys. Lab., Univ. Leiden, No. 122b (1911).

[3] G. J. Van Wylen and R. E. Sonntag, Fundamentals of Classical Thermodynamics (John Wiley & Sons, Inc., New York, N.Y., 1965).

[4] A. R. Winters and W. A. Snow, Capacity and economic performance of a large 5 °K helium refrigerator, Advances in Cryogenic Engineering (ed. K. D. Timmerhaus, Plenum Press, New York, N.Y., 1966), Vol. 11, p. 116.

[5] F. Simon, Helium liquefaction with performance of work, Z. Ges. Kälte-Ind. 39, 89 (1932).

[6] F. Simon, On the expansion method for liquefaction of helium, Proc. 7th Intern. Congress of Refrigeration 1, 367 (1936).

[7] G. L. Pickard and F. Simon, A quantitative study of the expansion method for liquefying helium, Proc. Phys. Soc. (London) 60, 405 (1948).

[8] L. E. Scott, Ideal yield of a Simon liquefier, Cryogenics 3, 112 (1963).

[9] C. E. Taylor, Sodium cryogenic coils, Proc. 1965 Symp. on Engineering Problems of Controlled Thermonuclear Research, CONF 650512 (1965), p. 152.

[10] J. W. Dean and D. B. Mann, The Joule-Thomson process in cryogenic refrigeration systems, NBS Tech. Note. 227 (1965).

[11] R. C. Muhlenhaupt and T. R. Strobridge, An analysis of the Brayton cycle as a cryogenic refrigerator, NBS Tech. Note. 366 (1968).

[12] S. C. Collins, R. W. Stuart, and M. H. Streeter, Closed cycle refrigeration at 1.85 K, Rev. Sci. Instr. 38, 1654 (1967).

[13] R. C. Muhlenhaupt and T. R. Strobridge, The single-engine Claude cycle as a 4.2 K refrigerator, NBS Tech. Note. 354 (1967).

[14] J. A. Rietdijk, The expansion-ejector, a new device for liquefaction and refrigeration at 4 K and lower, Intern. Inst. of Refrigeration, Commission 1, Boulder, Colo. (Annexe 1966–5), p. 241.

[15] J. Haisma and K. Roozendal, Investigation of the behavior of an ejector in the low temperature region beyond the λ-transition of helium, Intern. Congress of Refrigeration, 12th meeting, Commission 1, Madrid, Spain, Paper No. 1.37 (1967). To be published.

[16] G. J. Haaruis, A new type of helium liquefier, Intern. Congress of Refrigeration, 12th meeting, Commission 1, Madrid, Spain, Paper No. 1.36 (1967). To be published.

[17] R. W. Stuart, W. H. Hogan, and A. D. Rogers, Performance of a 4 K refrigerator, Advances in Cryogenic Engineering (ed. K. D. Timmerhaus, Plenum Press, New York, N.Y., 1967), Vol. 12, p. 564.

[18] A. Zürcher and H. Meier, Reciprocating compressors with non-lubricated cylinders and labyrinth pistons or plastic piston rings, Sulzer Tech. Rev. 49, No. 1 (1967).

[19] P. C. Wapato, Development of a 4.2 K cryogenic refrigeration system, Garrett Corp., Los Angeles, Calif., Aireseach Div., Final Rept. No. 66–0347, Contr. No. DA–36–039–AMC–03725(S), DDC AD486509 (1966).

[20] D. B. Colyer and R. L. Gessner, Miniature cryogenic refrigerator turbomachinery, Advances in Cryogenic Engineering (ed. K. D. Timmerhaus, Plenum Press, New York, N.Y., 1968), Vol. 13, in press.

[21] W. M. Kays and A. L. London, Compact Heat Exchangers (McGraw-Hill Book Co., New York, N.Y., 1964), 2d ed.

[22] W. H. McAdams, Heat Transmission (McGraw-Hill Book Co., New York, N.Y., 1954), 3d ed.

[23] M. Jakob, Heat Transfer (John Wiley & Sons, Inc., New York, N.Y., 1949), Vols. I and II.

[24] R. B. Fleming, The effect of flow distribution in parallel channels of counterflow heat exchangers, Advances in Cryogenic Engineering (ed. K. D. Timmerhaus, Plenum Press, New York, N.Y., 1967), Vol. 12, p. 352.

[25] C. B. Hood, CVI Inc., Columbus, Ohio. Private communication (1968).

[26] W. A. Snow, A. R. Winters, and R. B. Currie, Multipurpose high capacity helium refrigerator-liquefier, Proc. Inst. Environmental Sciences Annual Technical Meeting (1965), p. 305.

[27] H. Sixsmith and W. A. Wilson, The theory of a stable high speed externally pressurized gas-lubricated bearing, J. Res. NBS 68C, 101 (1964).

[28] C. E. Witter, Design of a closed-cycle helium temperature refrigerator, Advances in Cryogenic Engineering (ed. K. D. Timmerhaus, Plenum Press, New York, N.Y., 1966), Vol. 11, p. 107.

[29] M. Firth, D. E. Ward, and J. B. Gardner, A 73 watt, 3 K helium refrigerator using gas bearing turbines, Intern. Inst. of Refrigeration, Commission 1, Boulder, Colo. (Annexe 1966-5), p. 227.

[30] T. R. Strobridge and D. B. Chelton, Size and power requirements of 4.2 K refrigerators, Advances in Cryogenic Engineering (ed. K. D. Timmerhaus, Plenum Press, New York, N.Y., 1967), Vol. 12, p. 576.

[31] D. B. Colyer, General Electric Co., Private communication (1968).

TRADE NAMES AND UNITS: The appearance of trade names in this chapter was required to give adequate credit to those who contributed pictorial material used to illustrate typical devices. Such appearance in no way implies approval, endorsement, or recommendation of a specific product by the National Bureau of Standards. Deviations from SI units occur where needed for clarity because of prevailing practice in certain segments of the technology.

CHAPTER 5

Storage, Distribution, and Handling

L. E. Scott,[1] R. C. VanMeerbeke,[2] B. S. Kirk,[1] G. C. Nubel [1]

[1] Air Reduction Company, Murray Hill, N.J. 07971.
[2] Present address: Columbia Gas Systems, New York, N.Y.

153

5.1. INTRODUCTION

Many of the physical principles used today in liquefying and storing helium were known to Kamerlingh Onnes [1][3] and his colleagues when they first liquefied helium in 1908. The technology and commercial impetus to make liquid helium an everyday commodity developed in only the last 15 years.

In 1908, as today, workers in low-temperature physics have developed liquid helium technology primarily as a means to obtain an environment suitable for their experiments. Until recent years, it was necessary for a low-temperature experimenter to be proficient in cryogenic techniques, as well as in his own field of interest, in order to successfully conduct experiments in the helium temperature range. The introduction of the Collins cryostat in 1949 greatly reduced the experimental difficulties. This machine provided a working environment refrigerated to helium temperatures; a concept which was not utilized extensively. Modifications were made to allow liquid helium to be transferred from the machine, stored, and used at will, thus eliminating the machine as part of the experimental apparatus.

Since the development of the Collins machine, the demand for liquid helium has grown rapidly. By 1959, several industrial concerns were marketing liquid helium to scientific communities. The development of large liquefiers to support these markets has made liquid helium a readily avaliable commodity. In 1958, 700,000 liters (700 m^3) of liquid helium [2] were produced in the United States; essentially 100 percent was produced by Collins machines. In 1964, an estimated 1,700,000 l (1700 m^3) were produced [3], of which only 50 percent was made in Collins machines. By 1966, the total liquefaction capacity exceeded 12,000,000 l (12,000 m^3) per year.

The largest single boost to liquid helium production has been the realization that the production and shipment of liquid helium are the least expensive way of distributing gaseous helium [4]. Lower capital investments and lower distribution costs are possible with liquid distribution as compared to gaseous distribution, in much the same way that these benefits have been achieved for many years in distributing oxygen and nitrogen as liquids. The typical liquid helium consumer can now be supplied from large central liquefiers. Distribution is now made routinely by air and truck.

---

[3] Figures in brackets indicate the literature references at the end of this chapter.

This chapter describes the equipment and techniques used in the handling of liquid helium. Since many of the techniques are commonly used in handling other cryogenic fluids, emphasis is placed on methods which are unique with liquid helium. Many excellent publications contain information on the properties of insulation and construction materials suitable for low temperatures. This information will be presented only briefly, for the convenience of the reader. The last portion of the chapter describes a liquefaction and distribution system for handling liquid helium on a large scale.

5.2. STORAGE SYSTEMS

The low boiling point of helium (table 5.1) would appear to be the most difficult design criterion for liquid helium storage containers. It is only when we also consider the very small heat of vaporization of helium that the true problem of liquid helium storage becomes apparent: namely, limiting the heat transfer from the surroundings to the helium contents. The real significance of this is appreciated upon considering that the heat of vaporization of water is some 450 times that of helium on a volume basis. Without elaborate thermal protection, helium can exist as liquid for only the most brief periods.

TABLE 5.1. *Comparison of the physical properties of helium with other cryogenic fluids and water*

Property	He	H_2	N_2	H_2O
Density (lb/ft^3)...............................	7.798	4.418	50.46	62.43
Specific gravity................................	0.12	0.07	0.81	1.00
Normal boiling point (°F)...................	−452.10	−423.2	−320.36	212
Heat of vaporization (Btu/lb)..............	9.0	192.7	85.67	970.3
(Btu/gal)...	9.4	113	579	8090

Most of the problems have been successfully overcome in present containers, but not without high cost. Most small containers require an investment of about $25 per liter of capacity, making liquid helium storage very expensive compared with other products that are commercially shipped. When compared to equivalent gas storage, the investment for small liquid containers is six times greater than for standard gas cylinders. Very large (10,000-gal) liquid storage systems may cost only half as much as equivalent gas storage. Figure 5.1 illustrates the approximate cost of liquid containers now in existence.

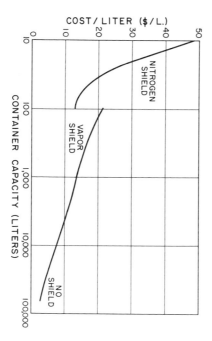

FIGURE 5.1. *Approximate cost, per unit storage capacity, for various size liquid helium containers.*

Two different design criteria are commonly applied to liquid helium containers depending upon the desired final product state, liquid or gas. If the product is to be used as liquid, the container is designed for constant venting of the vapor evolved from liquid evaporation because of heat leak. If a gas or vapor requirement exists, and the gas can be recovered at the destination or use point, then the container is designed for nonvented storage and transport, allowing the heat leak to cause a pressure increase in the container. Significant differences exist in the design and operation of the two systems.

5.3. VENTED CONTAINERS

5.3.1. Liquid Nitrogen-Shielded Containers

The most common container in use today is the double dewar. This design is best summarized by the description of Wexler [5]. Containers of this type are made by numerous manufacturers and have been produced in sizes ranging from 5 to 1200-1 capacity, the more common sizes being 25 to 50-1 capacity (see figs. 5.2 and 5.3).

The insulation system shown is high-vacuum insulation. Liquid nitrogen surrounds the liquid helium insulation space to reduce the heat transfer by reducing the temperature difference across the helium insulation system. The liquid nitrogen "shield," in turn, is insulated from ambient conditions by a similar high-vacuum insulation. Typical performance and specifications of these containers are shown in table 5.2.

An important contribution to the excellent performance of these containers is the refrigeration effect of the cold helium vapor vented through the neck tube. Helium is unique in that the heat of vaporization is relatively small compared to the specific heat of the vapor. As an example, a 4 K temperature rise of the cold vapor requires as much heat addition as the heat required to release the vapor from the liquid phase originally.

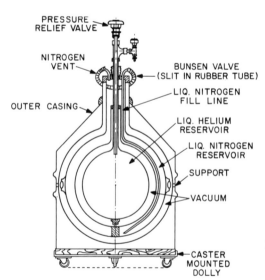

FIGURE 5.2. *Typical construction of small liquid nitrogen-shielded containers.*

FIGURE 5.3.   *Typical 25-liter, nitrogen-shielded, liquid helium container ready for shipment.*

Note the foam rubber protective rings around circumference and metal cylinder to protect the relief valve assembly.

TABLE 5.2.   *Representative capacities, evaporation rates and weights of nitrogen-shielded liquid helium containers*

CAPACITY		EVAPORATION RATE		WEIGHT—FULL
Helium (liters)	Nitrogen (liters)	Helium (liters/24 hr)	Nitrogen (liters/24 hr)	(lbs)
10	12 − 15	0.20 − 0.4	$1^{3}/_{4} - 3$	100 − 125
25	33 − 35	0.30 − 0.45	$2^{1}/_{4} - 4$	175 − 190
50	42 − 60	0.45 − 0.5	$2^{3}/_{4} - 4$	290 − 360
100	48 − 65	0.5 − 0.65	$4^{1}/_{2} - 5$	460 − 500

While venting, the cold vapor intercepts the heat being conducted down the neck tube, reducing the heat reaching the liquid vessel to a practically negligible amount. A mathematical analysis of this process can be found in Scott [6 (p. 239)]. The significance of the effect is shown in Wexler [5] and L. Scott [7], where a tenfold increase in container heat leak was found in nonvented containers versus vented containers.

Seemingly minor heat sources can have a measurable effect on the loss by evaporation. Radiation down the neck tube can be significant. Wexler [5] found that blackening the neck tube reduced evaporation losses in experimental dewars. Increase in evaporation rates has been observed by slightly tilting the container. This results from the bumper supports located in the vacuum annulus touching the warmer wall in the tilted position, which does not occur when the container is exactly vertical.

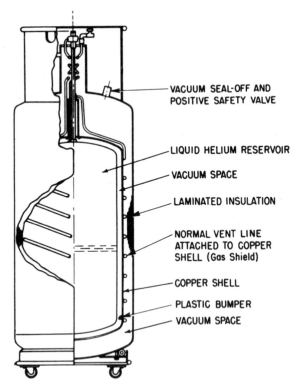

FIGURE 5.4. *Construction of a vapor-shielded container, using only one refrigerated shield.*

5.3.2. Vapor-Shielded Containers

The concept of using the refrigerating capacity of the vapor has been used to eliminate the need for liquid nitrogen shielding. Two methods have been used. The first of these (fig. 5.4) provides an intermediate heat shield between the ambient wall and the helium vessel. This shield is refrigerated by directing the escaping cold vapor through coils attached to the shield. The neck tube heat conduction is also intercepted at two or more points: at the bottom, the vapor flows up the neck for a short distance before entering the shield; and again near the top, the neck is refrigerated by continuing the tube coil from the shield to a physical attachment on the neck to provide heat exchange between the vapor and the neck. The insulation systems commonly used are: high vacuum alone between the helium vessel and the shield and evacuated multilayer insulation between the shield and the ambient shell.

In figure 5.5, an alternate method [8] is shown for utilizing the refrigeration of the vapor. The vapor does not pass through coils attached

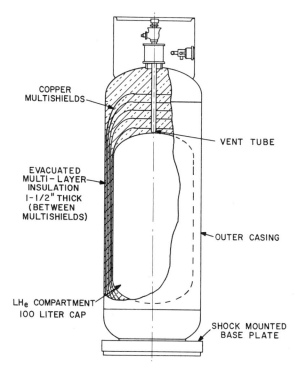

FIGURE 5.5. *Multiple vapor-cooled shields as described by Paivanas [8].*

FIGURE 5.7. *A 100-liter container using the single vapor-cooled shield concept (see fig. 5.4).*

The performance and dimensions are:
  Normal evaporation rate = < 1.5%/day
  Weight, full = 258 lbs.
  Inner and outer shell construction − stainless steel;
  Dimensions, Diameter = 22 inches; Height = 66 inches;
  Shock provisions = shock mount base. (Courtesy Cryogenic Engineering Company).

FIGURE 5.6. *A 100-liter container using the multiple vapor-cooled shield concept (see fig. 5.5).*

The specifications of this container are:
  Normal evaporation rate = 1.25%/day
  Weight, full = 250 lbs.
  Inner and outer shell construction − stainless steel;
  Dimensions, Diameter = 20 inches; Height = 63 inches;
  Shock provisions = shock mount base. (Courtesy Linde Division, Union Carbide Corporation).

to a shield, but passes directly up the neck. Numerous shields are placed in thermal contact with the neck. Multilayer insulation is used between each shield. While each shield is cooled at only one point, the area of neck attachment, temperature gradients along the shield are reduced to acceptable levels by using high thermal conductivity materials (such as copper) in the fabrication of the shield. In this system, heat passing radially through the insulation is intercepted and conducted along each shield to the neck tube, where it is absorbed by the escaping cold vapor.

Vapor-shielded containers presently have slightly higher rates of evaporation than nitrogen-shielded containers, but they have the distinct advantage of eliminating the requirement for liquid nitrogen. Containers of this general type have been made in sizes from 50-1 to 2000 gal capacity. Some representative illustrations are shown in figures 5.6 and 5.7.

5.3.3. The Vaporization Process

In a constant pressure vaporization process, such as a vented helium dewar, the relationship between the mass vaporized and the heat input is normally given by:

$$m_t = \frac{q}{h_v} \tag{5.1}$$

where $m_t =$ mass vaporized
$q =$ heat input
$h_v =$ heat of vaporization.

This relationship is commonly used to solve for the heat imput q by measuring the mass expelled from the container—either by gas meter or container weight loss—and equating this value to m_t. Several unique properties of helium may lead to the incorrect application of this simple relationship. Since the heat of vaporization is relatively small compared to the specific heat of the vapor, a small degree of superheat in the vapor leaving the container will mask the true heat leak of the container. The degree of superheat may vary with liquid level. Hence, the rate of gas evolution from the container will also vary with the content level. Also, the ratio of the saturated liquid density to the vapor density at 4.2 K is only 8 : 1 at 1 atm. Therefore, the vapor which fills the void resulting from liquid vaporization is not a negligible mass and must be added to an external measurement of vaporization losses.

A correction for vapor superheat may be made by measuring the temperature of the vapor at the point of exit from the liquid container and the true enthalpy change substituted for h_v in eq (5.1). A much simpler method is to confine loss rate measurements to full containers.

The vapor density error can easily be corrected by:

$$m_t = m \left(\frac{V_g}{V_g - V_L} \right) \qquad (5.2)$$

where m_t = total mass vaporized
$\quad m$ = mass vented from container
$\quad V_g$ = average specific volume of vapor in the container
$\quad V_L$ = specific volume of the saturated liquid.

At 1 atm, assuming zero superheat of the gas, this reduces to:

$$m_t = 1.15 \; m.$$

5.3.4. Atmospheric Pressure Variations

The apparent heat input calculated from loss rate measurements is greatly influenced by pressure changes on the evaporating fluid. Because of this, it is sometimes difficult to measure dewar loss characteristics when the container is vented and subject to atmospheric pressure variations. A correction for this process, for a full container, may be approximated [9] by equating the heat capacity of the fluid and the cooling effect of the vaporization loss due to flashing:

$$\frac{VC_s}{V_L} \left(\frac{\partial T}{\partial P} \right)_{\text{sat}} \frac{dP}{dt} = h_v \frac{dm_t}{dt} \qquad (5.3)$$

where V = container volume
$\quad C_s$ = liquid specific heat at saturation
$\quad P$ = container pressure
$\quad t$ = time
$\quad \left(\dfrac{\partial T}{\partial P} \right)$ = slope of the temperature-vapor pressure curve.

This equation may be solved for the rate of vaporization resulting from small pressure changes:

$$\frac{dm_t}{dt} = KV \frac{dp}{dt} \qquad (5.4)$$

where

$$K = \frac{C_s}{V_L h_v} \left(\frac{\partial T}{\partial P} \right)_{\text{sat}} .$$

If the values for the fluid properties of helium are used to solve for K, with convenient units,

$$c = 7.9 \times 10^{-3} V \left(\frac{dp}{dt}\right) \qquad (5.5)$$

where c = vaporization rate due to change in barometric pressure, scfh

  V = total container volume, liters

  $\left(\dfrac{dp}{dt}\right)$ = change in barometric pressure, mm/hr

For example, if the flash loss rate from eq (5.5) is compared with the normal evaporation rate of a full 100-l vapor-shielded container (about 1.5 percent per day), a change in atmospheric pressure at the rate of only 1 mm per hour will result in a 50 percent change in the measured liquid evaporation rate. For this reason, meaningful loss-rate measurements can be obtained only if the test is conducted over a long period of time, to average out the effects of pressure variations. The use of a precision regulator, controlling absolute pressure on the container, is an alternative.

FIGURE 5.8. *7800-gal liquid helium semi-trailer constructed of 5083–0 aluminum by Cryogenic Engineering Company.*

This trailer, built in 1962 for nonvented transport, is designed for 100 psig operating pressure. Heat leak is approximately 95 Btu/hr. Insulation is of the multilayer type. A tubular heat exchanger is attached to the inner vessel, for use during inital cool-down. (Courtesy: Cryogenics Division, NBS Institute for Basic Standards.)

5.4. NONVENTED CONTAINERS

Low-pressure, vented containers are the preferred method of storing and shipping liquid helium when the ultimate use requires a liquid-phase product. Low container pressures result in lower liquid transfer losses at the destination (see sec. 5.8.6) and the refrigeration available in the vented vapor may be used effectively to reduce vaporization

FIGURE 5.9.   *This 5300-gal semi-trailer, built in 1959, was the first large-scale unit ever constructed for nonvented liquid helium transport.*

The inner stainless steel tank is designed for a maximum operating pressure of 180 psig. An additional inner copper shell reduces thermal stratification of the contents and also is used to direct the vapor generated during filling into close contact with the heavy pressure shell. This latter feature reduces liquid consumed during cooldown by making maximum use of the gaseous reuseable heat. (Courtesy: Linde Division, Union Carbide Corporation.)

losses during transport. When the ultimate use of the product requires gaseous helium or both gas and liquid, it is more economical to conserve the vapor by not allowing the container to vent during the period of transport, and by allowing the temperature and pressure of the contents to increase. Containers designed for this service are less expensive than vented containers. This cost reduction is usually accomplished by omitting refrigerated shields at the sacrifice of greater heat input. Some liquid can usually be recovered at the destination (see sec. 5.8) by venting the container into a gaseous recovery system. The insulation systems used are the multilayer type in a high vacuum. Figures 5.8, 5.9, and 5.10 show several containers now in use.

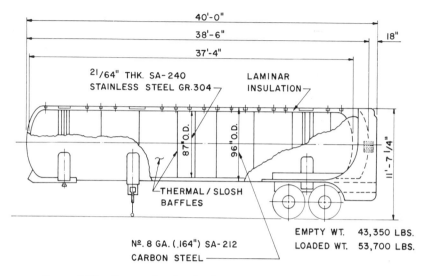

FIGURE 5.10.   *Construction details of 10,000-gal liquid helium semi-trailer.*
The trailer utilizes multilayer insulation to provide a 100 Btu/hr heat leak rate. Copper baffles are used to reduce thermal stratification and sloshing.

5.4.1. Pressure Rise

The heat added in a nonvented or constant-volume process may be equated to the change in internal energy of the contents [10]:

$$Q = \Delta U = \Delta H - v\Delta P \qquad (5.6)$$

where Q = total heat added to the system
U = internal energy function
H = enthalpy function
v = specific volume = container volume divided by total mass of liquid and vapor
ΔP = the pressure rise at constant volume.

The pressure-internal energy relationship may be conveniently plotted for various specific volumes as shown in figure 2.7 and described in chapter 2, if the contents are in thermal equilibrium (without temperature gradients). The process can be illustrated by following a line of constant volume (isochor) for the horizontal distance corresponding to ΔU or Q. If the vessel is initially partially full, a constant heat input will result in a linear pressure increase with time until the liquid-vapor dome is intersected. After that point, the pressure again increases at a nearly constant but much faster rate. It is interesting to note that at specific volumes less than that corresponding to the critical point, the liquid miniscus steadily rises until a single phase exists. At specific volumes greater than the critical, the liquid miniscus lowers until only a single phase exists.

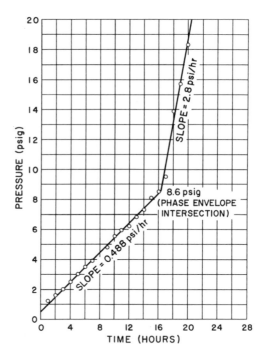

FIGURE 5.11. *Pressure rise in a nonvented, 25-liter, nitrogen-shielded helium dewar.*

The container initially contained 22¼ liquid liters. Note the sharp inflection in the curve, as the contents became single phase [10].

In the absence of temperature gradients (thermal stratification), the pressure rise can be accurately predicted and the transition from two phases to a single phase is sharply defined as shown in figure 5.11.

Thermal stratification usually will result in faster rates of pressure rise than a system in thermal equilibrium [10]; also, the phase transition point will be less clearly defined. These effects can usually be avoided by the use of construction materials of high thermal conductivity to distribute the energy input uniformly throughout the helium contents.

A nonvented transport container would be designed for a specified, no-loss transit time corresponding to an allowable pressure rise and initial specific volume or filling condition. The container would arrive at the destination with its contents at an elevated temperature and pressure, and possibly in the form of a single-phase, cold, dense, gas. Several discharge techniques for liquid gas recovery will be discussed later.

5.4.2. Supercritical Venting

If a nonvented vessel is delayed in transit, excessive gas losses can occur when the container pressure reaches the relief valve setting. An approximate expression [11] for the loss experienced in venting a single phase container is shown below:

$$\ln\,(m_f/m_i)=(1-K)Q/KPV \qquad (5.7)$$

where m_f = final mass in container
$\quad m_i$ = initial mass in container
$\quad Q$ = total heat input to expell mass $(m_i - m_f)$
$\quad P$ = venting pressure
$\quad V$ = volume of container
$\quad K$ = C_p/C_v
$\quad \ln$ = natural logarithm.

Considering a large vessel such as the semi-trailer shown in figure 5.10, a 30-W energy input would result in a 2 percent/day loss of gaseous product if the container was vented at 1 atm (see sec. 5.4.1). The same energy input would result in a 4.6 percent/day loss if the container were vented at 100 psig. However, if the container was initially shipped 100 percent full of liquid at 1 atm, a pressure of 100 psig would not be reached for a period of 7 days. During the 7-day period of pressure rise, no product would be lost.

5.5. INSULATIONS

As has been pointed out earlier in this chapter, the very small heat of vaporization and the low boiling temperature of liquid helium place severe requirements on insulation systems for this fluid.

As an example, the heat leak into a high-quality liquid helium container is such that it boils away only about one percent of the total capacity per day. The same heat leak into an equivalent volume of water would require more than five months to raise the water temperature one degree Celsius.

In addition, liquid helium is a comparatively expensive cryogenic fluid. Thus, the use of relatively complex and expensive insulation systems is economically justified. In fact, a common and effective method of insulating liquid helium storage containers involves the sacrifice of a less expensive cryogenic fluid, usually liquid nitrogen, to absorb part of the heat leaking into the container (sec. 5.3.1).

Part of the heat leak into any liquid helium container takes place through the necessary mechanical support members and plumbing. These aspects of liquid helium containers are treated elsewhere in this chapter. This section is concerned only with insulation materials and systems.

5.5.1. Types of Insulation

There are two broad categories of insulations: the evacuated and non-evacuated. The evacuated insulations can conveniently be subdivided into three major types: simple high-vacuum insulation, evacuated porous insulations, and evacuated multilayer insulations.

The non-evacuated insulations are porous materials such as expanded silicate powders or ceramic fibers in which the interstitial spaces are filled with atmospheric pressure gas. Because of their low installed cost, they are widely used in less demanding cryogenic insulation systems such as air liquefaction plants. However, their relatively low thermal effectiveness, which is due mostly to the high heat leak through the atmospheric pressure gas phase, generally precludes their use with liquid helium. Only evacuated insulations are normally used with liquid helium.

The simple high-vacuum insulation system is composed of a well evacuated space bounded by highly reflective walls. It is exemplified in the classical Dewar flask and the Thermos bottle and is illustrated

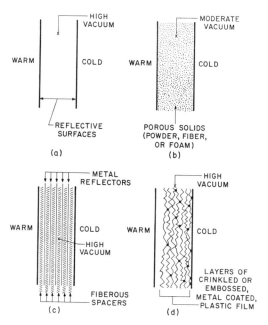

FIGURE 5.12.   *Three types of evacuated insulation: (a) simple high vacuum insulation; (b) evacuated porous insulation; (c) and (d) two general types of evacuated multilayer insulation.*

schematically in figure 5.12a. It is, structurally and conceptually, the simplest of the evacuated insulation systems. It has the least weight and least total heat capacity of any of the evacuated insulations, a feature which minimizes cooldown losses in equipment which undergoes frequent thermal cycling (transfer lines, for example). This insulation has the unique property that the heat leak is independent of the insulation thickness (at least for nonmicroscopic thicknesses), a characteristic particularly useful in insulating small equipment. When used between liquid nitrogen temperature and liquid helium temperature, simple high-vacuum insulation is normally the most effective insulation available. It is, however, not nearly so effective when used between room temperature and liquid helium temperature.

The evacuated multilayer insulations consist of a well evacuated, laminar assembly of many thin, highly reflective layers which are spaced apart in such a manner that poor thermal conduction takes place between adjacent layers. Two commonly used evacuated multilayer insulations are shown schematically in figures 5.12c and 5.12d. The insulation shown in figure 5.12c consists of multiple layers of thin metal reflectors separated each from the others by a spacer material. In figure 5.12d is shown an insulation composed of multiple layers which are crinkled or embossed in such manner that adjacent layers touch one another only at small, discrete, fairly widely spaced points. Between room temperature and liquid helium temperature, evacuated multilayer insulations are the most effective insulations yet developed. They are also the most expensive and difficult to install properly. In addition, they have relatively large total heat capacities which can introduce cooldown problems.

The heat leak through an evacuated multilayer insulation is inversely proportional to its thickness. The total heat leak can, in principle, be reduced to any desired extent by using a sufficient thickness of the insulation. Thus these insulations can be characterized by an apparent thermal conductivity (k_a), which is, however, highly anisotropic, being very small in the direction perpendicular to the layers but being several orders of magnitude higher in directions parallel to the layers. This anisotropy causes increased heat leak at any discontinuities in the insulation, such as penetrations by supports and plumbing.

In spite of their several drawbacks, the unexcelled thermal effectiveness of the evacuated multilayer insulations makes them extremely useful for applications between room and liquid helium temperatures, especially for storage containers in which auxiliary cooling is not employed.

The evacuated porous insulations, shown schematically in figure 5.12b, consist of finely dispersed solids — powders, fibers, or even foams — similar to those used in nonevacuated insulations, but which are enclosed within impermeable walls so that the interstitial gas can be evacuated to a moderately low pressure, 0.01 to 0.001 torr. This degree of vacuum is considerably poorer than that required for the other types of evacuated insulation, a factor in the comparatively low total cost of these insulations. In addition, they are simple to install, usually being poured directly into the evacuatable insulation space. However, they have roughly the same, relatively large, total heat capacity as do the evacuated multilayer materials.

The evacuated porous insulations can be characterized by an apparent thermal conductivity which is isotropic. Their apparent thermal conductivities are, however, roughly ten times greater than those of the better multilayer insulations. For this reason, these porous insulations are seldom used as the only insulation in liquid helium vessels. They are, however, sometimes used to insulate the liquid nitrogen vessels incorporated in shielded helium containers.

In the following sections, experimental heat transfer data, the mechanisms of heat transfer, and other properties of the evacuated insulations will be discussed, the greater emphasis being given to the simple high-vacuum and the evacuated multilayer insulations. It will become evident that there is a notable absence of published experimental data for these insulations at liquid helium temperature. Almost all of the data presented, therefore, will be for liquid hydrogen temperatures or higher.

5.5.2. Simple High-Vacuum Insulation

Heat transfer through a simple high-vacuum insulation system takes place by radiation transfer between the bounding walls and by free molecular conduction through the residual gas in the vacuum space. The radiation and free molecular conduction processes do not interact with one another. They can, therefore, be treated separately, and the total heat transfer rate taken as the sum of those evaluated for each process. Radiation and free molecular gas conduction heat transfer are important in all evacuated insulations, but because they occur in their least complicated form in the simple high-vacuum insulations, they will be discussed in some detail here.

Radiation Heat Transfer. Any two surfaces separated by a transparent medium will interchange thermal energy by a process of emitting and absorbing electromagnetic radiation. Basic to any discussion of this heat transfer process is the concept of the perfectly black surface, or blackbody, which is one that completely absorbs all of the electromagnetic radiation that impinges upon it. Such a blackbody must also emit radiation according to the Stephen-Boltzmann relation.

$$q/A = \sigma T^4. \tag{5.8}$$

In eq (5.8), q/A is the rate of thermal energy radiated per unit normal area, T is the absolute temperature of the blackbody, and σ is a fundamental physical constant having the value 5.67×10^{-12} W/cm²-K⁴ (1.712 $\times 10^{-9}$ Btu/hr-ft²-R⁴).

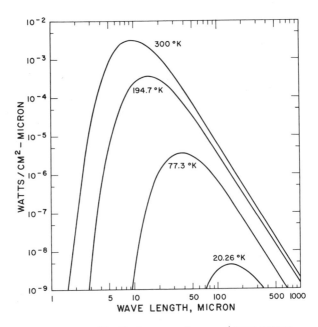

FIGURE 5.13.   *Blackbody spectra for several temperatures.*
The area under each curve is σT^4.

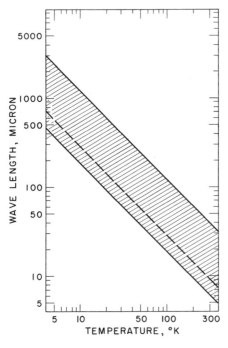

FIGURE 5.14.   *Band of wavelength of significance in radiation heat transfer at low temperatures.*

The shaded band includes the range of wavelength that accounts for 90 percent of the radiant energy emitted by a black or grey body at the indicated temperature. The dashed curve describes the wavelength of maximum radiation intensity as a function of temperature.

From eq (5.8) it follows that the rate of heat transfer between two extended perfectly black surfaces at temperatures T_1 and T_2 is

$$q/A = \sigma(T_1^4 + T_2^4). \tag{5.9}$$

The radiation emitted from a blackbody has a well-defined distribution of wavelengths, termed the blackbody spectrum for a particular temperature. Such spectra for several temperatures are shown in figure 5.13. For each temperature, these spectra extend over a wide range of wavelengths. As an example, the significant band of wavelengths can be selected as those which account for 90 percent of the total radiation intensity. The dashed curve in figure 5.14 shows the wavelength of maximum radiation intensity as a function of temperature, and the two solid curves define the band of wavelengths which accounts for 90 percent of the radiation intensity. It is important to recognize that these wavelengths are very long. They occupy the intermediate and far infrared regions of the electromagnetic spectrum and are far longer than the wavelengths of visible light (0.3 to 0.7 μm). Wavelengths as long as 40 μm are significant at room temperature, and wavelengths up to 150 μm (0.006 in) are significant at liquid nitrogen temperatures. These are dimensions easily measurable with a machinist's micrometer.

Practical surfaces do not emit or absorb radiation as effectively as would a blackbody; some part of the radiation incident upon practical surfaces is reflected. The radiation properties of real surfaces are characterized by their emittance, absorbance, and reflectance. The reflectance is the fraction of the incident radiation reflected by the surface; the absorbance is the fraction of the incident radiation absorbed by the surface; and for opaque materials, the sum of the absorbance and reflectance must be 1.

The emittance is the ratio of the intensity of radiation emitted by a real, isothermal surface to that which would be emitted by a blackbody at the same temperature as computed from eq (5.8). Kirchhoff's law requires that, for any given wavelength of radiation, the absorbance be numerically equal to the emittance. Most of the surfaces encountered in cryogenic insulations are "grey": their absorbance and emittance do not change much over the range of significant wavelengths. Kirchhoff's law can, therefore, be applied with good accuracy to values of absorbance and emittance averaged over the entire range of significant wavelengths.

In order to compute the rate of radiation heat transfer between two extended surfaces, eq (5.9) must be modified as follows to take into account the emittances of the two surfaces, ϵ_1 and ϵ_2:

$$q/A = \sigma \left[\frac{\epsilon_1 \epsilon_2}{\epsilon_1 + \epsilon_2 - \epsilon_1 \epsilon_2} \right] (T_1^4 - T_2^4). \qquad (5.10)$$

This equation is exactly correct for semi-infinite, parallel plates. It is also correct for semi-infinite, coaxial cylinders and concentric spheres when specular (rather than diffuse) reflection from the surfaces is assumed; in these cases q/A is referred to the inner surface area.

If diffuse reflection is assumed, the correct form for spheres and cylinders is eq (5.11), in which the subscripts 1 and 2 refer to the inner and outer surfaces, respectively.

$$q/A = \sigma \left[\frac{\epsilon_1 \epsilon_2}{\epsilon_2 + (A_1/A_2)(\epsilon_1 - \epsilon_1 \epsilon_2)} \right] (T_1^4 - T_2^4). \qquad (5.11)$$

Generally, reflections in cryogenic insulations have both diffuse and specular components. The assumption of diffuse reflection yields the higher q/A value and is, therefore, the conservative assumption.

In most cases encountered in cryogenic insulations, the factor A_1/A_2 is nearly 1, the emittances ϵ_1 and ϵ_2 are approximately equal, and both emittances are much less than 1. Under these conditions, both eqs (5.10) and (5.11) can be approximately simplified to the following form in which ϵ_{avg} is the arithmetic average of ϵ_1 and ϵ_2.

$$q/A = (1/2)\sigma\epsilon_{avg}(T_1^4 - T_2^4). \qquad (5.12)$$

This equation clearly shows that there are two ways to reduce the rate of radiation heat transfer: by reducing either the differences in the fourth powers of the surface temperatures or the average emittance of the surfaces.

In most high-vacuum insulation systems, the temperature of the colder surface is unimportant, for if the temperature of the colder surfaces is less than 31 percent of the warmer surface temperature, the fourth power of these temperatures will differ by a factor of more than 100. Radiation heat transfer in cryogenic insulations is, therefore, approximately proportional to the fourth power of the warm boundary temperature, a fact which explains the greatly enhanced effectiveness of simple high-vacuum insulations at low temperatures. In liquid helium storage vessels, for example, the reduction of the warm surface temperature from 300 to 77 K, by using either a liquid nitrogen or helium vapor cooled shield, will reduce the radiation heat transfer by 99.58 percent.

Once the boundary temperatures of the insulation are fixed by the overall design of the equipment, the lowest practical surface emittances must be obtained to minimize radiation heat transfer. The lowest emittance surfaces are clean, undistorted surfaces of pure metals, especially the metals having low electrical resistivities. Such surfaces can be routinely fabricated which have emittances of 0.02 or less, and eq (5.12) shows that the radiation heat transfer between two such low emittance surfaces will be only 1 percent of that which would take place between black surfaces.

There are a number of published compilations of experimentally measured surface emittance data. Among these are the compilations by Dickson and Jones [12]; Purdue University [13]; Reynolds, Corruccini, Fulk, and Burley [14]; Goldsmith, Waterman, and Hirschhorn [15]; and Gubareff, Janssen, and Torborg [16].

Some illustrative values of the emittances of various metal surfaces have been selected from these published compilations and are shown in table 5.3. Both monochromatic and total emittances are given, and no distinction is made between normal and total hemispheric emittances.* In addition to showing values for practical surfaces which can be produced by standard manufacturing methods, values are also shown for laboratory-quality surfaces in order to illustrate the very low emittance values that can be obtained by the most careful fabricating techniques. In fact, the room-temperature emittance shown for ultra-high vacuum deposited silver is the lowest experimental value yet reported for any room-temperature surface.

The values shown in table 5.3 make one point abundantly clear: emittance is not a true property of the bulk material; rather, it is a property of the surface itself. The emittance values are strongly dependent on the exact manner in which a surface is prepared. Because surface emittances are dependent on so many parameters, some of which are very difficult to measure, the literature data for emittances are valuable mostly as qualitative guides for the selection of materials and fabricating techniques which will yield low emittance surfaces. These qualitative guides, based both on experimental data and theoretical considerations, have been formulated by Scott [6] and Dickson and Jones [12].

---

*Normal emittances are those measured perpendicular to the surface, and total hemispheric emittances are averaged over the entire hemisphere from which the surface can be viewed. For low emittance surfaces, these two kinds of emittances differ by only about 20 percent.

TABLE 5.3. *Emittances of selected metal surfaces*

Material	Surface temperature K	Radiation*	ϵ
Aluminum			
Vacuum deposited at 10^{-10} torr	~ 300	10μm	0.0124
Vacuum deposited at 10^{-5} torr			
freshly deposited	~ 300	10μm	0.0155
		20μm	0.0122
		30μm	0.0104
aged in air several weeks	~ 300	10μm	0.0188
		20μm	0.0148
		30μm	0.0130
Clean, annealed bulk metal	300	300 K	0.038
	76	300 K	0.022
	4	300 K	0.014
Household foil	80	300 K	0.043 – 0.065
H–19 tempered foil			
bright side	76	300 K	0.056
dull side	76	300 K	0.063
Commercially vapor-deposited on polyester plastic film	76	300 K	0.04 – 0.05
Copper			
Vacuum deposited at 10^{-5} torr	295	10μm	0.0099
	82	10μm	0.0076
Electropolished	4.2	> 1.5μm	0.005
Electroplated	4.2	300 K	0.0042
Mechanically polished	4.2	300 K	0.0147
Commercial copper sphere	76	300 K	0.03
Gold			
Vacuum deposited at 10^{-9} torr	300	10μm	0.0061
		20μm	0.0060
		30μm	0.0058
Vacuum deposited at 10^{-5} torr	295	10μm	0.0101
	82	10μm	0.0076
0.0015 inch foil	76	300 K	0.01
Electroplated on stainless steel (1% silver in gold)			
0.00005-in thick	76	300 K	0.028
0.0001-in thick	76	300 K	0.027
0.0002-in thick	76	300 K	0.025
Vapor deposited on polyester in plastic film	76	300 K	0.02

Table 5.3. *Emittances of selected metal surfaces* — Continued

Material	Surface temperature K	Radiation*	ϵ
Silver			
Vacuum deposited at 10^{-9} torr....................	300	10μm	0.0047
		20μm	0.0044
		30μm	0.0042
Vacuum deposited at 10^{-5} torr....................	295	10μm	0.0113
	82	10μm	0.0093
Electropolished......................................	4.2	$> 1.5\mu$m	0.0044
Electroplated.......................................	76	300 K	$0.007 - 0.012$
Chemically deposited.............................	90	293 K	0.023
Alloys			
316 Stainless Steel			
finished to 2 μin rms............................	83	....	0.027
finished to 15 μin rms...........................	83	....	0.045
Yellow brass, shim stock...........................	76	300 K	0.029
Yellow brass, hand polished......................	77	273 K	0.10
Yellow brass, electropolished.....................	4.2	~ 300 K	0.018
Yellow brass, mechanically polished.............	90	293 K	0.046
Soft solder...	76	~ 300 K	$0.03 - 0.047$

*Entries in "Radiation" column given in micrometers (μm) refer to monochromatic radiation of that wavelength; entries given in K refer to blackbody radiation corresponding to that temperature.

Most importantly, the visual appearance of a surface is not a reliable indication of its emittance for the intermediate and far infrared radiation involved in cryogenic insulation. For example, organic lacquers and paints, even though they may be transparent to visible light, are very black to infrared radiation. And a highly polished stainless steel surface looks more reflective than the rather dull, matte surface of chemically deposited silver, but the silver has the lower emittance for thermal radiation.

Emittances generally decrease somewhat with decreasing surface temperatures. This is evident from some of the data in table 5.3 and is further illustrated by the data in figure 5.15 which show the measured emittances [17] of several surfaces as a function of temperature.

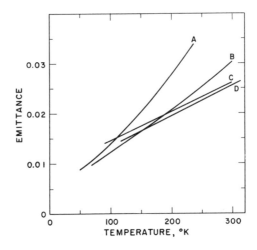

FIGURE 5.15. *Experimentally measured total emittances of several practical surfaces as a function of surface temperature illustrating the significant reduction of emittances at lower temperatures* [16].

A is for chemically cleaned copper;
B is for aluminum foil;
C is for chemically deposited gold;
D is for chemically deposited silver.

Surface contaminants, especially organic materials such as lubricants or even fingerprints, increase the emittance. Rough surfaces have higher emittances than do smooth surfaces; the characteristic dimensions of roughness are, however, related to the wavelength of the radiation. Irregularities small in comparison to the radiation wavelength cannot be "seen" by the radiation.

Any mechanical deformation (cold working) of the surface, such as occurs in mechanical polishing or burnishing, will increase the emittance. Dickson and Jones [12] have generalized that emittances decrease in the following order of surface preparation techniques: mechanical polishing, high-vacuum vapor deposition, electropolishing, and ultra-high-vacuum deposition.

Gas Conduction. Heat can be conducted from one surface to another by gas molecules. The ability of the gas to conduct heat is proportional to the heat capacity of the gas, to its density, to the mean-free-path of the gas molecules (the average distance a molecule travels between collisions either with other gas molecules or with the surfaces), and to the velocity of the molecules.

In roughly atmospheric pressure gases, the mean-free-path is entirely determined by collisions between gas molecules. As the pressure is reduced (but not too far), collisions between molecules become less frequent and the mean-free-path increases. This increase is, however, almost exactly offset by the decrease in the gas density, and the ability of the gas to conduct heat is unchanged. This is the region of viscous gas conduction.

As the gas pressure is further reduced, the collisions between gas molecules and the surfaces become more frequent than collisions between molecules, and the mean-free-path becomes limited by the distance between the surfaces. Still further reductions in pressure cannot increase the mean-free-path, but it does decrease the gas density; thus, the ability of the gas to conduct heat becomes proportional to the gas density or to its pressure. This is the region of free molecular gas conduction.

Evacuated insulations are always maintained at a pressure sufficiently low that free molecular gas conduction prevails. In insulation systems in which one wall is at liquid helium temperature, only helium and a small amount of hydrogen can exist as gases; all other materials are, for practical purposes, completely frozen out. The vapor pressure of hydrogen at 4.2 K is 7×10^{-7} torr [18]. The vapor pressure of nitrogen at 10 K is calculated to be about 1×10^{-30} torr [19].

Corruccini [20] has presented an illuminating review of free molecular conduction in cryogenic insulations. He shows that the rate of heat transfer by this mechanism is given by the following relation:

$$q/A = C\alpha p (T_2 - T_1).$$ (5.13)

In this equation, q/A is the rate of heat transfer per unit normal area (watts/cm^2), p is the gas pressure in the vacuum space measured by a gage at 300 K (torr), T_1 and T_2 are the temperatures of the two surfaces in degrees Kelvin, α is the average accommodation coefficient which is discussed below, and C is a numerical constant determined by the kind of gas involved. Corruccini gives the value for C as 0.0280 for helium, and 0.039 to 0.053 for hydrogen, depending on the temperatures involved.

The average accommodation coefficient, α in eq (5.13), is defined as follows:

$$\alpha = \frac{\alpha_1 \alpha_2}{\alpha_2 + \alpha_1 (1 - \alpha_2)(A_1/A_2)}.$$ (5.14)

Here, α_1 and α_2 are the accommodation coefficients for the inner and outer surfaces, respectively, and A_1/A_2 is the ratio of the surface areas.

The accommodation coefficient is a measure of the efficiency of thermal energy interchange that occurs when a gas molecule collides with the surface. It is less than or equal to 1, and its exact value depends upon the kind of gas, the temperature of the surface, and very strongly upon the exact conditions of the surface. Based on the very limited experimental data for the low-temperature accommodation coefficients on the sort of surfaces commonly used in simple high-vacuum insulations, Corruccini [20] has given suggested values for several gases. Those for helium and hydrogen are listed in table 5.4. He also points out that increased surface roughness and the presence of adsorbed gas films tend to increase the accommodation coefficient.

TABLE 5.4. *Suggested accommodation coefficients*

Temperature K	Accommodation coefficient	
	Helium	Hydrogen
300	0.3	0.3
80	0.4	0.5
20	0.6	1
4	1	1

It is important to note that the distance between the two surfaces does not appear in eq (5.13). In free molecular gas conduction, the rate of heat transfer is independent of the thickness of the gas layer. The spacing between the surfaces is important, though, in defining the pressure at which the transition from viscous to free molecular gas conduction takes place; the greater the spacing, the lower is the transition pressure. For spacing on the order of an inch, the transition pressure is 10^{-3} to 10^{-4} torr. For the microscopic spacing of surfaces found in some evacuated porous insulations, however, this transition pressure is near 1 atm.

Equation (5.13) shows also that the heat transfer by free molecular gas conduction is directly proportional to the gas pressure. In principle, then, this mode of heat transfer can be reduced to any desired extent by a sufficient lowering of the gas pressure. In practice, however, it is only necessary to reduce the gas pressure to such a level that gas conduction is negligibly small compared to the heat transferred by other modes, particularly by radiation.

For example, consider a simple high-vacuum insulation, the walls of which have an average emissivity of 0.02. Between 300 and 77 K, conservatively taking $\alpha = 1$ and assuming helium gas, eqs (5.10) and (5.13) show that the free molecular gas conduction is reduced to 10 percent of the radiation heat transfer at a pressure of about 7×10^{-5} torr. Considering wall temperatures of 77 and 4 K, as would be found in a liquid nitrogen-shielded helium container, the gas pressure must be reduced to about 2×10^{-7} torr before gas conduction is reduced to 10 percent of the radiation heat transfer.

The techniques for producing, maintaining, and measuring the vacuums required in evacuated insulations are far too broad an area to be summarized here. Dushman [21] and many other texts offer reviews of the entire area of vacuum technology, and Scott [6] gives a review aimed particularly at evacuated insulation technology.

5.5.3. Evacuated Porous Insulations

Radiation heat transfer is a major component of the total heat leak through evacuated insulations, particularly at temperatures not far below room temperature. We have seen in the preceding section that one effective way of lessening radiation heat transfer is to reduce the emittances of the two boundary surfaces in simple high-vacuum insulation.

Another effective method of reducing radiation heat transfer is that of filling the evacuated insulation space with a finely divided solid material such as powders or fibers. These porous materials reduce radiation heat transfer either by scattering or by absorbing and re-emitting radiation. At the same time, however, some additional heat transfer by conduction from particle to particle through the insulation is introduced. (This will hereafter be called solid-phase conduction.)

For not-too-thin layers of evacuated porous insulations, the resistance to radiation heat transfer is directly proportional to the total number of scattering and absorbing particles between the warm and cold boundaries; this is, of course, directly proportional to the thickness of the insulation layer. Similarly, the resistance to solid-phase conduction is proportional to the insulation thickness. Consequently, these insulations, in contrast to the simple high-vacuum insulations, can be characterized by an apparent thermal conductivity, k_a, which for one-dimensional, rectilinear heat flow is defined by the following integral form of the Fourier heat transfer law:

$$q/A = k_a (T_w - T_c)/L. \qquad (5.15)$$

The value of k_a is not a constant; it depends strongly on the values of T_w and T_c, the warm and cold boundary temperatures. But, for insulation thicknesses (L) of greater than ½ in or so, k_a is practically independent of thickness. Therefore, at least in principle, the total rate of heat transfer through evacuated porous insulations can be reduced to any desired extent by sufficiently increasing the thickness of the insulation layer.

The k_a of evacuated porous insulations is, again excepting very thin layers, independent of the boundary surface emittances. In addition, it is isotropic; that is, it has the same value in any direction. Thus, the value of k_a determined for particular boundary temperatures can be properly applied to other geometric cases (cylinders and spheres, for example) involving similar boundary temperatures by using standard, integral form, conduction heat transfer equations which are available in any standard heat transfer text.

Some representative values for the conductivities of evacuated porous insulations are listed in table 5.5 together with the boundary temperatures associated with each value. There is a notable lack of data for the cold boundary at liquid helium temperature; the value shown for perlite between 20 and 4 K appears to be the only one yet reported. From comparing the tabulated k_a values of several insulations for 77 and 20 K cold boundary temperatures (and the same warm boundary temperatures), however, one would expect that k_a values for 4 K cold boundary temperatures should be somewhat smaller than those shown for the 20 K cold boundary temperature.

The relative merits of evacuated porous insulations can be illustrated by comparison with a simple high-vacuum insulation having surface emittances of 0.02. Considering as the first case boundary temperatures of 300 and 77 K, the simple high-vacuum insulation would exhibit a heat leak of 4.6×10^{-4} W/cm². A good evacuated powder having a k_a of 4 μW/cm-K would require the very reasonable thickness of only 1.94 cm (0.76 in) to attain an equally low heat leak.

Upon comparing a liquid-nitrogen-shielded helium container with an unshielded helium container insulated only with an evacuated porous insulation, however, the picture is completely changed. The heat leak through the high-vacuum insulation from the nitrogen shield to the helium vessel is only 2×10^{-6} W/cm². Taking a fairly low k_a value of 2 μW/cm-K for an evacuated powder between 300 and 4 K, eq (5.15) shows that a 296-cm (116-in or 9.4-ft) thickness of insulation on the powder-insulated container would be required to equal the performance

TABLE 5.5. *Apparent thermal conductivity values for some evacuated porous insulations*

Material	Boundary temperature		k_a		Density	Reference
	Warm	Cold				
	K	K	$\dfrac{\mu W}{cm-K}$	$\dfrac{\mu Btu}{hr-ft-R}$	lb/ft^3	
Perlite, −30 mesh..........	304	76	10	578	8.7	24
	304	20	6.5	376	8.7	24
	76	20	2	115	8.7	24
	76	4	0.8	46	8.7	24
Expanded....................	304	76	6	350	12.5	23
carbon powder...........	300	20	3.5	200	12.5	−
Silica aerogel+.............	300	76	4.75	274	−	22
50%, 5μ dia alu-						
minum..................	300	20	3.75	217	−	22
Silica aerogel+.............	305	90	3.7	214	−	27
50% fine copper						
flake.....................	294	20	3.1	180	−	28
"AA" Fiberglas.............	303	77	5.7	330	8	29
isocyanate.................	300	77	100	5800	−	30
foam.......................	300	20	69.6	4020	−	30

of the liquid nitrogen-shielded vessel. Such a thickness is, of course, impractically large.

Thus, this illustration shows that evacuated porous insulations are not useful as the sole insulation in liquid helium vessels. Their use is normally restricted to the less stringent task of insulating the liquid nitrogen or vapor-cooled shields from room temperature in shielded helium containers.

Because the uses of evacuated porous insulations in liquid helium handling equipment are so restricted, they will not be discussed in any further detail here. Instead, the reader is referred to the reviews of Scott [6]; Beck, Kreith, and Kropschot [22]; Kropschot [23]; Fulk [24];

Glaser [25]; and to the more theoretical treatment by Larkin and Churchill [26].

5.5.4. Evacuated Multilayer Insulations

A very effective method of inhibiting radiation heat transfer between two extended, parallel surfaces has been known for many years: the use of floating radiation shields. Radiation shields are thin sheets of reflective material, metal foil for example, which are placed between and parallel to the two surfaces. Floating radiation shields are those which are supported in such a tenuous manner in a high vacuum that each can exchange energy with its surroundings only by radiation heat transfer. The term "floating" refers to the temperatures of the shields, which are determined entirely by the condition of radiation equilibrium.

In order to illustrate the effectiveness of floating radiation shields, let us consider a high-vacuum insulation system into which has been placed a number, n, floating shields and assume that all surfaces have the same low emittance, e_{avg}. With the same assumptions involved in eq (5.12), the radiation heat transfer through this system is as follows:

$$q/A = 1/2 e_{avg} \sigma (T_1^4 - T_2^4)/(n+1). \tag{5.16}$$

A comparison of this equation with the analogous equation for a simple vacuum insulation, eq (5.12), shows that the presence of n floating radiation shields reduces the radiation heat transfer by the factor $1/(n+1)$. Thus, the introduction of one floating shield reduces radiation transfer by 50 percent; three, by 75 percent; and nine, by 90 percent.

Needless to say, it is enormously difficult to fabricate any large number of truly floating radiation shields within a reasonable insulation thickness. Some systems incorporating only a few shields have been built, but these have generally been used only for very specialized applications.

The evacuated multilayer insulations, however, offer a practical method of approximating a large number of floating radiation shields within a reasonable insulation thickness. This is accomplished by supporting each thin radiation shield (reflector) more or less uniformly over its surface, each shield being supported by its neighbors, and the whole array being supported by one or both walls of the insulation space. Obviously, this mechanical support is accompanied by some thermal contact, and evacuated multilayer insulations are effective only because such thermal contact can be kept small.

Broadly, there are two methods by which thermal contact between adjacent reflectors is kept small in evacuated multilayer insulations. One method is to place a spacer sheet made of a low-density, usually fibrous, low thermal conductivity material between each pair of reflectors. Such has been illustrated in figure 5.12c. The other method requires that the reflectors be made of a low thermal conductivity material: polyester plastic film coated with a very thin (few hundred Angstroms) layer of metal such as aluminum. These reflectors are either crinkled or embossed so that when they are placed against one another, they touch only at small, discrete, comparatively widely spaced points. Such an insulation is shown schematically in figure 5.12d.

There are, naturally, many variants of the multilayer insulation theme, many of them protected by patents, and many different materials for reflectors and spacers have been tried. Most multilayer insulations use either aluminum foil or aluminum-coated polyester film for reflectors. The most common spacer material is fine glass fiber in the form of thin mats, cloth, or paper. In addition, synthetic fiber netting, thin sheets of plastic foam, powders, and embossed plastic sheets are sometimes used as spacers [31]. In experimental insulations, even a multitude of tiny springs of plastic monofilament has been attached to the reflectors to act as spacers [32].

Multilayer insulation normally is applied to the inner vessel of a cryogenic container, and subsequently, the outer vacuum shell is assembled around it. Most commonly, the insulation is applied by spirally wrapping a continuous strip of reflector or reflector-spacer pair onto the object being insulated. Less common and generally less effective techniques include the prefabrication of multilayer assemblies quilted together with needle and thread [33] and the application of reflective plastic film reflectors in a shingle fashion [34]. Another technique involves supporting a fairly rigid, prefabricated, multilayer assembly between widely spaced, stand-off supports [35].

Spiral wrapping is most easily accomplished on cylindrical surfaces. The application to compound-curved surfaces, such as eliptical tank heads and spheres, usually requires that the layers be cut in a gore pattern and carefully interleaved to prevent thermal shorts between different layers of the insulation. In this respect, the insulations using only crinkled or embossed plastic film reflectors have the advantage of being more conformable to compound-curved surfaces than are the aluminum foil–glass fiber insulations. Furthermore, when multilayer insulations, particularly those using metal foil reflectors, are spirally wrapped on small-diameter objects, there can be significant heat conduction along the spiral path of aluminum. This can be prevented by slitting small gaps in the foil at intervals. Finally, for reasons we will get to shortly, the tension under which multilayer insulations are wrapped is critically important to obtaining optimum performance.

From this discussion, it should be clear that there is a considerable amount of art involved in the proper application of multilayer insulations. Much of this art is proprietary. In addition, it can be seen that the proper installation of multilayer insulation can be complicated and time-consuming, an important factor in the comparatively high installed cost of this type of insulation.

In a well-evacuated multilayer insulation (vacuums of 10^{-4} torr or better are required), heat is transferred from shield to shield through the insulation by two processes, radiation and solid-phase conduction. These two processes interact strongly with each other. Equation (5.16) offers only a crude approximation for the radiation heat transfer: first, the shield temperatures are not the same as they would be if they were truly floating radiation shields, and second, the spacer materials in many insulations further inhibit radiation transfer by the same scattering and absorption-reemission processes that occur in evacuated porous insulations. There is even less quantitative understanding of solid-phase conduction in these insulations. It exists and it is significant in the overall heat transfer through the insulation. In truth, the relative contributions of radiation and solid-phase conduction to the total heat transfer in this type of insulation have yet to be measured in an exact and unambiguous manner. Although the quantitative understanding of the heat transfer mechanisms in evacuated multilayer insulations is quite limited, they are at least qualitatively understood.

A uniform multilayer insulation has a fixed number of reflectors per unit thickness. The resistance to radiation transfer is proportional to the total number of reflectors and, hence, to the total insulation thickness. The resistance to solid-phase conduction is, by the nature of the process, also directly proportional to the insulation thickness. Therefore, as is the case with evacuated porous insulations, the multilayer insulations can be properly characterized by an apparent thermal conductivity, k_a, which is independent of the insulation thickness, but is definitely dependent on the warm and cold boundary temperatures. Furthermore, if the sample is thick enough to include a large number of reflectors (50 or more, say) the k_a value is practically independent of the emittance of the boundaries. In contrast to the evacuated porous insulations, though, the k_a values for evacuated multilayer insulations are extremely anisotropic; for some insulations using metal foil reflectors, the value of k_a in the direction parallel to the reflectors has been reported to be 10^6 times greater than the k_a in the direction perpendicular to the reflectors [36].

The total heat transfer rate through a multilayer insulation is markedly increased by compressive forces resulting either from compression between the bounding surfaces of the insulation space or from the tension applied during the wrapping of the insulation. Most of the increase presumably takes place in solid-phase conduction. According to the best available theories, the increase in heat leak should be proportional to between the 1/2 and 2/3 power of the applied compressive load. This has been strikingly confirmed experimentally for many insulations by Black and Glaser [31] for compressive loads ranging from 15 psi down to 0.01 psi, which is little more load than that produced by the weight of the insulation itself.

Although compressive loading of any given evacuated multilayer insulation sample increases the total heat leak, this same compressive loading also decreases the thickness of the sample. For small compressive loads, the sample thickness decreases more rapidly than the total heat leak increases. This results in a net reduction in k_a. Beyond some optimum compressive load, the situation reverses, and k_a begins increasing with increased compression. Curves illustrating this effect for several multilayer insulations are shown by Glaser, Black, and Doherty [36]. Rather than describing an optimum compressive load for a particular multilayer insulation, however, this optimum is usually specified by an optimum insulation density expressed in number of reflectors per unit insulation thickness (reflectors per inch). For maximum insulation effectiveness, then, the insulation density must be very carefully controlled during installation.

The published k_a values for several representative evacuated multilayer insulations are given in table 5.6. As was found for evacuated porous insulations, there is a notable lack of published data for helium temperature cold boundaries [37–39]. Noting the general decrease in k_a as the cold boundary temperature is reduced from 77 to 20 K, it may be surmised that the k_a for boundary temperatures of 300 and 4 K should be somewhat less than those shown for 300 to 20 K.

In discussing the evacuated porous insulation, it was calculated that an impractically large thickness of insulation would be required to equal the insulating performance of a nitrogen-shielded liquid helium

TABLE 5.6. *Apparent thermal conductivities of some evacuated multilayer insulations*

Material	Layers per inch	Boundary temperature		k_a		Density	Reference
		Warm	Cold				
		K	K	$\dfrac{\mu W}{cm\text{-}K}$	$\dfrac{\mu Btu}{hr\text{-}ft\text{-}R}$	$lb./ft^3$	
1-mil Al foil—0.2 mm bonded........	66	300	76	0.7	40	7.5	37
glass fiber mat...	66	300	20	0.5	28	7.5	37
1-mil Al foil—8-mil glass...........	50	300	76	0.5	28	8.7	37
fiber paper........	50	300	20	0.4	23	8.7	37
Al foil—glass fiber................	50–100	300	76	0.38	22	5.5	38
paper..............	50–100	300	20	0.36	21	5.5	39
(proprietary).......	75–150	300	20	0.17	10	7.5	28
¼-mil, crinkled aluminum coated polyester film..... no spacer (proprietary)	106	289	77	0.42	24	—	32

container. If one makes the same calculations for a container insulated only with a very good evacuated multilayer insulation having a k_a of 0.2 μW/cm-K, one finds that only a 29.5-cm (11.6-in) thickness of insulation between 300 and 4 K is required to equal the performance of the liquid-nitrogen-shielded container.

As was stated earlier, the residual gas pressure within an evacuated multilayer insulation must be reduced to 10^{-4} to 10^{-5} torr, a somewhat lower pressure than is required by evacuated porous insulations. The proper evacuation of multilayer insulations can be quite time-consuming. Some materials, particularly plastic films and organic binders in spacer materials, often contain sizable quantities of absorbed gases which are only slowly liberated. And since either metal foil or plastic film reflectors are impervious to gas flow, the gases being pumped away must flow along the narrow, obstructed channels between the reflectors until they can escape at an edge or other discontinuity in the insulation.

In cases where a high evacuation rate is required in a multilayer insulation, the impediment to gas flow can be significantly reduced by perforating the reflectors so that gas can flow outward through the thickness of the insulation [36, 40]. Naturally, the perforations decrease the effectiveness of the reflectors; so the size, number, and spacing of the perforations must be judiciously selected so as to attain adequate pumping speed without too seriously reducing the insulating effectiveness.

One final problem in properly applying evacuated multilayer insulations will be mentioned: the effects of mechanical penetrations through the insulation layer. Penetrations by mechanical supports and fluid conduits can not be avoided, but their presence can cause a deterioration in the performance of these highly anisotropic insulations. This results because the comparatively large amount of heat being conducted along the penetrating member can be transferred to the radiation shields, and this heat can then be conducted along each shield for a considerable distance around the penetration. The result is the increase of the shield temperatures above their equilibrium value and a net increase in heat transfer. This effect can be lessened by thermally decoupling the insulation from the penetration. One method of accomplishing this is to leave a gap between the insulation and the penetration which is then filled with an isotropic insulation such as glass fiber.

Of course, if the penetration is a member which can absorb heat, a cold-vapor vent line for example, the penetration can actually improve the performance of the insulation by reducing the shield temperatures below their equilibrium values. In these cases, good thermal coupling rather than decoupling is desirable. A multilayer insulation system in which this situation is exploited is described in section 5.3.2.

Here much emphasis, perhaps too much, has been given to the problems that may be encountered in properly applying evacuated multilayer insulations. These problems are, however, quite real, and they should be anticipated in designing and selecting insulations for liquid helium containers. In spite of the difficulties and expense of using evacuated multilayer insulations, the fact remains that they are the only insulations effective enough to make practical the insulation of liquid helium storage vessels without recourse to auxiliary cooling in the form of liquid nitrogen or helium vapor-cooled shields.

5.6. SLOSHING AND THERMAL OSCILLATION HEATING EFFECTS

The commercial distribution of liquid helium in large capacity semitrailers, described in section 5.9, demands a relatively sophisticated cryogenic design. While multilayer insulation techniques have played a very important role in reducing heat leak, other effects must be considered. Thermal stratification, for example, produces excessive pressure rise for a given heat leak. The energy of sloshing in the vessel and thermal oscillations in the interconnecting piping also contribute to the overall heating effects.

5.6.1. Sloshing

Accelerations of the trailer, associated with speed or direction changes and road disturbances, will produce sloshing of the liquid within the vessel. Energy thus gained by the liquid will eventually be converted to heat through friction. This heat will cause product vaporization or pressure rise additive to that caused by heat leak. The energy of the sloshing liquid, due to given input accelerations, is therefore a significant design consideration of a liquid-helium vessel.

The literature on energy of sloshing is very scant, particularly that applicable to a horizontal cylindrical vessel. Arthur D. Little, Inc. [41] found that basic relationships for surface waves developed by Lamb [42] could be used if the cylindrical vessel was approximated by an equivalent rectangular tank. From this basis, it can be shown [43] that vertical accelerations (road disturbances) will produce no sloshing. Rough estimations also show that sloshing energy due to rotational accelerations is small compared to that of longitudinal or latitudinal accelerations.

Equation (5.17), developed by Arthur D. Little, Inc., gives the specific sloshing energy input to the liquid for sloshing in the direction of a given acceleration. Note that a deceleration has the same effect as an acceleration and that starting and stopping of a trailer have additive effects:

$$dq = \frac{16a^2 L^2}{\pi^4 J h (n+1)^2} \tag{5.17}$$

where dq = energy input in Btu/lb
    a = acceleration in g's
    L = total length of tank in feet
    h = height of the liquid in feet
    n = number of full transverse baffles
    J = work-energy equivalent, 778 ft-lb/Btu.

An order of magnitude approximation of the energy input for a helium trailer can be obtained as follows [43]. A typical cryogenic trailer on a 30-hr trip receives approximately 1600 accelerations and decelerations, averaging 0.04 g, from starting, stopping, and routine speed changes. For the helium trailer described in section 5.9 with eight full transverse baffles, the total energy gained for such a trip is about 15 Btu for a 90 percent full load. While this heat gain is significant, it is roughly equivalent to $1/200$ of the normal heat leak while stationary. This estimate is only for longitudinal sloshing, the type with the greatest effect. The sloshing energy for the same trailer without baffles would increase by a factor of 80, an indication that baffles are necessary. Sloshing may be eliminated by transporting single-phase fluid, which eliminates the liquid-vapor interface. In practice this is normally the case, since nonvented transport containers are shipped liquid full. The single-phase state will occur during transit in partially full vessels as the rising pressure approaches the critical point of 2.26 atm.

Sloshing is observed with other cryogenic fluids in trailer transport, but a quantitative correlation of the effects has not been made. The mixing effect of sloshing is apparent in transport vessels subject to temperature stratification (see sec. 5.4.1); the mixing serves as a temperature equalizing mechanism which causes the pressure to drop. The handling of trailers, as reported by various drivers, is adversely affected by the sloshing motion of the liquid.

5.6.2. Thermal Oscillations

Thermal oscillations may occur spontaneously in tubes connecting a liquid helium reservoir to ambient temperatures. The existence of this phenomenon is quite well known (see, for example Clement [44], Scott [6], and Wexler [5]) and is commonly used to detect liquid levels in helium dewars. Thermal oscillations, or pressure oscillations, as they are often called, in a storage or transport container cause a heat pumping effect which may increase the heat leak into a helium reservoir up to 1,000 times that of normal conduction in a tube.

A recent paper by Bannister [45] discusses pressure oscillations in some detail, presenting quantitative as well as qualitative results. Physically, the oscillation is a traveling wave phenomenon which transports energy from the warm end of the tube to the cold end and which ejects discrete pulses of warmed vapor from the cold end. Several results are mentioned which may be helpful in liquid helium equipment design. The frequency of oscillations has been computed by Norton [46] for certain tube configurations. Bannister correlated the pressure amplitude as a function of the slenderness ratio (length to diameter) shown in figure 5.16. The significant result is the heat pumping rate shown in figure 5.17 as a function of oscillation intensity (amplitude times frequency).

The oscillation amplitude is maximum when the cold end of the tube is 5 to 15 cm above the liquid surface. Below the liquid surface, both the amplitude and the frequency are reduced. Bannister noticed that the oscillation intensity could be increased by heating the tube along a portion of its length and, thus, could be reduced by cooling a portion of its length. This is currently done in dewar design by thermally shorting the vent lines to the liquid nitrogen or helium vapor refrigeration

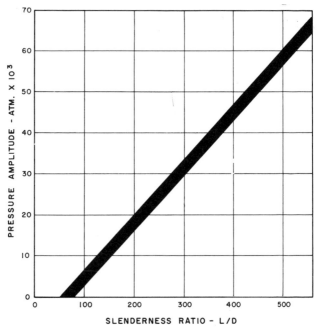

FIGURE 5.16. *Thermal oscillation—pressure amplitude vs. slenderness ratio for tube exposed to a liquid helium reservoir* [45].

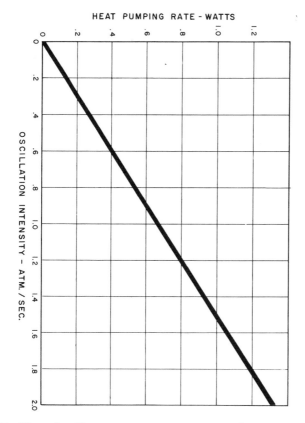

FIGURE 5.17. *Thermal oscillation—heat pumping rate vs. oscillation intensity (amplitude times frequency) for tube exposed to a liquid helium reservoir* [45].

shield. It was also noted that the increased oscillation intensity served to depress the temperature profile of a tube at the cold end of the tube. Finally, the heat pumping is significant only when the cold end is in the vapor phase. This seems reasonable, since more energy is required to pump liquid up and down a tube than to move cold vapor.

Experience with various types of liquid helium dewars indicates that oscillations are not self-sustaining in a freely venting tube. For this reason, oscillations are not usually a problem in a properly venting dewar. It is apparent that restricting the flow, particularly in the cold end, with foam, sintered metal, fibers, beads, etc., will reduce the effects of thermal oscillations, but this also restricts the flow. Another technique is to place expanded sections of tubing or accumulators in the connecting piping to dampen the oscillation energy in the cold regions.

5.7. CONTAINER DESIGN

5.7.1. Materials of Construction

There is little need to provide details on materials and construction for cryogenic equipment. This is covered quite well in the literature, e.g., Bell [47] and Kropschot [48]. Usually, materials suitable for cryogenic service with other low-temperature fluids are also appropriate for liquid helium storage and transport vessels. Some special distinctions exist, however, between 4.2 K service and 77-90 K service, and rather than attempting to discuss the entire area of cryogenic materials selection, the special requirements for 4.2 K service are emphasized.

Generally, copper, aluminum, nickel, their respective alloys, and austenitic stainless steels may be used for vessel construction. Support members may be metallic (stainless and high-strength alloys, such as Hastalloy B or A-286 stainless) or nonmetallic (fluorocarbon polymers, polyester fiber, etc.). Data compilations for these and other materials are given by McClintock and Gibbons [49] and by Schwartzberg, Good, Keys, and Kieter [50] among other sources. Actually, there has been very little mechanical testing done at helium temperatures, and most published curves are extrapolated from 77 K or 20 K down to 4.2 K. A comparison of common cryogenic materials suitable for helium service is given in table 5.7 as the ratio of yield stress to thermal conductivity.

Copper has special application for small helium dewars because of its ductility for spinning and its low surface emissivity in the polished condition. Electrolytic tough pitch copper is used for anti-slosh (sec. 5.6.1) and de-stratification (sec. 5.4.1) baffles because of its high thermal conductivity. Aluminum has not been very widely used for helium equipment. Since stainless steel is usually used for interconnecting piping (low conductivity), aluminum to stainless transition joints are required. These have traditionally been avoided because of their susceptibility to vacuum leaks; however, more reliable joints are becoming available. Aluminum does have an economic and weight advantage and there exists a successful 7,000-gal helium trailer designed for air transport, manufactured by the Cryogenic Engineering Company (fig. 5.8) using a 5083-O aluminum alloy.

Type 304 and 304L austenitic stainless is commonly used. Type 304 has better properties in general, but 304L has better impact properties in the weld heat affected zone. This is attributed to its lower carbon content. The common 9 percent nickel steel, while much used for liquid oxygen and nitrogen service, has very poor impact properties below 77 K, especially in the heat affected zone. Carbon steel, such as SA–212, is often used for outer shells which are not subjected to low temperatures. Cryogenic transport vessels, regardless of operating pressure, are considered as pressure vessels, and therefore must satisfy pertinent state and local codes where they apply. Most of these codes incorporate the ASME Pressure Vessel Code. Vessels subject to interstate usage, as is most transport equipment, come under the jurisdiction of the Interstate Commerce Commission. There are presently no general regulations for cryogenic transport, and, although ICC specification MC331 generally applies, special permits must be obtained for hazardous fluids and for operation above 25 psig. Liquid hydrogen, for example, fits into the first category and the liquid helium trailers described in section 5.9.1 are in the second. Apart from general safety and transport restrictions, the

TABLE 5.7.   *Comparison of materials used for support members**

Material	σy	k	$\sigma y / k$
	(1,000 psi)	*(Btu/hr/ft/F)*	
Aluminum 2024..............................	55	47	1.17
Aluminum 7075..............................	70	50	1.4
Copper, ann...............................	12	274	0.044
Hastelloy [a] "B"..............................	65	5.4	12
Hastelloy [a] "C"..............................	48	5.9	8.1
"K" Monel [b].................................	100	9.9	10.1
Stainless Steel 304, ann.....................	35	5.9	5.9
Stainless Steel (drawn 210,000 psi)......	150	5.2	29
Titanium, pure..............................	85	21	4.0
Titanium alloy (4Al–4Mn)................	145	3.5	41.4
Dacron [c]....................................	20	†0.088	227
Mylar [c].....................................	10	†0.088	113
Nylon [c].....................................	20	0.18	111
Teflon [c]....................................	2	0.14	14.3

*σy is the yield stress and k is the average thermal conductivity between 20 and 300 K.
†Room-temperature value.
[a] Haynes Stellite Company.
[b] International Nickel Company.
[c] E.I. du Pont.

ICC requires vessel design according to Section VIII of the ASME Boiler and Pressure Vessel Code. To satisfy the Code for vessels operating below −325 F, notch impact tests of weld samples must be performed at the operating temperature, which is −450 F for liquid helium. The value of impact tests at this temperature is questionable. With current techniques, the sample must either be cooled on the anvil or transported from a helium bath to the anvil during the 5-s period allowed by the Code. Since the specific heat is extremely low in the range of 4 to 20 K, and the temperature difference so great (300 K), it is probable that the sample would warm considerably, possibly to 30 or 40 K.

The Compressed Gas Association represents another endeavor to regulate uniformly the design of cryogenic transport equipment. This is an effort of the industrial gas industry to provide for the safe transport of compressed and liquefied gases. Two pertinent documents published by the CGA are Pamphlet S−1.2, Safety Relief Device Standards for Cargo and Portable Tanks for Compressed Gases, 1966 edition [51]; and the "Proposed Insulated Cargo Tank Specification MC−341 for Low Temperature Liquefied Gases" [52]. As of this writing, the latter document is not final, but will be proposed to ICC for inclusion in the appropriate regulations.

5.7.2. Vacuum Retention

Vacuum insulation techniques and their application to helium dewar and equipment design are discussed generally in sections 5.3 and 5.5. Because of the cryopumping in the insulation space, about 11,000 l/s/ft^2 for air, the initial or warm level is not as important as the vacuum integrity, and since helium is the only gas that will not cryopump, the leak rate between the helium vessel and the vacuum space has the greatest effect. Most liquid helium equipment is fabricated under the scrutiny of mass spectrometer leak testing of both the individual components and the final piece of equipment. A purchase specification of a 1,000-l helium dewar, for example, might require mass spectrometer leak testing with no detectable leak at a sensitivity of 10^{-9} atm-cm^3/s. Such a design specification would vary with the size of the vessel and the amount of re-evacuation that could be tolerated. An activated charcoal or molecular sieve adsorbent attached to the helium vessel will adsorb helium and hydrogen outgassing from the metal walls and the insulation material.

There are several types of vacuum sealoff devices commonly used for liquid helium equipment. The leaded pinchoff tube is most used for small dewars where the need for re-evacuation is infrequent. Larger vessels and transfer lines usually include a high-vacuum valve, and many of these have locking devices to prevent accidental opening. The Richards [53] sealoff valve, often used, is equipped with a removable bonnet.

Burst disks or vacuum-relief devices are included on larger transfer lines and helium vessels to prevent over-pressurization of the vacuum space. The relief capacity of the device should handle the maximum boiloff from a ruptured inner vessel. A combination of a Richards-type sealoff and vacuum-relief valve is available from several manufacturers. Current vendor literature on these and similar devices is often very helpful in making final component selections.

Liquid helium transfer lines may require re-evacuation several times a year. A poor vacuum will show up during use as a uniformly cold, wet, or frosted transfer line. Individual cold spots, particularly at elbows and fittings, indicate poor construction or failure of internal spacers. A well designed and constructed transfer line will always feel warm to the touch and any signs of moisture or frost will indicate excessive heat leak. A helium transfer line containing air may be re-evacuated to below 1×10^{-2} torr in the warm condition. It will then cryopump to below 1×10^{-6} torr when used in helium service.

5.7.3. Internal Supports

Low heat leak is a prime design criterion for liquid helium vessels. Generally, the more rugged the support, the greater the heat leak. Therefore, the design of the support system requires a careful balance between low heat leak and adequate strength. Consequently, low-loss helium containers cannot be made invulnerable to damage resulting from rough, improper handling. Repair charges are high, up to 30 percent of initial cost for nitrogen-shielded dewars and up to 50 percent of cost for the vapor-shielded type.

The first liquid helium dewars of nitrogen-shielded design were intended for use within the laboratory and were handled rather carefully. Centralized production facilities have since created the need for long-distance trucking and air shipment of helium. Common carrier shippers and commercial truckers, however, are unpredictable and often unreliable in their treatment of fragile equipment.

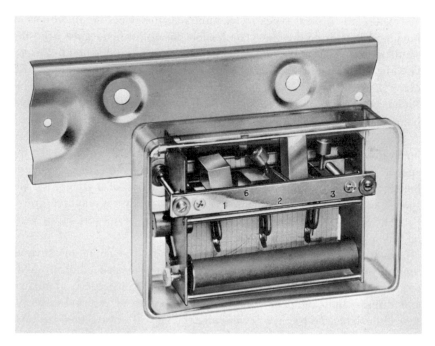

FIGURE 5.18. *Impact-O-Graph recording g-meter, three-directional, 0 to 15 g range.*
(Courtesy Impact-O-Graph Corp.)

While firm g-load design limits are still a gray area, one guideline has been established by the Air Force. Military Specification MIL–A–8421B (USAF) 5 May 1960 provides the following design criteria for air transportable equipment. For flight and taxing loads, a structural design suitable for 3 gs in any direction is required; and for emergency landing conditions, equipment must withstand $4\frac{1}{2}$ gs in the vertical direction and 8 gs longitudinally for 0.1 s without external breakage. It is the authors' opinion that this design limit should be met for vacuum retention to prevent release of cold vapor in a crash condition.

A preliminary field study was performed by Air Reduction Company [54] to determine the actual g-loads encountered during various phases of transportation of liquid helium dewars. A recording g-meter (fig. 5.18) was used to record the number and magnitude of shocks in three directions. Results show that a dewar, secured in place during trucking, receives very small shocks—less than 2 gs in the vertical direction and less than 1 g in either the lateral or longitudinal direction. Miscellaneous handling, however, which includes loading and unloading operations, contributes many shocks ranging from 1 to 3 gs in all directions, with higher single shock up to 8 gs in any direction. As a result of this study, the following g-load specification was established by Airco for all liquid helium dewars up to 500-1 in size:

g Load Design Limit

	Vertical	*Lateral*
Static loads (sustained)...............................	5	6
Short duration loads (about 0.1 s)....................	25	15

FIGURE 5.19. *500-liter vapor-shielded liquid helium dewar (Airco Cryogenics Division).*
Note the rubber shock mount system and the vacuum jacketed liquid withdrawal valve.

There are some techniques used by various manufacturers to reduce the impacts of handling. Rubber ring cushions in the base will absorb a portion of the shock before it reaches the vessel. Sponge rubber rings around the circumference of a vessel protect it from lateral bouncing. The rubber shock mount system shown on the dewar in figure 5.19 reduces the impact of short duration shocks by a factor of $2\frac{1}{2}$ to 5. One manufacturer (Airco Cryogenics Div.) uses the Impact-O-Graph meter to monitor the handling of dewars as part of the warranty conditions.

The appearance of a shipping package is another facet. The initial trend of transporting helium dewars in a rugged crate seems to be diminishing. Many suppliers have the opinion that the crates create an impression of ruggedness, which is not warranted. "Careful handling" and "fragile" warning signs are also useful in reducing structural failures.

Trailers, on the other hand, are not subjected to the unpredictable handling received by small dewars. This is because they are in constant contact with the road and attached to a limited acceleration vehicle. Sufficient experience has been gained in trailer transport of other cryogenic fluids to provide adequate design data. The Compressed Gas Association (1966) makes the following recommendation on g-load design as an addition to existing ICC Regulations.

Minimum* Static g Loadings

Vertical downward......................	2.0
Vertical upward.........................	1.0
Longitudinal.............................	1.0
Lateral...................................	0.5

*Based on $\frac{1}{4}$ ultimate strength

5.7.4 Neck Plug Hazards

Helium, hydrogen, and neon are the three air-solidifying cryogenic fluids. The boiling points of these fluids—4.2, 20.4, and 27.2 K, respectively—are all below the solid point of air, 62 K, and the nitrogen-oxygen system eutectic, 50 K. Air that is drawn into a dewar vent line or neck tube will condense and freeze, forming a solid plug. This will prevent further venting and cause pressure to build to the burst point of the container. Helium vessels, being the coldest, are most susceptible to this hazard, and because of the increased heat leak in the nonvented condition, the pressure will rise more rapidly. The potential hazard of neck plugging is increased with normal barometric pressure fluctuations, air transport (see sec. 5.7.5), and by opening the dewar to the atmosphere for product transfer.

During 1961 and 1962, several malfunctions of liquid helium containers caused a temporary embargo to be placed by the airlines on the air shipment of this cargo. In 1963, dual-neck, nitrogen-shielded helium dewars were introduced and readily accepted by the industry. Work done by L. Scott [7] on pressure rise rates and burst pressures strongly supported the use of dual-neck dewars. As of this writing, all major producers of liquid helium distribute it in vessels equipped with some type of dual relief passage.

Experience has shown that double-neck or dual relief passage design has effectively reduced the hazards of neck plugging. If a plug forms in the normal vent line or fill connection, a second relief passage with a higher relief valve setting will prevent excessive pressure buildup. This is achieved in most dewars with a double concentric neck design (figs. 5.20 and 5.21); the inner tube serves as the access port and normal vent

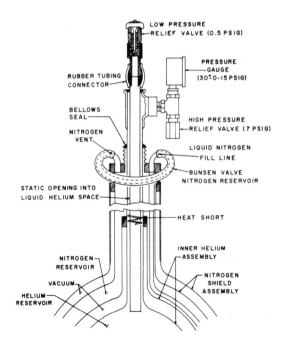

FIGURE 5.20.   *Dual neck and relief valve arrangement for a typical nitrogen-shielded helium dewar.*

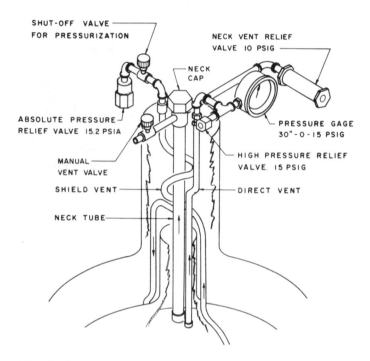

FIGURE 5.21. *Dual vent and relief valve arrangement for a typical vapor-shielded dewar.*

and the outer annulus acts as an emergency relief passage. Loss rate measurements for nitrogen-shielded dewars indicate a 5 to 15 percent increase in heat leak for a dual-neck dewar, compared to a single-neck dewar, with slightly lower loss rates when venting from the inner tube (L. Scott, [7]). The cold vapor venting up the neck tube keeps the heat leak increase to a minimum (see sec. 5.3.1).

Vapor-shielded dewars generally have an independent secondary vent, rather than a double-neck design, to achieve the dual relief capacity. There are actually three relief passages for a typical vapor-shielded helium dewar (figs. 5.21 and 5.22). The shield vent, with a relief valve set for the desired operating pressure (0.5 to 3.5 psig), is dependent on the neck vent or access tube, as they are interconnected a short distance up the neck from the inner vessel. The secondary relief passage runs directly from the inner vessel to an external relief valve set to relieve below the design pressure of the vessel. Other relief valves would have intermediate pressure settings.

A technique for reducing the possibility of a neck plug occurring is described by Neary [55]. A closed-system operation of the dewar elimi-

FIGURE 5.22. *External view of a typical vapor-shielded helium dewar (Cryogenic Engineering Company), showing access port (center), primary and secondary relief valves, and pressure gage.*

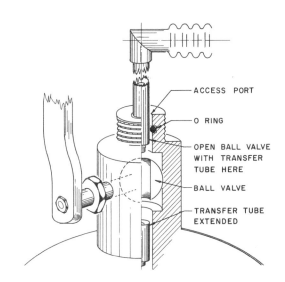

FIGURE 5.23. *Ball valve transfer tube access port for helium dewar.*
(Linde Division, Union Carbide Corporation.)

nates any portion being opened to the atmosphere. The neck tube access, terminating in a ball valve and O-ring adapter, as shown in figures 5.23 and 5.24, will receive a transfer tube while maintaining a positive pressure on the vessel. In this case, since the vessel need not be blown down

FIGURE 5.24. *Top view of a 100-liter multi-shielded helium dewar showing ball valve access port, relief valves, and accessories.*

(Linde Division, Union Carbide Corporation.)

to atmospheric pressure prior to a transfer, the operating pressure should be maintained at the desired transfer pressure, 2 to 3 psig. The open type dewar is maintained at low pressures, 0.5 to 1.0 psig, to reduce flash losses of depressurization, which are treated in more detail in section 5.8.

A permanently installed liquid line on a dewar will eliminate the need for access to the inner vessel. The line must terminate with a vacuum-insulated valve and appropriate bayonet connection and will serve for both filling and withdrawal. A vessel using this construction is shown in figure 5.19.

Neck plugs do occur in spite of careful handling during normal dewar usage, and they must be removed. A neck plug may be noticed by lack of venting when the pressure gage shows a higher reading than the relief valve setting, or by finding an obstruction on insertion of a transfer tube. The standard practice for removing neck plugs is to insert a copper or brass rod or tube down the neck. This source of heat will easily melt the ice plug. Care must be taken in this technique to avoid burns from the escaping cold helium vapor. Gloves and safety glasses are appropriate. A plug saw is available which is inserted into the neck and rotated. The saw drills a hole in the plug to relieve the pressure and then removes the plug in a manner similar to a typical hardware hole saw. One other technique is to blow warm helium gas down the neck or vent line which may melt the plug. This was tried in one case by the author on a small curved vent line (one of several vent lines on the dewar) without success. In this case, the entire dewar was warmed to ambient temperature to remove the plug.

5.7.5. Air Transport and Absolute Pressure Relief Valves

The variations in ambient pressure during air transport have particular importance as they affect shipments of liquid helium. During flight, the aircraft cabin pressure decreases to values ranging from 12.2 to 8.3 psia, which corresponds to equivalent altitudes of 5,000 to 15,000 ft, respectively (fig. 5.25). This reduction in external pressure imposed on a helium dewar causes depressurization of its contents and resulting very high flash rates. A typical air shipment of liquid helium would lose 15 to 20 percent of its contents (fig. 5.26) if allowed to vent to the reduced pressure.

A subsequent increase in cabin pressure occurs as the aircraft descends, creating an external pressure which is higher than the dewar pressure. This back pressure causes an influx of air into the neck tube or vent lines through valves unintentionally left open or through relief valves which may not reseat to reverse flow. A neck plug may occur or the dewar may arrive at its destination under partial vacuum. The economic loss of high flash rates is coupled with the hazard of neck plugging and venting in a closed space.

The potential of a neck plug occurring can be reduced by venting through either an absolute pressure relief valve or a differential relief valve preceded by a heat exchanger. An absolute pressure relief valve

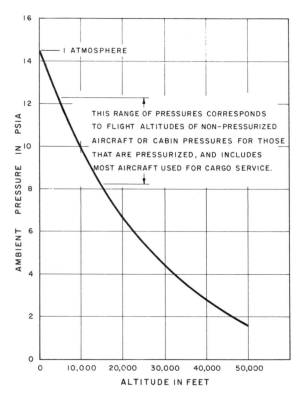

FIGURE 5.25.   *Ambient pressure vs. altitude, showing range of cabin pressures for commercial aircraft in cargo service.*

(fig. 5.27) controls the absolute pressure within the dewar by sensing the pressure with respect to an evacuated bellows within the relief valve. The net effect of the absolute pressure relief valve is to maintain a constant venting rate, proportional to the heat leak. This prevents a decrease of pressure in the vessel below that of the absolute pressure setting, which, for this service, ranges from 15.2 to 18.5 psia.

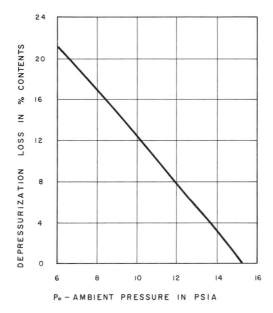

FIGURE 5.26.   *Helium dewar depressurization losses, loss in percent liquid contents vs.* p_0 *when vessel is depressurized from 15.2 psia to reduced ambient pressure* p_0.

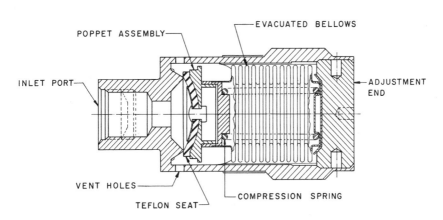

FIGURE 5.27.   *Absolute pressure relief valve maintains constant absolute pressure of venting vessel.*

(Courtesy of Tavco, Inc.)

The external heat exchanger does not control the vessel pressure, but only serves to preheat the venting vapor prior to the relief valve. The heat exchanger has sufficient surface to prevent freezing of the valve for large evaporation rates encountered in air shipments. It is assumed that a differential pressure relief valve maintained at ambient temperature will always reseat and seal tight in the reverse direction; even if this is not true, the heat exchanger is of sufficient length and volume so that small quantities of air that may leak through the valve will not reach the cold portions of the neck or vent lines.

The airlines, through their regulatory organizations, are in accord with either of these solutions for preventing general malfunction of a dewar in air transport. The International Air Transport Association and the Air Traffic Conference of America make the following statement in the latest IATA Regulations [56]:

"Changes in pressure and temperature, resulting from altitude variations, can cause malfunction of safety relief devices and plugging of vent lines unless the relief valves are specifically designed for these conditions. Failure of a liquid compartment to vent excess pressure can be prevented by placing safety relief devices to the vapor space on lines connected separately to the liquid compartment, by use of an absolute pressure safety relief device, or by use of a differential pressure relief device preceded by a heat exchanger."

Large quantities of helium escaping into the aircraft cabin reduce the oxygen concentration, and because of the high velocity of sound in helium, it also changes the pitch of the human voice. This problem is more serious in larger helium shipments. For example: A 500-l dewar, not equipped with a functioning absolute pressure relief valve, will vent more than 2500 scf of gaseous product into the aircraft cabin in a typical air shipment. A pitch of voice increase is easily noticed with helium concentrations as low as 5 percent [57], but the change in voice pitch does not cause severe disruption of communication until helium concentrations above 50 to 60 percent are reached [58].

While communication intelligibility should not be a problem, the increase in voice pitch does serve as a warning of decreased oxygen concentrations. Figure 5.28 illustrates that a 5 percent helium + 95 percent air mixture at a pressure of 10 psia causes a sufficient reduction of oxygen to impair human performance [59]. Helium reduces the partial pressure of oxygen, already reduced because of the altitude, leading to symptoms of hypoxia. The tissues most sensitive to oxygen deficiency, such as the central nervous system (brain and eyes), are the first to be affected. The above comments apply equally well to a venting dewar in any enclosed space. See chapter 6 for more detailed information on this safety aspect.

A detailed analysis of a specific situation of helium venting is difficult because of the volume and air circulation rate for a particular aircraft, but the above discussion does point to the need for absolute pressure control of a venting helium vessel. It is important to note that the heat exchanger-relief valve combination does not prevent the depressurization flash losses.

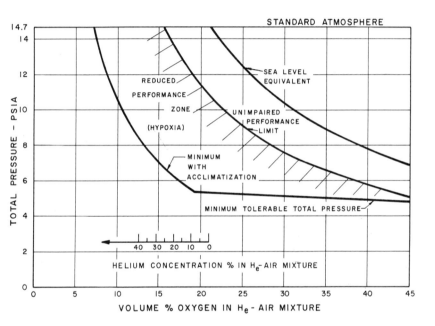

FIGURE 5.28. *Helium concentrations in helium-air mixtures at subatmospheric pressures, showing effect of reduced oxygen concentrations on human performance* [59].

5.7.6. Catastrophic Loss of Vacuum

The insulation systems in liquid helium storage vessels must be maintained at a high vacuum in order to be effective. In well constructed vessels, the insulation vacuum undergoes very little deterioration with time since all residual gases except helium are effectively cryopumped by the 4.2 K surface in the insulation space.

Of greater importance is the effect of instantaneous or sudden loss of vacuum caused by accidental structure failure. Most failures in helium vessels are attributable to mishandling of the equipment. The failure often occurs as a rupture of the neck tube and inner vessel support members, but it may sometimes occur as a piercing of the outer shell. The effect, in either case, is a drastic increase in heat leak and evaporation rate with a subsequent rapid pressure rise — possibly to the point of rupturing the vessel.

Adequate venting capacity must be provided to prevent excessive pressure buildup in the event of accidental loss of vacuum. High capacity relief valves on the helium vessel and burst disks or vacuum-relief devices on the insulation space are important design considerations for liquid helium equipment. Emphasis must be placed on selection of the reliable relief valves on the inner vessel because of the high rate of pressure rise resulting from increased heat leak.

One solution is to calculate the lost-vacuum heat leak from non-evacuated insulation characteristics and to provide a venting capacity which will prevent excessive pressurization of the vessel. Experience has shown, however, that air condensing on the inner vessel will give a much higher heat input than predicted. A theoretical solution becomes rather involved and difficult because of the lack of data on air flow through various insulations.

Experimental tests offer a practical solution to the problem. Such a test was performed by Airco and by Superior Air Products on a 25-l, nitrogen-shielded, helium dewar [7] and by Cryogenic Engineering Company [60] on a 100-l, vapor-shielded dewar. In both of these instances, the tests resulted in the accepting of a particular size relief valve, rather than the actual determination of a venting capacity.

These results were later extrapolated for larger size vessels, up to 1,000-l capacity, based on the assumption that a similar design would have a lost-vacuum heat leak directly proportional to the surface area of the inner vessel. The subsequent occurrence of structural failures and loss of vacuum in commercial liquid helium container transport has confirmed the experimental and extrapolated value selections.

A method of relief valve sizing, advocated by the Compressed Gas Association, is applicable and commonly used for larger cryogenic vessels (liquid semi-trailers). A formula based on predicted insulation properties from Pamphlet S–1.2 is generally accepted as adequate by the member CGA companies. The reader is referred to that publication for full details [51].

5.8. TRANSFER OF LIQUID HELIUM

The transfer of liquid helium has always required a high degree of sophistication in equipment and procedures. The properties of helium which affect liquid transfer are the low temperature and low latent heat. The small difference in the saturated vapor and liquid densities is also important. Since some vaporization may occur during transfer, and the two phases, liquid and vapor, differ in density by a factor of only 8, they do not always separate well. The problems, techniques, and equipment vary greatly with the particular instance of transfer. The end use may be liquid, cold vapor, or compressed gas; the flashed vapor may be recovered or vented to the atmosphere; and product purity may or may not be important.

The losses which occur during transfer may be divided into equipment related losses and procedure related losses. The equipment most commonly used is described in the following section. The losses which are inherent with various transfer procedures are described starting in section 5.8.3.

5.8.1. Transfer Line Design

Liquid helium transfer lines may be made from rigid or flexible (convoluted) metal tubing; copper, bronze, and stainless steel are the most common materials. A typical example is illustrated in figure 5.29. Small transfer lines are usually made as a single unit, but larger ones may be fabricated as individual segments with special couplings.

Simple high-vacuum insulation is commonly used to minimize cooldown losses even at some sacrifice in heat leak, especially in small lines. Evacuated multilayer insulation is used in some larger lines.

In any vacuum-insulated transfer line, the outer jacket must be sealed to the inner helium line at both ends in order to form the vacuum space. When the inner line is cooled, it contracts while the warm outer jacket does not. This differential thermal contraction is easily taken up in flexible transfer lines, but in rigid lines, some means of accommodating this contraction must be incorporated. Some rigid transfer lines use Invar or similar alloys for the inner tube to minimize the thermal contract. Most commonly, though, bellows-type expansion joints are placed in either the inner line or outer jacket.

Transfer lines of any appreciable length require additional mechanical supports (spacers) to prevent the inner line from directly

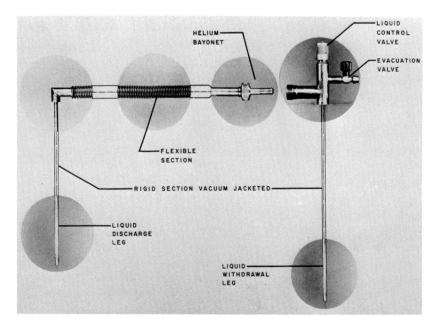

FIGURE 5.29. *Composite 3/16-in-I.D. flexible liquid helium transfer line.*
Note 1/4 to 1/2-in helium-hydrogen bayonet and 1/4-in vacuum jacketed control valve. (Linde Division, Union Carbide Corp.)

touching the outer jacket. These supports are comparatively large sources of heat leak. They are, therefore, made of low thermal conductivity plastic or thin metal alloy sheet, and they are designed to have small, near point contacts with the inner line and the outer jacket. Flexible lines require more supports for a given length than do rigid lines, but even flexible lines are made with heat leaks as low as 1 Btu/hr-ft (~ 0.01W/cm) for sizes up to ½-in inside diameter.

Heat Leak. Liquid helium is always transferred at, or very near, saturated conditions. Sub-cooling can be achieved for short periods by pressurization, but for reasons which will become apparent in section 5.8.3, excessive pressurization is undesirable. The transfer line heat leak will therefore vaporize a portion of the liquid transferred. The vapor thus formed creates two-phase fluid flow with resulting increased pressure drop. This is not as serious with helium, however, as it is with most other fluids. The relative similarity of the liquid and vapor densities and viscosities allows mixed flow to occur with little interference of the two phases. Pressure drop for liquid helium, for example, with 10 percent vapor by weight, may only be two or three times that for 100 percent liquid flow.

Valves. Vacuum jacketed, extended stem valves are generally suitable for liquid helium. Thin-wall stainless steel tubing is commonly used for the stem material, and the hollow stem may be evacuated to eliminate gaseous conduction along its length. A double-stem design similar to that shown in figure 5.30 allows all welded construction in the vacuum space and thus avoids O-ring or mechanical seals. Several valves used in helium service are shown in figure 5.29 (small size) and figures 5.30 and 5.31 (larger sizes). These have relatively low heat leaks, all welded construction in the vacuum space, and easily replaceable seats. Either O-rings or packed stems at the warm end are used on the helium space. The valve in figure 5.30 includes a connection to the helium space for a purge valve or safety relief device.

Other types of specialty liquid valves are described in the literature [6, 61]. These two references also provide excellent background for cryogenic transfer and for design and selection of related equipment.

Couplings. Vacuum jacketed, bayonet couplings are available in a wide variety of sizes and configurations. The ever-present problem of the industrial gas industry, that of mating connections, is thus very serious. The use of adapters, in addition to being costly, is often prohibitive because of increased heat leak. Several commonly used bayonet couplings will be described.

Two bayonet couplings used in early helium service are shown in figures 5.32 and 5.33. The first is widely known as the Air Force hydrogen bayonet and is used extensively for that fluid. It has a short length, about 7 in, compared to its 2-in diameter and has a relatively high heat leak for liquid helium. The NASA bayonet (fig. 5.33) has a length of about 14 in for its 1-in-diam inner line, which results in very low heat leak. Check valves at the liquid end and a bleed valve on the vapor space are advantageous operating features. This particular device, however, is more elaborate than is necessary for most applications.

The current trend is toward simplified construction and longer heat leak paths, up to 15 in. Two examples are shown in figures 5.34 and 5.35; both are supplied by the manufacturer with added length for helium service. An O-ring at the warm end provides an adequate seal on the annular gas space to prevent leakage. The cold end may or may not have an additional sealing surface. If a liquid seal is not used, the mating annular passage is very narrow to minimize convection currents in the

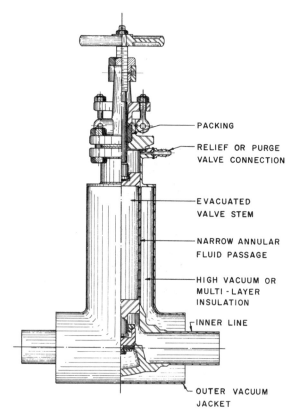

FIGURE 5.30. *Typical vacuum jacketed liquid helium valve, showing thin-wall evacuated stem design with warm end connection on the helium gas space.*

(Courtesy Consolidated Precision Company)

gas space. It is desirable to orient the bayonet in a horizontal or cold end down position. If this is not done, convection currents and possibly liquid seal leakage will greatly increase the heat leak and cause the O-ring seal to freeze and possibly leak. Experience with the Cryenco bayonet (fig. 5.34) shows that it performs well with or without a Teflon liquid seal when tilted at least 25° from the horizontal position.

One more bayonet is shown in figure 5.36, the Linde helium-hydrogen bayonet. This has a relatively short heat path (about 4 in), but has a sufficiently low heat leak for use with small helium transfer lines such

FIGURE 5.31.   *Typical vacuum-jacketed liquid helium valve.*

(Courtesy CVI Corporation)

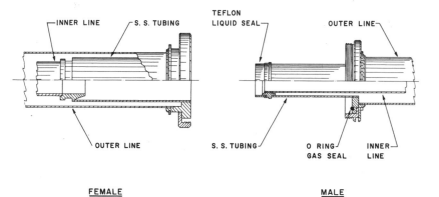

FIGURE 5.32.   *Air Force type hydrogen bayonet used for helium service, 2-in diam and 7-in length.*

Note Teflon liquid seal and O-ring gas seal.

as figure 5.29. It has an advantage of being interchangeable in $\frac{1}{4}$-in and $\frac{1}{2}$-in line sizes, and its use is well established in both helium and hydrogen service.

A slight, intentional gas leak in a bayonet actually reduces the total liquid evaporation resulting from bayonet heat leak [62]. The escaping helium vapor intercepts the normal heat conducted in the coupling, much the same as does the vapor vented through the neck of small dewars.

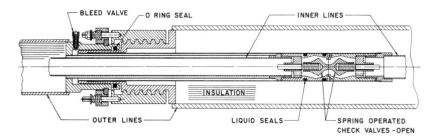

FIGURE 5.33.   *NASA helium bayonet, 1-in diam and 14-in length.*
Note liquid and gas product seals, spring operated check valves on the liquid line, and bleed valve on the gas space.

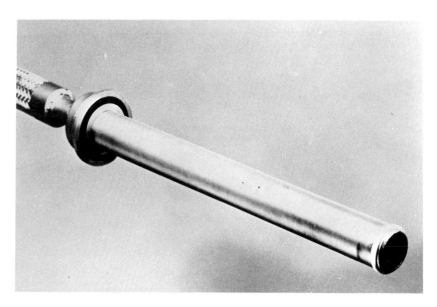

FIGURE 5.34.   *Liquid helium bayonet, male half, 1-$\frac{1}{4}$-in diam, 15-in length.*
Note Teflon seal on liquid end and O-ring seal at the warm end. (Courtesy Cryogenic Engineering Company)

FIGURE 5.35. *Liquid helium bayonet assembly, a warm end O-ring seal is shown, but a narrow mating annulus eliminates the need for a liquid end seal.*

(Courtesy CVI Corporation)

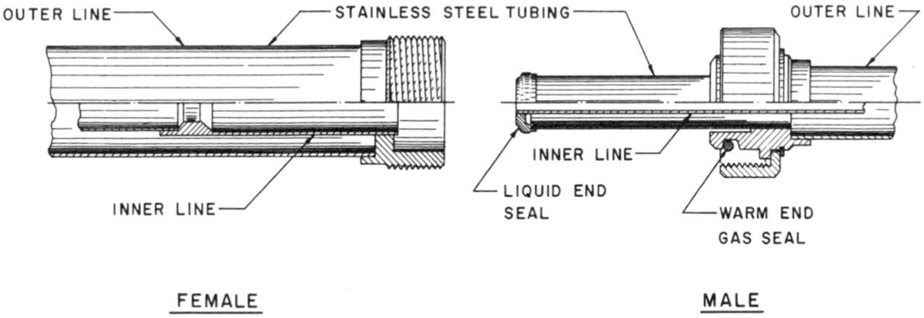

OUTER LINE — STAINLESS STEEL TUBING — OUTER LINE

INNER LINE —

INNER LINE —

LIQUID END SEAL

WARM END GAS SEAL

FEMALE   MALE

FIGURE 5.36. *Liquid helium-hydrogen bayonet $1/4$-in or $1/2$-in diam 4-in length, metal-to-metal liquid seal, and O-ring gas seal.*

Liquid Nitrogen Shielding. For more stringent heat leak requirements, the transfer line may be shielded with liquid nitrogen. It is possible to construct a three- or four-wall transfer tube, consisting of a vacuum jacketed helium line completely enclosed within a nitrogen line. The nitrogen portion may or may not be vacuum insulated, depending on economic considerations. Nitrogen-shielding of valves and couplings is also possible and perhaps more desirable since these are sources of high heat leak. A simpler method of shielding is by nitrogen tracing. Small diameter copper tubing is thermally bonded to the transfer line jacket, valve, or bayonet connection. Liquid nitrogen is then circulated through the tubing to reduce the outside jacket temperature.

5.8.2. Cooldown Losses

Cooldown of equipment with a cryogenic fluid consumes a quantity of product porportional to the mass and specific heat of the vessel and inversely proportional to the heat capacity, latent plus sensible, of the cryogen. Helium has a low latent heat and large cooldown losses are common. On the other hand, if the high sensible heat of helium vapor is utilized, the losses may be reduced by a factor of 15 or 20. For example, if only the latent heat of helium (9.02 Btu/lb) is used, 15.3 l of liquid will vaporize in cooling 1 lb of stainless steel from 300 K to 4.2 K, whereas, if it were possible to use all of the available refrigeration capacity of the vapor, only 0.36 l would be required.

In examining the heat capacity of structural materials versus temperature, it is clear that most of the refrigeration is required at the higher temperatures. Table 5.8 gives the specific heat and enthalpy versus temperature for several metals [6, 63]. By precooling a piece of equipment to intermediate temperatures with less expensive cryogenic fluids, in particular nitrogen, considerable helium can be saved. While the latent heat of 15.3 l of liquid helium is required to cool 1 lb of stainless steel from 300 K to 4.2 K, that of only 0.70 liters is required to cool the same mass from 77 K (nitrogen boiling point) to 4.2 K. A similar

TABLE 5.8.   *Specific heat and enthalpy vs. temperature for several common metals*

Tempera-ture K	Specific heat — Btu/lb — F			Enthalpy — Btu/lb		
	Cu [63]	Al [63]	18–8 S.S. [6]	Cu [63]	Al [63]	18–8 S.S.*
4.2	0.000024	0.000068	0.00031	0.0000646	0.000231	0.000085
20	0.00184	0.00213	0.0011	0.0146	0.0206	0.012
77	0.0466	0.0803	0.038	2.35	3.61	1.74
100	0.0607	0.115	0.057	4.57	7.63	3.76
300	0.0923	0.216	0.114	34.3	73.3	38.1

*Determined by graphical integration — $H = \int_0^T c_p dt$.

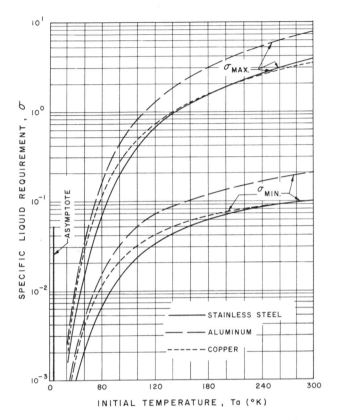

FIGURE 5.37. *Specific liquid helium requirement for cooldown vs. initial equipment temperature.*

Maximum liquid requirement, σ_{max} from eq (5.18) and minimum liquid requirement σ_{min} from eq (5.19) [64].

savings is possible if advantage is taken of the high sensible heat of helium, and for cooling other structural materials. In any event, it is clear that some degree of precooling is desirable.

Complete cooldown of a piece of equipment using only the latent heat is an extreme which may be considered as the maximum liquid requirement. The cooldown consumption in this case may be found by dividing the enthalpy change of the equipment from initial to final temperature and dividing by the latent heat of helium (eq 5.18). Results are shown as maximum specific liquid requirement versus initial temperature in figure 5.37 for cooling to saturated liquid temperature.

$$\sigma_{\max} = (h_1 - h_2)/\lambda \qquad (5.18)$$

where $\sigma_{\max}$ = maximum specific liquid requirement in pounds of cryogen per pound of metal.
  h_1 = initial specific enthalpy.
  h_2 = final specific enthalpy.
  λ = latent heat of cryogen.

A minimum liquid requirement may be defined as the liquid required to cool a system to its operating condition if all of the refrigeration available in the liquid is utilized. A unique treatment of this problem by Jacobs [64] gives a reliable estimate of the consumption by considering the ideal case. The technique simply assumes that the temperature of the leaving fluid is equal to the temperature of the warmest part of the equipment. This is the limiting case of effective heat exchange. The minimum specific liquid requirement is given by eq (5.19) in terms of initial and final equipment temperature:

$$\sigma_{\min} = \int_{T_c}^{T_a} \left\{ C_e \left[\lambda + \int_{T_s}^{T_e} C_{pf} dT_f \right]^{-1} \right\} dT_e \qquad (5.19)$$

where $\sigma_{\min}$ = minimum specific liquid requirement,
  T_a = initial equipment temperature,
  T_c = final equipment temperature,
  T_s = saturation temperature of fluid,
  T_e = equipment temperature,
  C_e = equipment specific heat,
  λ = latent heat of fluid,
  C_{pf} = isobaric specific heat of fluid vapor.

In addition to the double integration above, we require information regarding the specific heats of the equipment and vapor. Since the specific heats are not constant and are not available as analytic functions of temperature, numerical or graphical integration is necessary. This was done using tabulated specific heat data for helium, specific heat and enthalpy data for copper, aluminum, and 18-8 stainless steel, and subject to the condition that the final equipment temperature is equal to the saturated liquid temperature [64]. Figure 5.37 gives the minimum specific liquid requirement, $\sigma_{\min}$, as a function of initial equipment temperature using helium as the cooling fluid. Curves are shown for aluminum, copper, and stainless steel materials and comparing the maximum consumption from eq (5.18) to the minimum consumption from eq (5.19). While the minimum liquid requirement represents an ideal situation, this may be approached by careful cooldown techniques.

Several techniques for minimizing cooldown losses follow directly from the above. They are: use of thin-wall construction and materials having low specific heat for parts in contact with helium; precooling with liquid nitrogen; and utilization of the sensible heat of helium during cooldown. There are other considerations also deducible from the above, but more directly resulting from experience. A slow transfer rate during cooldown, especially for transfer lines, will take advantage of longer fluid equipment contact and higher overall heat transfer rates. Observance of the vapor flow leaving the equipment and estimation of its temperature (condensation, frost, liquid air, etc.) will aid in judging the rate of liquid flow for cooldown.

The liquid discharge should be located at or near the bottom of the receiver. The liquid thus vaporized will displace the warm vapor upwards and contact the vessel wall in an approximately counterflow arrangement. If liquid is discharged at the top of a warm vessel, the large quantity of helium vapor can entrain liquid as droplets and carry them out through the vent. Also note that inherent in the cooldown with liquid helium, the vessel must be filled with saturated vapor at 4.2 K. This requires 0.13 ft^3 of liquid for every cubic foot of volume, which is later displaced as a flash loss when the vessel is filled with liquid.

Finally, heat exchange between the incoming liquid and the existing warm vapor should be prevented, as this will vaporize product. The transfer tube should be completely vacuum jacketed, including the portion that extends into the inner vessel. The effect is also evident in liquid discharge, where the warm pressurization gas can vaporize the liquid being withdrawn. In one case, a 20-in length of uninsulated line, exposed to the warmer gas above the liquid, completely vaporized 80 lb/hr of helium being withdrawn.

5.8.3. Pressure Transfer

We shall for the purpose of discussion, consider transfer of liquid helium in several separate categories; there is considerable overlap of these categories. Several methods of transfer are illustrated in figure 5.38. The conventional pressurized transfer will be considered first; gravity, liquid pumping, and cold vapor compression methods are discussed in the following section. Liquid and vapor may be transferred

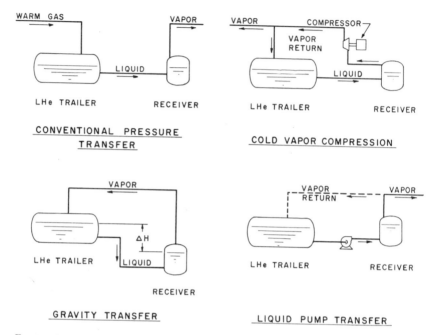

FIGURE 5.38. *Comparative liquid transfer techniques, illustrated for transfer from a liquid semi-trailer to storage vessel.*

without external work or additional pressurization if the storage vessel pressure is sufficiently high. Several techniques are illustrated in figure 5.39. While the actual liquid transfer is straightforward (see sec. 5.8.1), the behavior of the product remaining in the storage vessel during withdrawal is given special consideration as depressurization (see sec. 5.8.5).

An energy addition is required for pressurization; this may be vessel heat leak, warm helium gas addition, or provision for a heat source within the container. Normally, heat leak provides a portion of the initial pressurization, as well as a minor contribution during the transfer. The relationship of heat leak to pressure rise is treated in section 5.4.1.

The heat added by insertion of warm transfer tubes is of some importance in product transfer from small dewars. The warm transfer tube vaporizes liquid as it is placed in the dewar, and if a gas seal is provided at the outlet of the neck tube, the vapor thus generated provides a source of pressurization. The pressurization achieved in this manner may be sufficient to transfer from 20 to 30 l of helium without the use of additional pressurizing gas.

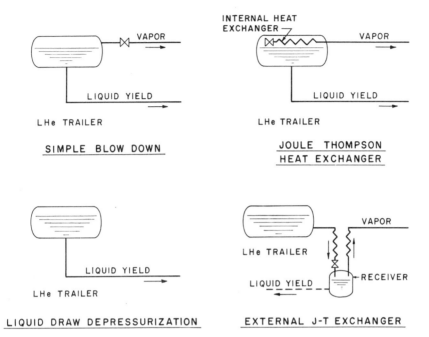

FIGURE 5.39. *Comparative liquid extraction and trailer depressurization techniques.*
Use of an internal or external J–T exchanger increases the liquid yield and reduces flash losses.

For substantial liquid transfers, helium gas pressurization is usually required, if not to achieve initial pressure buildup, then to maintain the necessary pressure during liquid withdrawal. The source of warm gas is usually from high-pressure gas cylinders with the helium gas at essentially ambient temperature. A mass and energy balance yields the following relations for such an addition of mass to a constant-volume system:

$$m_1 v_1 = (m_1 + m_g)v_2 \tag{5.20}$$

$$h_g m_g + m_1 u_1 = m_2 u_2 \tag{5.21}$$

where
$h_g =$ specific enthalpy of gas added,
$m_1 =$ initial system mass,
$m_g =$ mass of gas added,
v_1 and $v_2 =$ initial and final specific volumes,
u_1 and $u_2 =$ initial and final specific internal energies,
$v =$ volume of system.

Generally, m_g and u_2 are unknown. A further simplification may be made by assuming that the mass of warm gas added is small compared to the system mass, an assumption which is valid for most purposes.

$$m_g(h_g - h_v) = m_1(u_2 - u_1) \qquad (5.22)$$

where h_v = enthalpy of saturated vapor at final conditions and u_2 is the internal energy at the final pressure and initial specific volume of the system.

In either case such a pressurization often results in an end state which lies in the subcooled liquid region, i.e., to the left of the saturated liquid line on a temperature-entropy chart (see fig. 2.4).

Once the desired transferring pressure is obtained, a continuing supply of heat or warm gas is necessary throughout the transfer period. As liquid is withdrawn, cold vapor must be generated to fill the void space. An optimum or ideal transfer efficiency may be calculated under the assumption that the equilibrium exists at saturated conditions. For every unit volume of liquid withdrawn, a quantity must remain behind to fill the void as a unit volume of vapor. Transfer efficiency = 100 $(\rho_L - \rho_V)/\rho_L$, where ρ_L and ρ_V are the liquid and vapor densities at the transfer pressure P_2 [5]. At 1 atm pressure, a transfer efficiency of 86.8 percent is calculated from the above. This also assumes that the mass of the pressurization gas is negligible. Figure 5.40 shows the heat addition in Btu per pound of liquid transferred as a function of the transfer pressure, and the equivalent heat addition in terms of warm pressurization gas [65].

Lowering the temperature of the pressurization gas reduces the amount of vaporization, although larger quantities of gas are required. Two techniques to lower the temperature of helium used for pressurization are: use of a liquid nitrogen pre-cooler; and returning the flash gas with a cold vapor compressor (see fig. 5.38). A more complete mass, volume, and energy balance then becomes:

$$m_1 v_1 = m_2 v_2, \qquad (5.23)$$

and $\qquad m_g h_g + m_1 u_1 = m_2 u_2 + m_e h_e, \qquad (5.24)$

where subscripts g, 1, 2, and e represent gas added, initial conditions, final conditions, and exit conditions, respectively.

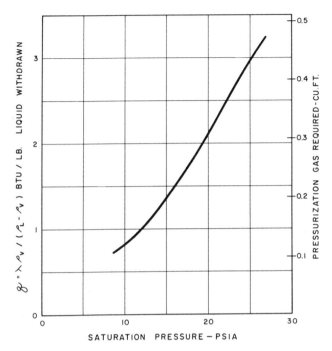

FIGURE 5.40. *Liquid helium transfer, required heat addition, q, for constant pressure liquid withdrawal and equivalent warm pressurization gas consumption vs. transfer pressure* [65].

The greatest source of error in transfer efficiency calculations is thermal stratification. If no heat transfer takes place between the gas and liquid phases, a 100 percent efficient transfer is possible. This situation may be approached by quick pressurization with rapid liquid withdrawal. Many theoretical treatments of this topic can be found in the Advances in Cryogenic Engineering. A recent paper by Epstein [66] gives a generalized technique for calculating the pressurization gas requirement for cryogenic fluid transfer with confirming experimental results.

As stated earlier, liquid may be transferred under pressure, without external pressurization if the initial container pressure is sufficiently high. This technique is used in the system described in section 5.9. As liquid is withdrawn, the vessel pressure decreases to a point where either no liquid remains or atmospheric pressure is reached. An analysis of this system was made by Canty [65] assuming no thermal stratification. His results are shown in figure 5.41, which shows the pressure changes as a function of the percent liquid withdrawn for various initial pressures. The limit of withdrawal or "liquid empty" curve is also shown.

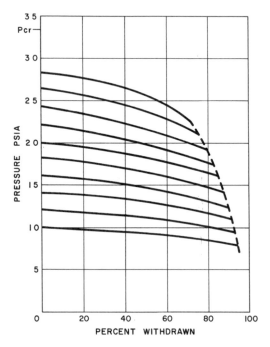

FIGURE 5.41. *Pressure history vs. percent withdrawn for a helium vessel initially liquid full without external pressurization; the dashed line indicates the pressure at the liquid empty point.*

Note that the quantity of liquid that may be withdrawn down to 14.7 psia is a function of the initial pressure [65].

Throttling Losses. The transfer of a liquid at or near saturated conditions involves what is commonly called a throttling flash loss. This flash is attributed to the isenthalpic pressure drop. The properties of helium are such that this flash or loss rate is unusually high. Because of helium's low critical temperature, the degree of subcooling that can be achieved by quick pressurization of the liquid is only 1 or 2 K. The throttling loss is predicted by an isenthalpic expansion from storage pressure P_1 to receiver pressure P_2 (usually 1 atm). We may properly consider the subcooling by taking the initial enthalpy as that of the saturated liquid at the storage temperature. Equation (5.25) gives the percent flash when transferring liquid from P_1 to P_2.

$$\text{wt \% flash} = 100 \, \frac{h_{l1} - h_{l2}}{h_{v2} - h_{l2}} \qquad (5.25)$$

where h_{l1} = enthalpy of liquid at P_1.
 h_{l2} = enthalpy of saturated liquid at P_2.
 h_{v2} = enthalpy of saturated vapor at P_2.

Figure 5.42 presents the flash loss versus storage pressure for saturated liquid conditions. This is not the total transfer loss, but only that due to throttling the flow. Even so, the advantage of low transfer pressures is obvious. There are instances when fluid throttling is essential for collecting liquid in the receiver—for example, if the storage

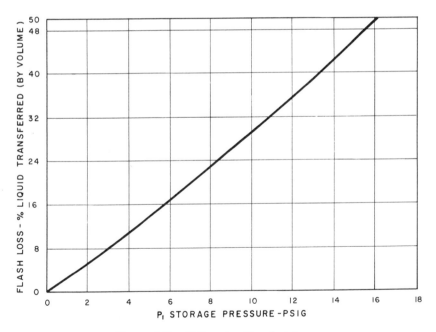

FIGURE 5.42. *Helium throttling flash losses.*

Loss in percent liquid transfer vs. storage pressure p_1 for an isenthalpic expansion from p_1 to 14.7 psia.

vessel contains supercritical fluid. This expansion is the same phenomenon as that across a Joule-Thomson valve in a liquefier.

Pressure Drop. In view of the potential for high flash losses, it is indeed fortunate that pressure drop with liquid helium is generally lower than for other cryogenic fluids.

The flow in transfer lines is almost always turbulent. The Fanning equation, in the form of eq (5.26), is thus appropriate with friction factors taken from a Moody diagram.

$$\Delta p = 2f \frac{V^2}{g_c} \frac{L}{D} \tag{5.26}$$

For liquid helium in long smooth tubes, the following correlation by Koo for high values of the Reynolds number, $N_R = Du\rho/\mu$, is applicable.

$$f = 0.00140 + 0.125/N_R^{(0.32)} \tag{5.27}$$

The viscosity of helium is quite small. The table below compares values for liquid and gaseous helium to those for nitrogen.

Viscosity* lb/ft-hr

	Gas	Liquid
Helium..........................	0.0030	0.0046
Nitrogen.......................	.013	.39

*These values for saturated conditions at 1 atm.

The resulting high Reynolds numbers for a particular flow rate give low friction factors for helium. For a given volume flow rate, the pressure drop of liquid helium is an order of magnitude less than for nitrogen. This helps in keeping flash losses to a minimum. Experience has shown, for example, that adequate transfer rates for small experimental apparatus may be achieved with dewar pressures of only 1 or 2 psig when transferring through a typical ⅛-in transfer line.

The Fanning equation is also applicable for flow through corrugated metal hose, but it is difficult to determine the correct friction factor. An equivalent roughness (ϵ/D on a Moody diagram), taken as the ratio of depth of convolution to maximum diameter, gives poor results.

A more practical method of predicting pressure drop for flow through corrugated hose was developed by Hawthorne and von Helms [67]. Their correlation assumes fluid flow through uniformly spaced orifices, where every convolution represents an orifice. The results of this work are presented in eq (5.28).

$$\Delta p = N \left[1 - \left(\frac{D}{D + 0.438\ S} \right)^2 \right]^2 \frac{V^2 \rho}{9266} \qquad (5.28)$$

where Δp = pressure drop in psi
N = number of corrugations
D = inside diameter, inches
S = corrugation pitch, inches
V = fluid velocity — ft/s
and ρ = fluid density — lb/ft^3.

Experimental results with water, and qualitative results with liquid nitrogen give good agreement with this expression. While there is no experimental evidence to verify its use for liquid or gaseous helium, reasonable agreement is expected. Additional details are available in the original paper [67].

5.8.4. Gravity and Pump Transfer

Any comparison of gravity with pumping transfer methods is, for the present, academic. A review of the literature on cryogenic pumping reveals no commercial applications of liquid helium pumping. However, pump transfer techniques may well be developed in the near future.

A fairly large difference in the elevation of the source and receiving vessel is needed to create the pressure differential necessary for the gravity transfer of liquid helium. This is caused by the small liquid density of 0.78 lb/ft^3. At the normal boiling point, a 1-ft liquid head exerts a pressure of only 0.054 psi. When flashed or displaced cold vapor (4.2 K) is returned to the storage vessel, the driving pressure for liquid transfer is reduced to only 0.046 psi/ft of head. This occurs when liquid is transferred in a closed cycle from a storage vessel to a receiver (see fig. 5.38). In both cases, the driving pressure differential is reduced with increased saturation pressure as illustrated in figure 5.43.

One instance where gravity transfer may play an important role is in a large liquid distribution system. If the storage vessel is placed above

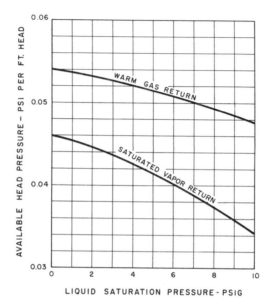

FIGURE 5.43. *Available head pressure vs. saturated transfer pressure for gravity liquid helium transfer.*

Warm gas return implies external pressurization and saturated vapor return implies a closed cycle transfer.

the receiving dewar, the transfer is essentially one of displacement; the liquid displaces cold vapor from the trailer, which in turn fills the void space of the liquid withdrawn from storage. Additional refrigeration is needed only to compensate for heat leak and flash losses which are normally small.

The present state of cryogenic pumping precludes the use of centrifugal pumps for liquid helium, but we should not ignore the potential for such use. A centrifugal pump coupled with an active inducer section, such as that designed by Pesco [68] for hydrogen service, seems to be a reasonable way to overcome the low NPSH requirement of liquid helium. Also, one should note that the pump discharge would generally be in the supercritical region and possibly the suction as well. If such a pump is operated in the range of subcooled liquid to supercritical vapor, the fluid process would not likely enter the two phase region at all but pass to the left of the saturated liquid line on a temperature-entropy diagram. The operation is then similar to a cold vapor compressor because of the high compressibility of helium. A cold vapor compression liquid transfer scheme is shown in figure 5.38. The vapor compressor provides the driving force for the transfer—essentially producing a pressurized transfer. This technique is especially appropriate for large (1000 to 10,000 gal) liquid helium transfers.

One further liquid pump will be mentioned. A positive displacement pump described by Darrel and Schock [69] is driven by a superconducting solenoid completely immersed in the helium reservoir. The oscillating solenoid pump has a capacity of less than 0.5 l/min, but presumably this capacity could be increased. An advantage of this pump is the relative ease of automatic flow control.

There has been some work on high pressure helium pumps intended for cylinder filling. A pump designed by Linde for helium-hydrogen service [70] was intended for use in conjunction with a trailer mounted vaporizer and liquid trailer; it is capable of producing 6000 psig gas for high-pressure storage [71]. The design was proved in hydrogen service, but never tested with liquid helium.

Insofar as positive displacement pumps for liquid helium are concerned, several factors must be considered. The isentropic compressibility of liquid helium is about twice that of nitrogen, requiring very small clearance volumes to achieve good volumetric efficiency. Frictional heating within the pump is best removed on the discharge side, to avoid interference with the suction flow. The discharge stream should contact the cold end of the pump barrel for efficient heat interception. Finally, because of the low NPSH requirement, the use of a fore-pump is desirable.

5.8.5. Depressurization

We are considering vessel depressurization separately to avoid the necessary complexity of an overall transfer analysis and to more closely observe the behavior of the contents of a vessel during the process. A depressurization may be attributed to liquid or vapor withdrawl, or simply a blowdown to gain access. The two aspects receiving special attention are the liquid yield and product flash losses.

The depressurization process is shown on a temperature-enthalpy chart for helium in figure 5.44. This adiabatic process is essentially reversible and, therefore, isentropic. We may assume that the vessel was initially filled at 1 atm to a given percent full (1) and allowed to pressurize by heat leak along a constant volume line to (2) and to (3). The depressurization then begins at (3), at a given specific volume and

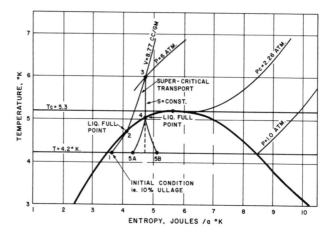

FIGURE 5.44. *T–S diagram illustrating the condition of a liquid
helium vessel: filled to 10% ullage at 1.0 atm.*

(1), pressure rise during transit to liquid full point (2), and to 6 atmospheres (3) isentropic
product withdrawal to liquid full point (4), and liquid (5B) or vapor (5A) withdrawal to 1
atmosphere. No gas addition during cycle.

pressure. A constant entropy line (average entropy of the fluid remaining)
determines the point at which the vessel is completely full of saturated
liquid. Below the saturation curve, a phase separation occurs. If vapor
is withdrawn (from the top), the product leaving has a higher energy
than that within the vessel and the process ends at (5A) with decreased
entropy and increased liquid. When liquid is withdrawn, the product
leaves at a lower energy level than that within the vessel and the process
ends at (5B) with less liquid remaining. More product may be withdrawn from the vessel in process (3)–(5B), however, without addition of
heat or warm gas to the vessel.

An entropy balance is convenient because of the isentropic process,
but the variation in leaving conditions requires a stepwise calculation.
The process, however, may be simplified by taking the expansion in two
steps [72]. The first step from (3) to (4) is strictly isentropic, where s_3
and s_4, as specific properties, are equal. From the saturated liquid line
(4) to either (5A) or (5B), average leaving conditions are used, rather than
successive steps. The result for vapor withdrawal is given by eq (5.29)
which gives the quantity of liquid remaining after depressurization [72].

$$Y = 100 \frac{v_l}{v_b} \left[\frac{v_g(s_e - s_b) + v_b(s_g - s_e)}{v_g(s_e - s_l) + v_l(s_g - s_e)} \right] \qquad (5.29)$$

where $s_e = (s_d + s_g)/2$
    Y = liquid yield as percent of initial volume,
    v_l = specific volume of saturated liquid at final pressure,
    v_g = specific volume of saturated vapor at final pressure,
    v_b = specific volume of saturated liquid at initial pressure,
    s_l = entropy of saturated liquid at final pressure,
    s_g = entropy of saturated vapor at final pressure,
    s_b = entropy of saturated liquid at initial pressure,
    s_d = entropy of saturated vapor at initial pressure.

Results of the above are presented in figure 5.45 for depressurization of a vessel full of liquid at pressure P_1 down to 1 atm, giving the percentage liquid loss as a function of P_1.

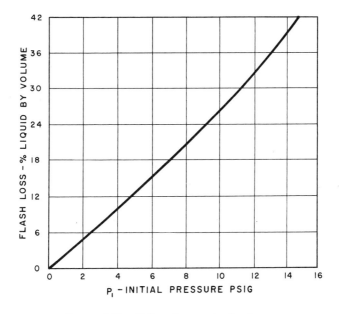

FIGURE 5.45. *Helium depressurization losses.*
Isentropic depressurization (expansion) of dewar contents from storage pressure p_1 to 1 atm.

If the depressurization takes such a long time that heat leak becomes a factor, the heat addition may be treated separately, as shown in section 5.4.1, again, as a repetitive step calculation. Should a mass addition also be involved, a First Law analysis, as shown in section 5.8.3, is more effective. It may be possible to assume average leaving conditions in some cases, rather than resorting to successive step calculations.

Two techniques are useful for increasing the liquid yield: (1) where the liquid remaining in the trailer is maximized, and (2) where more liquid is recovered from the product leaving. Their use, of course, depends on the ultimate aim of the helium transfer.

A heat exchanger and expansion valve located within the storage vessel is shown in figure 5.39. The flow is throttled to 1 atm and 4.2 K by the valve preceeding the heat exchanger. The existing fluid, now colder than that within the vessel, absorbs heat energy with the net effect of increasing the quality of the liquid remaining after the vessel is depressurized to some pressure below $P_c = 33.2$ psia. A comparison of this depressurization with an ordinary vapor blowdown is shown in figure 5.46 for a trailer which was initially filled with liquid at 4.2 K and later depressurized from a pressure P_1 to 1 atm. The yield is shown as percentage recovery of liquid in the trailer.

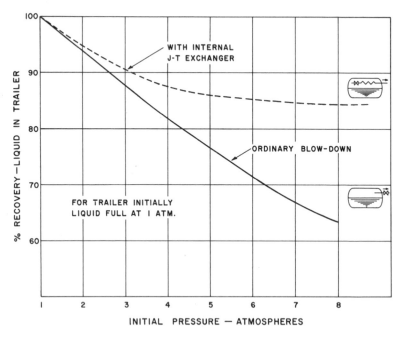

FIGURE 5.46. *Percent liquid recovery in trailer vs. initial pressure for depressurization to 1 atm.*

Ordinary blowdown vs. internal J–T heat exchanger (increased liquid yield).

Greater efficiency of liquid transfer can be achieved with the external Joule-Thomson exchanger [73], as shown in figure 5.39. Liquid is withdrawn from the trailer and, after heat exchange with helium vapor at 4.2 K, is throttled to 1 atm. The flashed vapor is used to precool the incoming liquid. Ideally, the vapor will leave at the same temperature as the trailer; but, because liquid is being withdrawn, rather than vapor, more product will be transferred. In addition to being more efficient, the external Joule-Thomson exchanger may be used as part of the transfer system. This may be done by using the annular space of a three wall transfer tube as the heat exchanger. The performance of this type of exchanger may be compared to the Joule-Thomson exchanger of a helium liquefier. Again, stepwise calculations are necessary because of the variation of inlet conditions to the exchanger as trailer pressure drops.

5.8.6. Flash Gas Recovery

The cost of helium, whether liquid or gas, and the indication of the order of magnitude of flash loss in the previous sections clearly illustrate the importance of giving serious economic consideration to a flash gas recovery system. The greatest volume of liquid helium handling is that of small dewar filling, and in all commercial installations for this purpose, some type of gas recovery system is available.

For a liquid-gas helium distribution network described in the following section, flash gas recovery is an integral part of the gaseous product handling. Flash gases from dewar filling at liquid-gas conversion stations are heated further in the normal vaporizer and then compressed for gas cylinder filling. Where liquid transfer is a part of a liquefier or cryostat production, any flash gas is recovered and returned as makeup to the liquefier.

The two significant problems for helium gas recovery are capacity of the gas system and contamination of product with air and moisture. Liquid helium transfers generate large volumes of flash gas from precooling, heat leak, and liquid displacement. A relatively high-volume compressor is required to maintain adequate fill rates unless low-pressure gas storage is used to take up slack between gas generation and compressor capacity. Low-pressure gas storage equipment is generally of the dry type with flexible rubber or plastic composite lining, and compressors are preferably nonlubricated. This equipment is chosen to eliminate or minimize helium contamination. A gas recovery system may include a charcoal bed adsorber at liquid nitrogen temperature to remove impurities, as in many helium liquefiers.

In general, and specifically for systems without adsorbers, considerable attention is given to purging all lines and receiving vessels with gaseous helium before introducing liquid. There are two techniques which have proven to be satisfactory in purging contaminants. A pressure purge is a periodic buildup of pressure with warm gas and blow down to atmosphere. This must be done several times to achieve any degree of success. A vacuum purge is more certain, provided that the gaseous helium back fill is sufficient to vaporize any condensed or frozen impurities. This should also be repeated two or three times for best results.

Finally, the liquid nitrogen precool described in section 5.8.2 may cause serious difficulties in purging. As much liquid nitrogen must be removed as possible and the remainder vaporized with warm helium gas before purging can be successfully achieved. A pressure transfer is used to remove liquid nitrogen from a dewar, similar to a helium transfer. As an added note of caution, flexible transfer lines should not be precooled with nitrogen, as liquid will collect in the bellows sections, which are difficult to purge. Cleanliness is also important, and all pieces should be cleaned, dried, and capped—especially bayonets and lines that might be exposed to the weather and condensed moisture.

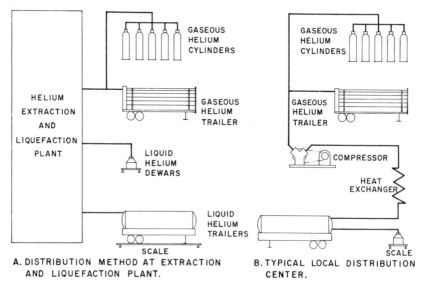

A. DISTRIBUTION METHOD AT EXTRACTION AND LIQUEFACTION PLANT.

B. TYPICAL LOCAL DISTRIBUTION CENTER.

FIGURE 5.47. *Schematic presentation of bulk liquid helium distribution systems.*

5.9. LARGE-SCALE LIQUID AND GASEOUS HELIUM DISTRIBUTION

Traditionally, helium has been shipped as a compressed gas in high-pressure tubes mounted on truck trailers or rail cars, as described in chapter 1. The most common tube trailers typically haul up to 40,000 scf* of helium compressed to approximately 2,400 psig. More recently, designs using longer trailers and tubes made of higher strength steels have increased the carrying capacity to nearly 130,000 ft³. The U.S. Bureau of Mines has operated gas rail cars for many years. During this time, many design improvements have been made; at present, the maximum capacity of newer units is about 345,000 ft³ at pressures to 4,000 psig.

TABLE 5.9. *Comparison of helium shipping containers*

Typical units	Helium capacity	Helium weight (W_H)	Container's weight (W_C)	Ratio $W_C : W_H$
	scf	lbs	lbs	
Standard cylinder	285	3	135	45
Standard trailer	40,000	415	26,800	65
Jumbo trailer	130,000	1,345	56,600	42
Rail car	300,000	3,100	234,000	75
Dewar (500-l)	13,350	138	1,100	8
Liquid trailer (10,000-gal)	1,000,000	10,350	43,350	4

Commercial shipment of liquid helium was started in the late 1950's with shipments to various consumers of liquid helium for research purposes [74]. Recent technological advances in cryogenic insulation and helium liquefaction coupled with rapidly growing markets for helium and the liberalized Helium Conservation Act of 1961 has made practical the transport of liquid helium even when the end use is gaseous helium. The distribution of helium as a liquid rather than a gas offers potential economic advantages comparable to those now achieved in distributing and handling oxygen, hydrogen, argon, and nitrogen in liquid form.

The weight advantage offered by shipping liquid is shown in table 5.9 and results in much lower transportation charges. The capital cost

---

*Industry standard of measurement is cubic feet at 1 atm and 70 F (scf).

of a liquid helium trailer is approximately one and one-half times that for a gas rail car; however, compared to a rail car, a liquid trailer can complete twice the deliveries in a given time and has three times the capacity. Therefore, liquid trailers require only one-fourth of the capital investment of gas rail cars to distribute the same amounts of helium. This savings in transportation cost and capital investment is only partially offset by the investment and operating cost of a helium liquefaction system. The ability to supply either liquid or gas from distribution centers is a further advantage of liquid transport systems.

5.9.1. The Airco Distribution System

In May 1966, the Air Reduction Co., Inc., started transporting liquid helium in semi-trailers from a new helium separation and liquefaction facility to four distribution centers within the United States [75]. Figure 5.47 is a block diagram showing the major components of and the products handled in this system.

Production Facility. Helium for commercial bulk distribution is obtained from natural gas in an integrated purification and liquefaction plant. The Kansas Refined Helium Company plant in Otis, Kans. [75–

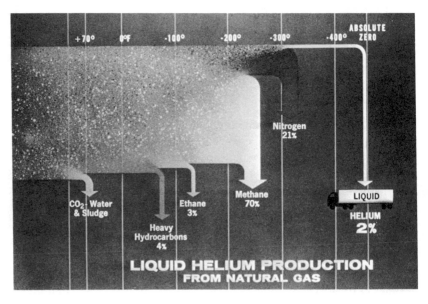

FIGURE 5.48.   *Flow diagram illustrating, in simplified form, a typical helium extraction and liquefaction process.*

77], (sec. 3.3.1) produces more than 800 l/hr of 99.995 percent helium. This plant currently has the largest single storage tank for liquid helium— a 32,000-gal, liquid nitrogen-shielded unit with a 1 percent per day evaporation rate. Basically, the plant process involves the following steps: (1) preliminary gas cleanup, (2) heavy hydrocarbon removal, (3) methane and nitrogen stripping, (4) final helium purification, and (5) helium liquefaction. Figure 5.48 shows a simplified flow schematic; a more detailed process discussion can be found in chapter 1.

System Operation. The distribution sequence starts with the liquid helium trailer being completely filled with liquid (at 16 psia) at the liquefaction plant. Filling and billing are done by weight (fig. 5.49). Extreme accuracy in weighing is important. Liquid helium is valued as high as $15 per pound. Thus a full trailer contains over $150,000 of product. Weighing errors, due to scale inaccuracies, snow and ice buildup on the trailer, etc., can be costly.

The liquid trailers are normally refilled in about 4 hours. Upon completion of the fill, the trailer vent is closed and the trailer is trans-

FIGURE 5.49. *The 10,000-gal liquid helium semi-trailer is weighed on a truck scale when making custody transfers of its 11,000-lb lading.*

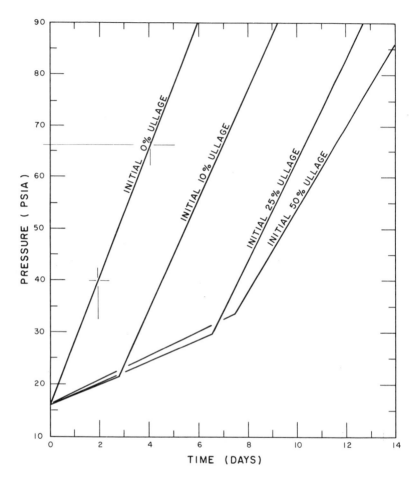

FIGURE 5.50. *Pressure rise in 10,000-gal liquid helium trailer as a function of time, showing percent full dependency relation.*

ported, within 48 hours, to any of several transfilling locations. During transport, heat leak into the trailer will cause a pressure rise rate of about 0.5 psi per hour (see fig. 5.50).

With the nonvented mode of operation for the liquid helium trailer, its contents will be a single-phase, cold, dense, fluid when it arrives at the transfilling location. Normal procedure is to depressurize the vessel to reestablish two-phase product. This is accomplished by withdrawing the dense fluid from the trailer through a manifold, heat exchanger, and compressor into gas trailers and cylinders. During this

FIGURE 5.51. *At a transfilling facility, liquid helium is pressure transferred from the liquid semi-trailer into various size liquid dewars, as required.*

All transfilling hoses are vacuum insulated. Gas generated in the operation is recovered and compressed into cylinders or trailers. The dewars are filled on a scale and contents checked by level probe. Normal trailer pressure is 5 psig. (Courtesy Air Reduction Co., Inc.)

depressurization period, liquid containers are not normally filled. Optimum trailer discharge pressure has been found to be 4 to 5 psig. This permits liquid withdrawal rates of up to 6 gal/min and minimizes flash generation while filling liquid containers.

It is possible to obtain liquid helium from the trailer immediately upon its arrival at a local distribution site, even if the product is in the supercritical condition. This can be accomplished by transferring the product directly into dewars, utilizing a transfer tube incorporating a throttling valve. The efficiency of this method can be increased by including a heat exchanger [73] in the transfer tube as discussed in section 5.8.5. This method is not normally used because varying trailer head pressure makes automatic flow control more difficult, and because all vapor generated must flow out through the limited vent passage of the dewar neck tube; this limits the transfer rate.

When liquid dewars are being filled, as in figure 5.51, all gas generated in the operation is collected, warmed, and compressed. Since the compressor is a constant capacity machine (7000 scfh in the system being described), it limits the rate at which liquid transfers can be accomplished while still maintaining a no-loss system. When dispensing 500,000 ft^3 per week of product from a 10,000-gal liquid trailer, as much as 65 percent of the product can be recovered as liquid.

If approximately 95,000 scf of product is withdrawn daily, the trailer pressure will remain constant. Should product demands exceed this figure, the 100 Btu/hr trailer heat leak will not sustain the trailer pressure and external pressurization would be required. Since the trailers are not equipped with pressure building coils, gas from the fourth stage of the compressor is used to maintain a minimum pressure of 5 psig.

Liquid Trailers. The liquid helium trailer is the key component in a bulk liquid helium distribution system. It must be designed to transport and dispense the product without loss. Therefore sloshing effects during transportation (sec. 5.6.1) and thermal oscillations (sec. 5.6.2) must be minimized, requiring costly design features.

One of a fleet of tractor-trailer units is illustrated in figure 5.10. The tanks of these trailers have a nominal capacity of 10,000 gal. Heat leak is limited to 100 Btu/hr by the use of evacuated multilayer insulation and a special support system. Eight baffles in the tank restrict the motion of the liquid, which makes the trailers more manageable on the road and reduces the mechanical damage that would result from unrestrained surges during abrupt changes of speed or direction. The baffles reduce sloshing of the liquid when the trailers are in motion and temperature stratification when they are stationary.

The trailer design also incorporates a pneumatic type suspension on the rear tandem for smooth-riding characteristics to minimize mechanical energy input into the liquid during transport.

The support system for the inner vessel is designed in accordance with proposed ICC specification MC 341 given in section 5.7.3.

The trailers are normally operated in the 100 percent full condition (0 percent ullage) and sealed for shipment. As is shown in figure 5.50, the rate of pressure rise is nearly constant and more rapid than that experienced with trailers less than 100 percent liquid full. Since the trailers have a 125 psig maximum operating pressure, the nonvented hold time, when 100 percent filled, can be as much as 9 days. Trailers filled to 90 percent of capacity (or approximately 9,600 gal of liquid) have a slower rate of pressure rise until the density change creates a liquid-full condition, at which point the contents become single-phase and the rate of pressure rise approximates that of a trailer initially filled to 100 percent of capacity. The nonvented hold time, when initially filled to 90 percent is 14 days. Actual operating data proved the validity of the internal energy method for calculating heat leak rate or rate of pressure rise, as discussed in section 5.4.1 using the data of figure 2.7.

Saturated helium vapor is one-eighth the density of liquid (at 1 atm); therefore, a 10,000-gal trailer may contain 1500 lb or more of cold helium vapor when emptied of liquid. The remaining dense vapor can be extracted by warming, either from trailer heat leak or external pressurization, to raise the residual gas temperature. Trailers are normally returned to the liquefaction plant with a 250 to 400-lb residual. This requires that about 11,000 Btu be added after the trailer is empty of liquid. Ambient temperature helium pressurizing gas will provide approximately

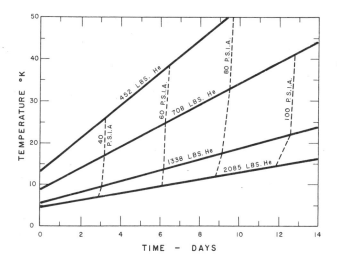

FIGURE 5.52. *Graphical presentation of the variation of residual lading pressure and temperature with time, for various residuals, in 10,000-gal liquid helium semi-trailer with a 100 Btu/hr total heat rate.*

FIGURE 5.53.   *Compression equipment in a liquid helium transfilling facility.*

The four-stage, nonlubricated compressor delivers 7200 scfh of 3000 psig helium gas with a 1 psig inlet. The trace oxygen, dewpoint and hydrocarbon analyzers (shown left center) continuously monitor the product and automatically shut down the compressor when contaminants in the 4 ppm range are detected.

650 Btu/lb per pound; therefore, about 17 lb of pressurizing gas is required for this operation.

The unloaded trailers are returned to the liquefaction plant without further venting. The heat leak into the trailer warms the residual helium gas and thereby increases its pressure. Figure 5.52 shows the rate of increase of both temperature and pressure for several values of the amount of cold vapor left in the unloaded trailer. It is noteworthy that the rate of pressure rise is substantially independent of the amount of cold gas left in the trailer.

Upon the trailer's return to the liquefaction plant, it is cooled to approximately 5 K with liquid helium and filled for another shipment. Refrigeration used to cool a trailer directly reduces the quantity of helium liquefied by the plant during the cooldown period. A compromise is made on the residual product returned in the trailer to maximize both trailer payload and plant production.

Gas Handling and Compression. A second major component of the bulk liquid distribution system is the gas recovery compressor. The compressor (see fig. 5.53) is a four-stage machine which boosts 15.5 psia, 70 F, helium to 3000 psig for gas trailer and cylinder filling. To prevent product contamination, the first three stages of the compressor are of the nonlubricated piston type with Teflon seals and rings. The fourth stage is a hydraulically actuated diaphragm. The fourth stage could not be of the Teflon ring type because current Teflon ring technology is limited to about 1500 psig. Temperature instrumentation with

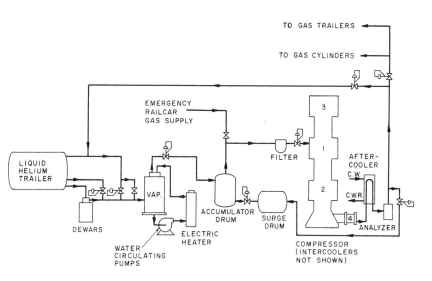

FIGURE 5.54. *Flow schematic for liquid helium transfilling station.*

The facility operates automatically once started. All gas generated in the transfilling operations is recovered and compressed into suitable gas distribution containers.

a high-temperature alarm and shutdown is installed on each of the first three stages to protect the Teflon rings from temperatures above 300 F. Ring and diaphragm life should be in excess of a thousand hours. The machine has a capacity of approximately 7000 scfh when operating within design conditions.

Figure 5.54 shows the piping for the major components at the local transfilling stations. The operator has the option of:

1. Removing either liquid or dense vapor from the trailer for compression into gas cylinders and trailers (after warmup to ambient conditions in a heat exchanger).

2. Filling of liquid dewars from the trailer and gas recovery from the dewars.

3. Combination of 1 and 2.

After the operator has selected the desired operational pattern, pressure actuated control valves automatically control flows from the trailer and to the compressor. Once the controls are set, liquid dewars can be filled as required without upsetting the remainder of the system.

Gas Purity. Local liquid helium transfilling stations have no facilities for repurification should the helium become contaminated during shipping or handling. Therefore, as the helium is compressed into cylinders or gas trailers, it is constantly monitored for moisture and oxygen, which would indicate product contamination from the atmosphere, and for total hydrocarbons, which indicate a malfunction in the compressor diaphragm or seals.

Moisture is monitored on an electrolytic type analyzer with a 0 to 10 ppm range; oxygen is monitored electrochemically also over a 0 to 10 ppm range; and hydrocarbons are detected by ultraviolet means using a fluorescent additive in the compressor hydraulic fluid. The system is shut down automatically should either the oxygen or hydrocarbon contaminant level increase to 4 ppm or the moisture to 2 ppm.

In the electrolytic moisture analysis [78], a sample gas stream is passed through a capillary tube containing phosphoric anhydride (P_2O_5) which absorbs all the moisture. Rhodium electrodes, embedded in the P_2O_5, are electrically energized, electrolyzing all the absorbed moisture. According to Faraday's law, the amount of current needed to effect the electrolysis is directly proportional to the absorbed water.

The electrochemical oxygen analyzer [79] is based upon the principle that the flow of electrical energy to an anode (cadmium or lead) from a cathode (silver) is proportional to the quantity of oxygen consumed in a galvanic oxygen reaction in alkaline solution.

REFERENCES

[1] H. K. Onnes, Koninkl. Ned. Anad. Wetenschap., Proc. **11**, 168 (1908).

[2] D. B. Mann and L. E. Scott, Unpublished results of a questionnaire survey conducted by the Cryogenic Engineering Laboratory, National Bureau of Standards, Boulder, Colo. (1959).

[3] A. P. Calvert, Air Reduction Company, Inc., New York, Private communication (1965).

[4] R. E. Brown, Economic and other aspects of the distribution of Navy helium in liquid form, Advances in Cryogenic Engineering (ed. K. D. Timmerhaus, Plenum Press, New York, 1957), Vol. **3**, p. 114.

[5] A. Wexler, Transfer of liquefied gases, Experimental Cryophysics (ed. F. E. Hoare, L. C. Jackson, and N. Kurti, Butterworths, London, 1961), Chapter 7.

[6] R. B. Scott, Cryogenic Engineering (Van Nostrand, Princeton, N.J., 1959).

[7] L. E. Scott, Neck plug hazards in liquid helium shipment, Advances in Cryogenic Engineering (ed. K. D. Timmerhaus, Plenum Press, New York, 1964), Vol. **9**, p. 374.

[8] J. A. Paivanas, et al., Multishielding—An advanced superinsulation technique, Advances in Cryogenic Engineering (ed. K. D. Timmerhaus, Plenum Press, New York, 1964), Vol. **10**, p. 197. (See also U.S. Patent 3,133,422.)

[9] R. J. Corruccini, Private communication, National Bureau of Standards, Boulder, Colo. (1954).

[10] L. E. Scott, R. F. Robbins, D. B. Mann, and B. W. Birmingham, Temperature stratification in a nonventing liquid helium dewar, J. Res. NBS **64C**, 19 (1960).

[11] E. Brown, National Bureau of Standards, Boulder, Colo., Private communication (1959).

[12] P. F. Dickson and M. C. Jones, Infrared reflectances of metals at cryogenic temperatures—A compilation from the literature, NBS Tech. Note 348, U.S. Dept. of Commerce, Washington, D.C. (1966).

[13] Purdue University, Data Book, Thermophysical Properties Research Center, Lafayette, Ind. (1967).

[14] M. M. Reynolds, R. J. Corruccini, M. M. Fulk, and R. M. Burley, Radiometry, American Institute of Physics Handbook (ed. D. E. Grey, McGraw-Hill, New York, 1963), Section 6K.

[15] A. Goldsmith, T. E. Waterman, and H. J. Hirschhorn, Handbook of Thermophysical Properties of Solid Materials (MacMillan Co., New York, 1961), 5 volumes.

[16] G. G. Gubareff, J. E. Janssen, and R. H. Torborg, Thermal Radiation Properties Survey, Minneapolis-Honeywell Regulator Co., Minneapolis, Minn. (1960), 2d ed.

[17] R. P. Caren, Low temperature emittance determinations, thermophysics and temperature control of spacecraft and entry vehicles, Progress in Astronautics and Aeronautics (ed. G. B. Heller, Academic Press, New York, 1966), Vol. **18**, p. 61.

[18] J. C. Mullins, W. T. Ziegler, and B. S. Kirk, The thermodynamic properties of parahydrogen from 1° to 22° K, Tech. Rept. No. 1, Project A–593, Engineering Experiment Station, Georgia Institute of Technology, Atlanta, Ga. (Contract CST–7339, National Bureau of Standards, Boulder, Colo., 1961).

[19] W. T. Ziegler and J. C. Mullins, Calculation of vapor pressure and heats of vaporization and sublimation of liquids and solids, especially below one atmosphere, IV. Nitrogen and fluorine, Tech. Rept. No. 1, Engineering Experiment Station, Georgia Institute of Technology, Atlanta, Ga., Project A–663 (1963).

[20] R. J. Corruccini, Calculation of gaseous heat conduction in dewars, Advances in Cryogenic Engineering (ed. K. D. Timmerhaus, Plenum Press, New York, 1958), Vol. **3**, p. 353; R. J. Corruccini, "Gaseous Heat Conduction at Low Pressures and Temperatures," Vacuum **7, 8**, 19 (1957–58).

[21] Saul Dushman, Scientific Foundations of Vacuum Technique (John Wiley & Sons, New York, 1962).

[22] D. R. Beck, F. Kreith, and R. H. Kropschot, A new steady state calorimeter for measuring heat transfer through cryogenic insulation, Advances in Cryogenic Engineering (ed. K. D. Timmerhaus, Plenum Press, New York, 1964), Vol. **9**, p. 64.

[23] R. H. Kropschot, Low temperature insulation, Applied Cryogenic Engineering (ed. R. W. Vance and W. M. Duke, John Wiley & Sons, New York, 1962), Chapter 6, p. 152.

[24] M. M. Fulk, Evacuated powder insulations for low temperatures, Progress in Cryogenics (ed. K. Mendelssohn, Heywood & Company, Ltd., London, 1959), Vol. I, p. 65.

[25] P. E. Glaser, Heat transfer mechanisms in evacuated powder insulations, International Developments in Heat Transfer, 829–837, ASME, New York (1963).

[26] B. E. Larkin and S. W. Churchill, Heat transfer by radiation through porous insulations, A.I.Ch.E. Journal **5**, 467 (1959).

[27] P. M. Riede and D. I-J. Wang, Characteristics and applications of some superinsulations, Advances in Cryogenic Engineering (ed. K. D. Timmerhaus, Plenum Press, New York, 1960), Vol. **5**, p. 209.

[28] M. A. Dubs and L. I. Dana, Superinsulation for the large scale storage and transport of liquefied gases, Problems of Low Temperature Physics and Thermodynamics (ed. A. Van Itterbeck, MacMillan Co., New York, 1962), p. 71.

[29] R. M. Christiansen, M. Hollingsworth, Jr., and N. M. Marsh, Jr., Low temperature insulating systems, Advances in Cryogenic Engineering (ed. K. D. Timmerhaus, Plenum Press, New York, 1960), Vol. **5**, p. 171.

[30] L. R. Stoecker, On the evacuation of plastic foams to reduce their thermal conductivity, Advances in Cryogenic Engineering (ed. K. D. Timmerhaus, Plenum Press, New York, 1960), Vol. **5**, p. 273.

[31] I. A. Black and P. E. Glaser, Effects of compressive loads on the heat flux through multilayer insulations, Advances in Cryogenic Engineering (ed. K. D. Timmerhaus, Plenum Press, New York, 1966), Vol. **11**, p. 26.

[32] R. C. Getty, J. P. Clay, E. J. Kremzier, and K. E. Leonhard, Experimental evaluation of some selected lightweight superinsulation for space vehicles, Advances in Cryogenic Engineering (ed. K. D. Timmerhaus, Plenum Press, New York, 1966), Vol. **11**, p. 35.

[33] I. Ishaghoff and J. M. Canty, Quilted superinsulation, Advances in Cryogenic Engineering (ed. K. D. Timmerhaus, Plenum Press, New York, 1964), Vol. **9**, p. 46.

[34] R. T. Parmley, D. R. Elgin, and R. M. Coston, Shingle multilayer insulation for space vehicles using cryogenic fluids, Advances in Cryogenic Engineering (ed. K. D. Timmerhaus, Plenum Press, New York, 1966), Vol. **11**, p. 16.

[35] Technical Brochures on Dimplar Cryogenic Insulation, Industrial Research & Development, Inc., Los Angeles, Calif. (1967).

[36] P. E. Glaser, I. A. Black, and P. R. Doherty, Multilayer insulation, Mech. Eng. **78**, 23 (1965).

[37] R. H. Kropschot, Cryogenic insulations, J.ASHRAE (Sept. 1959). R. H. Kropschot, Multiple layer insulations for cryogenic applications, Cryogenics 1, No. 3 (1961). R. H. Kropschot, J. E. Schrodt, M. M. Fulk, and B. J. Hunter, Multiple layer insulations, Advances in Cryogenic Engineering (ed. K. D. Timmerhaus, Plenum Press, New York, 1960), Vol. 5, p. 189.

[38] J. B. Loser, C. E. Moeller, and M. B. Thompson, Thermophysical properties of thermal insulating materials, ML–TDR–64–5, AD 601 535 (1964).

[39] I. A. Black and P. E. Glaser, The performance of a double-guarded cold plate thermal conductivity apparatus, Advances in Cryogenic Engineering (ed. K. D. Timmerhaus, Plenum Press, New York, 1964), Vol. 9, p. 52.

[40] C. R. Navikas, Insulation construction for cryogenic containers, U.S. Patent 3,241,702 (1966).

[41] Arthur D. Little, Inc., Cambridge, Mass., Private communication (1964).

[42] Horace Lamb, Hydrodynamics (Dover Publications, New York, 1945), 6th ed.

[43] R. Van Meerbeke, Thermal stratification and sloshing in liquid helium trailers, Advances in Cryogenic Engineering (ed. K. D. Timmerhaus, Plenum Press, New York, 1968), Vol. 13, p. 199.

[44] J. R. Clement and John Gaffney, Thermal oscillations in low temperature apparatus, Advances in Cryogenic Engineering (ed. K. D. Timmerhaus, Plenum Press, New York, 1960), Vol. 1, p. 302.

[45] J. D. Bannister, Spontaneous pressure oscillations in tubes connecting helium reservoirs to 300° K environments, Liquid Helium Technology (International Institute of Refrigeration, Commission I, Boulder, Colo., 1966), p. 127.

[46] M. T. Norton, Cryogenics Division, NBS, Institute for Basic Standards, Boulder, Colo., Private communication (1965).

[47] J. H. Bell, Jr. Cryogenic Engineering (Prentice-Hall, Englewood Cliffs, N.J., 1963).

[48] R. H. Kropschot, Mechanical properties of materials, Applied Cryogenic Engineering (ed. R. W. Vance and W. M. Duke, John Wiley & Sons, New York, 1962b), Chapter 3, p. 152.

[49] R. M. McClintock and H. P. Gibbons, Mechanical properties of structural materials at low temperatures, NBS Monograph 13, (Supt. of Documents, U.S. Govt. Printing Office, Washington, D.C., 1960).

[50] F. R. Schwartzberg, S. H. Good, R. D. Keys, and T. F. Kiefer, Cryogenic Materials Data Handbook (Martin Company, Denver, Colo., 1964). (Contract AF33 657)–9161; OTS, PB171809.

[51] Compressed Gas Association (500 Fifth Avenue, New York, 1966), Safety relief device standards for cargo and portable tanks, Pamphlet S–1.2. See also: Compressed Gas Association, Handbook of Compressed Gases (Reinhold, New York, 1966), p. 210.

[52] Compressed Gas Association (500 Fifth Avenue, New York, 1964 revision), Proposed insulated cargo tank specification MC–341 for low temperature liquefied gases, Docket 1204.

[53] R. J. Richards, A high-vacuum seal-off valve, Rev. Sci. Instr. 25, 520 (1954).

[54] R. C. Van Meerbeke, Commercial handling of liquid helium dewars, Advances in Cryogenic Engineering (ed. K. D. Timmerhaus, Plenum Press, New York, 1967), Vol. 12, p. 646.

[55] R. M. Neary, Air solidifying cryogenic fluids, Paper 64–WA.SAF–1, ASME Safety Conference, New York (1964).

[56] International Air Transport Association Regulations (1965), Sec. IV, p. 35, 10th ed., Item No. 865, Montreal.

[57] R. G. Biel, Frequency analysis of vowels produced in a helium-rich atmosphere, J. Acoust. Soc. Am. **34**, 347 (1962).

[58] J. P. Cooke, Verbal communication intelligibility in oxygen-helium and other breathing mixtures at low atmospheric pressures, Aerospace Med. **36**, 1167 (1965).

[59] National Aeronautics and Space Administration, Bioastronautics Data Book, Washington (1964).

[60] Cryogenic Engineering Company, Private communication (1963).

[61] P. D. Fuller and J. N. McLagan, Storage and Transfer of Cryogenic Fluids (ed. R. W. Vance and W. M. Duke, John Wiley & Sons, New York, 1962), Chapter 9.

[62] D. B. Chelton, U.S. Patent 3,034,319 (1962).

[63] A compendium of the properties of materials at low temperatures (ed. V. J. Johnson), WADD Technical Report 60–56, Part II.

[64] R. B. Jacobs, Liquid requirements for the cooldown of cryogenic equipment, Advances in Cryogenic Engineering (ed. K. D. Timmerhaus, Plenum Press, New York, 1963), Vol. **8**, p. 529.

[65] J. M. Canty, Pressure phenomena during transfer of saturated cryogenic fluids, Advances in Cryogenic Engineering (ed. K. D. Timmerhaus, Plenum Press, New York, 1961), Vol. **6**, p. 272.

[66] M. Epstein, Prediction of liquid hydrogen and oxygen pressurant requirements, Advances in Cryogenic Engineering (ed. K. D. Timmerhaus, Plenum Press, New York, 1965), Vol. **10**, p. 303.

[67] R. C. Hawthorne and H. C. Von Helms, Flow in corrugated hose, Product Engineering **34**, 98 (June 10, 1963).

[68] C. A. Schalla, Liquid hydrogen booster pump for aerospace ground-support systems, Advances in Cryogenic Engineering (ed. K. D. Timmerhaus, Plenum Press, New York, 1964), Vol. **9**, p. 521.

[69] B. Darrel and K. Schock, An electrically pumped liquid helium transfer system, Advances in Cryogenic Engineering (ed. K. D. Timmerhaus, Plenum Press, New York, 1966), Vol. **11**, p. 607.

[70] C. F. Gottzmann, High-pressure liquid-hydrogen and helium pumps, Advances in Cryogenic Engineering (ed. K. D. Timmerhaus, Plenum Press, New York, 1960), Vol. **5**, p. 289.

[71] J. W. Marshall, Logistic supply and handling of liquid helium, Paper 61–AV–10, ASME Aviation Conference, Los Angeles, Calif. (1961).

[72] L. E. Scott, Ideal yield of a Simon liquefier, Cryogenics **3**, 111 (1963).

[73] L. E. Scott and J. Kleinbaut, U.S. Patent 3,306,061 (1967).

[74] H. M. Long, The commercial production, storage and distribution of liquid helium, Liquid Helium Technology (International Institute of Refrigeration, Commission I, Boulder, Colo., 1966), p. 187.

[75] G. C. Nubel and H. Hover, Description of a bulk liquid helium distribution system, Liquid Helium Technology (International Institute of Refrigeration, Commission I, Boulder, Colo., 1966), p. 329.

[76] S. Ergenc and Ch. Trepp, A large-scale helium liquefier, Sultzer Tech. Rev. **4811966,** No. 4, 11215.

[77] Ch. Trepp, A large-scale helium liquefier, Liquid Helium Technology (International Institute of Refrigeration, Commission I, Boulder, Colo., 1966), p. 215.

[78] F. A. Keidel, A novel, inexpensive instrument for accurate analysis for traces of water, The Pittsburgh Conference on Analytical Chemistry and Applied Spectroscopy (1956).

[79] P. A. Hersch, Galvanic determination of traces of oxygen in gases, Nature **169,** 792 (1952); see also British Patent 707,323.

CHAPTER 6

Safe and Efficient Use of Liquid Helium

Hugh M. Long [1] and Paul E. Loveday [1]

[1] Linde Division, Union Carbide Corporation, Tonawanda, N.Y. 14150.

6.1. INTRODUCTION

Liquid helium is used in a wide variety of research and engineering projects, and personnel without previous experience with the unique characteristics of this fluid must frequently plan the operation. Chapter 2 emphasized the very low latent heat of vaporization, the low critical pressure, the low density ratio of saturated liquid to saturated vapor, as well as the high volume ratio of 530 R (294 K) vapor to saturated liquid. These properties of helium require careful planning, since one small oversight can cause complete failure to provide the desired liquid helium environment, in addition to exposing personnel to unwarranted hazards.

This chapter outlines some of the considerations necessary to achieve safe and efficient use of liquid helium. It presents general safety precautions and contains specific sections on liquefaction, transport, storage and transfer, and cryostat apparatus. A summary and conclusions section is also included. The reader is cautioned to study his specific operation, because the material presented herein can serve only as reminders rather than firm recommendations. Liquid helium technology is so young and applications so varied that existing rules and regulations cannot provide complete answers, though the referenced design guides should be helpful.

Designers of liquefaction and transport equipment use new technology not yet available in established design guides and regulations. For research applications, only the prudence of the designer can insure safe performance. It is hoped that the material in this chapter will provide adequate stimuli toward the development of safe design procedures.

Zabetakis [1] [2] has summarized the physiological, physical, and chemical hazards, as well as additional commentary on laboratory, plant, and test site safety. He also includes a Safety Data Sheet for each cryogenic fluid, plus many pertinent references.

Industrial Safety Data Sheets are available from the National Safety Council, 425 North Michigan Avenue, Chicago, Ill. 60611, and Chemical Safety Data Sheets can be obtained from the Manufacturing Chemists Association, Inc., 1825 Connecticut Avenue, N.W., Washington, D.C. 20009. Such sources of information can be very helpful in planning operations using other materials associated with helium liquefaction and its applications.

---

[2] Figures in brackets indicate the literature references at the end of this chapter.

6.2. HANDLING LIQUID HELIUM

The potential hazards in handling liquid helium stem mainly from four important properties:

a. The liquid is extremely cold (helium is the coldest of all cryogenic liquids).

b. The ultralow temperature of the liquid helium will condense and solidify air.

c. Very small amounts of liquid are converted into large volumes of gas.

d. Helium is non-life supporting.

In addition, there are potential hazards due to the mandatory use of vacuum-insulated vessels and transfer lines, and to changes in physical properties of materials between ambient and low temperatures.

6.2.1. General Precautions

Prior to using liquid helium, the specific operation should be reviewed with respect to the following list of precautions.

Cover eyes and exposed skin. Accidental contact of liquid helium, or cold issuing gas, with the skin or eyes may cause a freezing injury similar to a burn. Protect your eyes and cover the skin where the possibility of contact with cold fluid exists.

Keep air and other gases away from liquid helium. The low temperature of liquid helium or cold gaseous helium can solidify any other gas. Solidified gases and liquid allowed to form and collect can plug pressure-relief passages and foul relief valves. Plugged passages are hazardous because of the continual need to relieve excess pressure produced when heat leaks into the cold helium. Therefore, always store and handle liquid helium under positive pressure and in closed systems to prevent the infiltration and solidification of air or other gases.

Keep exterior surfaces clean to prevent combustion. Atmospheric air will condense on exposed helium-cooled piping. Nitrogen, having a lower boiling point than oxygen, will evaporate first from condensed air, leaving an oxygen-enriched liquid. This liquid may drip or flow to nearby surfaces. To prevent the possible ignition of grease, oil, or other combustible materials which could come into contact with the air-condensing surfaces, such areas must be cleaned to "oxygen-clean" standards. Any combustible foam-type organic polymer insulations should be carefully applied to reduce the possibility of this air condensation-oxygen enrichment process — which if followed by an impact could set off an explosive burning of the foam.

Pressure-relief devices must be adequately sized. Most cryogenic liquids require considerable heat for evaporation. Liquid helium, however, has a very low latent heat of vaporization. Consequently, it evaporates rapidly when heat is introduced, or when liquid helium is first transferred into warm or partially cooled equipment. Failure of the container vacuum can occur, adding appreciable heat. Pressure-relief devices for liquid helium equipment must, therefore, be of adequate capacity to release helium vapor resulting from such heat inputs, and thus prevent excessive pressure hazards. A quantitative method for determining the required relief device capacity for liquid helium containers is discussed in section 6.4.4.

Keep equipment area well ventilated. Although helium is non-toxic, it can cause asphyxiation in a confined area without adequate ventilation. Any atmosphere which does not contain enough oxygen for breathing can cause dizziness, unconsciousness, or even death. Helium, being colorless, odorless, and tasteless, cannot be detected by the human senses* and will be inhaled normally as if it were air. Without adequate ventilation, the helium will displace the normal air and give no warning that a non-life-supporting atmosphere is present. Store liquid containers in well-ventilated areas.

6.3. HELIUM LIQUEFACTION

6.3.1. Safety in Liquefier Design

Liquefier and refrigerator design has been covered in chapters 3 and 4. Safety features to be considered and incorporated in the design and operation of liquefaction equipment (because of the low temperature) have already been enumerated. In addition to these requirements, the design requirement for pressure vessels as outlined by ASME Codes [2] should be met. The usual safety considerations associated with compressed gases and machinery vibrations must also be incorporated in the design [3, 4].

The ever-present possibility of plugging due to impurities and the limitation on the length of operating periods imposed by removal of these impurities must be kept in mind during the design of liquefiers. Proper venting and incorporation of relief devices for traps are mandatory. Adsorbent traps must be designed to prevent adsorbent dust from entering the system and to contain the adsorbents even under the

---

*The pitch of the human voice is raised by high helium content, but this should not be used to gauge safe environments.

sudden depressurization due to emergency pressure relief. An adsorbent that generates minimum dust should be chosen.

Pressurized gas when cooled to low temperatures must be treated as liquid, and pressure relief devices (or expansion volumes) must be provided to cope with the pressure buildup caused by warming. For the same reason, all piping that passes into low-temperature regions and that may be isolated by valving must have a safety relief device or expansion volume.

Vacuum-insulated enclosures should be provided with safety-relief devices on the vacuum space, even if they are continuously pumped. Some details of relief design will be given in the following section on transport and storage equipment.

Liquefaction systems incorporating helium recovery from cryostats require carefully designed purification systems. In addition, if oil-sealed gas holders are employed, care must be taken to prevent discharge of oil into the system.

The following philosophy of Dr. A. J. Croft [5] was employed in the design of a liquid hydrogen facility and might well be adopted in design and operation of other cryogenic installations.

Any plant which embodies compressed gases or low-temperature liquids may explode from various physical causes, including faulty design and faulty operation. Where hydrogen is involved, there is the added possibility of chemical explosion. These dangers have to be thoroughly guarded against and a balanced approach to them is one of the hardest tasks for a designer of a liquefaction system. It is very easy to obscure real dangers by a mass of impressive precautions against improbable ones.

An order of priority for looking into the safety of a system may be made out as follows:

(a) In principle, one could eliminate danger altogether by paying enough attention to the design, materials, workmanship, and testing which go into a liquefaction plant. This is the first and most important line of defense.

(b) Next, still assuming a perfect system, one must look for every possible error on the part of the operator and allow for it if an accident might result.

(c) Then one must assume that either or both of these lines of defense have failed and that an accident occurs. The plant must be designed and precautions taken so as to reduce as far as possible any likelihood of injury to the operator or other people or serious damage to the building.

In particular, the last injunction — which can be paraphrased as "fail-safe design" — should be strictly followed in helium facilities even though the inert nature of helium renders it far safer than the other common cryogens. Indeed, a real concern with the design of helium apparatus is the inherent safety of its use, which can easily lead to complacency and possibly inadequate attention to safety.

6.3.2. Safety in Liquefier Operation

The general safety procedures for a liquefier parallel those of a chemical plant [6]. The moderate pressures in helium liquefiers and the chemical inactivity of helium can lead to complacency. However, the possibility of frozen impurities causing plugs in low-temperature piping and heat exchangers is reason enough to guard against this complacency. Unattended operation of liquefiers should be avoided because of the great hazard due to unobserved contamination during periods when pressures may inadvertently fall below atmospheric pressure. The principal source of danger is the inherent time-limitation on operation due to the impurities and the need to remove the impurities in limited-capacity traps for proper operation. Care must be exercised in venting traps which may contain hydrogen, oxygen, and hydrocarbons in mixture ratios which are dangerous. Although traps are sometimes provided at different temperature levels in an attempt to selectively remove oxygen and hydrogen, this selectivity is difficult between oxygen and the hydro-carbons, which liquefy at nearly the same temperature. Vent lines from various traps should not be manifolded, and each trap should be provided with a safety device, preferably a blowout disk. Traps should be purged separately unless a very high dilution is used to ensure low contaminant levels in the purge gas. Helium gas must be used for low-temperature purges. It is desirable that helium be employed for high-temperature purges as well, since this will eliminate the possibility of freezeup during cooldown. If nitrogen is used for high-temperature purge and thaw, then a further helium purge is required before cooldown.

The safety procedures for transferring liquid helium will be covered in a subsequent section of this chapter. One condition however, which is usually confined to the liquefier, is the cooling of warm containers prior to filling. In order to conserve liquid helium, the containers are usually precooled with liquid nitrogen and then purged with helium gas. There is danger that a residue of nitrogen will be frozen in the bottom of the container and subsequently plug the transfer lines or possibly the apparatus into which the helium is transferred. A safer procedure is to precool with gaseous helium which has been cooled with liquid nitrogen, thus eliminating free nitrogen from the helium compartment altogether. The next best procedure is to employ gaseous nitrogen only, although this is difficult in practice.

6.4. TRANSPORT AND STORAGE

Usually, the "use point" for helium is physically separated from the liquefier, sometimes only by a hallway but at other times by a continent or an ocean. This factor, coupled with the characteristics of helium which result in a sizable loss of the available liquid when removed from a storage vessel, has led to combining transport and storage into a single piece of equipment. Such equipment ranges in capacity from a tiny flask of a liter or two to a large semitrailer containing 40,000 l.

Some of the small equipment (up to about 25-l capacity) is fabricated from copper using techniques described by Wexler [7]. Larger equipment is usually fabricated using applicable provisions from the ASME Code or Department of Transportation Regulations and Specifications. To insure safe and economical storage and transport of liquid helium, close attention must be paid to equipment design.

6.4.1. Codes and Regulations

Until recently most domestic liquid helium shipments were made with a very slight positive pressure in the container, up to about 3 psig. Recent trends to bulk liquid helium distribution from large commercial liquefaction sources, as described by Nubel and Hover [8], have led to shipment of pressurized liquid helium. In such shipments the initial pressure is quite low (about 1 psig), and the heat leak to the helium during transportation is permitted to raise the internal energy rather than evaporate liquid. Thus the pressure increases during shipment, sometimes well in excess of the 25 psig (40 psia) value which places the shipment under regulatory control of the Department of Transportation [9] (DOT). Such regulatory control is independent of the quantity shipped. Ultimately, equipment used in such shipments must be designed, fabricated, and tested according to approved DOT Specifications; there are additional DOT Regulations which govern the conditions under which such DOT Specification Containers may be shipped. Since commercial pressurized liquid helium distribution is a new operation, the Compressed Gas Association is working with the DOT to obtain formal approval of the Specifications and Regulations [10].

For both cargo and portable tanks, the liquid helium container must meet the requirements of the ASME Code for design, materials, fabrication procedure, and test. Until such time as specific Regulations and Specifications are published by DOT, pressurized liquid helium shipments above 25 psig will be handled by Special Permit from DOT. Each shipper must obtain such a permit.

While most of the transport and storage containers having less than 1000-lb water capacity are operated at pressures so low that existing DOT and ASME rules do not apply, DOT Specification 4L, Paragraph 78.57 [9] can be used as a guide to the types of material specifications, joining procedure requirements, tests, and product identification which are desirable. (This Specification includes a formula for calculating vessel thickness and service pressure, hence does not reference the ASME Code.)

Air shipment of liquid helium is permitted under conditions defined by the International Air Transport Association (IATA) [11]. Liquid helium is not accepted for shipment on passenger aircraft, but when properly packaged and labeled is shipped on cargo aircraft. Nonpressurized liquid helium (i.e., in containers open to the atmosphere) is never accepted because of the solid air plugging hazard discussed in chapter 5. Present regulations permit shipment of up to 500 kg (4000 l) of low-pressure liquid helium (< 25 psig), and up to 140 kg (1120 l) of pressurized liquid helium (> 25 psig). Section 5.7.5. discusses the characteristics of relief devices and absolute pressure relief valves in the air transport environment, and summarizes current IATA requirements for venting of helium containers. These requirements are of a qualitative nature. Recommendations for quantitative relief-device sizing procedures are summarized later in this chapter. IATA does not require use of containers fabricated to specification, but it is strongly recommended that the specification guides described above be used in designing equipment for air transportation service.

6.4.2. Materials and Methods of Fabrication

Hansen [12] and Zenner [13] have emphasized the need to avoid low-temperature embrittlement in selecting suitable materials for fabrication of equipment for the low-temperature fluids. The ASME Code at present requires impact tests for SA–240 stainless steel used for liquid helium service; such tests are not required for some wrought aluminum alloys. Many other nonferrous materials are no doubt suitable for use in liquid helium equipment, but the ASME Code requires the designers to conduct suitable tests to satisfy the ductility requirements. Data on other materials are becoming available through extensive work done by various Government agencies [2, 14, 15].

While many materials will eventually prove suitable for use in liquid helium equipment, to date most existing equipment employs SA–240 Type 304 or 304L stainless steel, or SB–209 Alloy 5083 aluminum for material exposed to these extremely low temperatures. In addition to the base metal considerations, close attention must be paid to weld procedures, requirements for which are outlined in Section IX of the ASME Code, in order to achieve safe and reasonable equipment. Inadequate welds are not only hazardous from a strength viewpoint, but may also make it impossible to achieve the high vacuum required for efficient insulation of the container.

6.4.3. Insulation

Thermal insulations have been described in detail in chapter 5. It is obvious that careful design and application must be achieved to attain reasonable performance, whether the insulation system is based on liquid nitrogen shielding, cold gaseous helium shielding (single or multishield), or multilayer insulation. From a safety standpoint, the characteristics of the insulation system are tremendously important. Vacuum failure may occur in either the outer jacket or inner container. If a flaw should develop in the vacuum jacket, then air would enter the vacuum space. Any exposed metal surface which is cooled by liquid helium will serve as a condensation point for liquid or solid air, adding to the vessel heat flux. Similarly, a helium leak will flood the insulation space with helium, also leading to much greater heat flux across the insulation system. If helium gas generated by this increased heat influx is not removed from the liquid container at a sufficient rate, the pressure will increase to the burst point. Both types of heat flux behavior in addition to fire exposure should be checked for the specific insulation system, and the capacity of the conduit and relief devices of the inner container sized to assure adequate flow. Since gases leaking into the vacuum space can be cryopumped or cryosorbed and thus retained within the space, it is extremely important to protect the insulation system with an adequate pressure-relief device. Otherwise the equipment could be destroyed either by implosion of the inner vessel or by rupture of the outer vessel when the container is warmed.

Typical heat leak performance for various currently available designs is summarized in table 6.1. One point needs to be emphasized, and that is the large difference in heat leak to the inner vessel for venting and nonventing operation, which may vary markedly, depending

TABLE 6.1. *Heat leak performance for existing liquid helium transport and storage equipment*

Equipment	Normal capacity	Type of insulation system	Venting		Non-venting
			Heat leak	Percent of capacity	Heat leak
	Liters		*Btu/hr*	*per day*	*Btu/hr*
25-liter liquid-nitrogen-shielded dewar (Supairco, Hofman, and others).	23	Radiation with liquid nitrogen cooled shield.	0.05	1.6	0.5
LSHe–101 or –102 (Linde)............	100	Multishielded multilayer cooled by evaporated helium.	0.15	1.25	2.5
LSHe–500 (Linde).................	500	Multishielded multilayer cooled by evaporated helium.	0.7	1.0	12
500-liter vapor shielded container (Hofman).	500	Single radiation shield cooled by evaporated helium, with crinkled Mylar multilayer to jacket.	0.9	1.5	10
12,000-liter tank (Linde)...............	12,000	Multishielded multilayer cooled by evaporated helium.	10	0.8	67
37,000-liter semi-trailer (Linde)........	37,000	Multilayer.................	98	2.4	100

on the specific type of insulation system. For the small liquid nitrogen-shielded dewars, the nonvented heat leak is approximately ten times the vented heat leak; for multishielded dewars the ratio is over 15 to 1; while for the 40,000-l semitrailer the increase is only a few percent. Thus, the method of operation of the equipment should be based on the overall system requirements. If the end use is primarily in the liquid state, a continuously venting system may be more efficient.

6.4.4. Conduits and Piping Components

Liquid helium transport and storage containers are used in a wide variety of operations; hence many factors can influence their safe and efficient handling. Small containers of 500 l or less are designed to provide the user with a great deal of flexibility in removing the product from the container. A major feature is the neck access tube, which permits a wide variety of transfer lines to be inserted. This versatility can lead to unsafe conditions if proper operating procedures are not followed.

Neck plug hazard. A neck plug occurs when air condenses and freezes in a neck tube or vent line when either is open to the atmosphere. The pressure in the dewar is now unable to vent and will rise to the point of rupturing the vessel. The potential hazard is increased with fluctuations in barometric or ambient pressure and is also increased while making product transfers.

The dual relief passage is the most effective method of eliminating neck plug hazards. If a plug occurs in the normal vent line or fill connection, the second relief passage with a higher relief valve setting will prevent excessive pressure rise. This is achieved in most dewars with a double concentric neck design, as shown in figure 5.20 of chapter 5.

From a safety viewpoint, great care must be taken to keep air from entering the container when inserting and removing transfer lines, to prevent formation of a solid air plug. It is mandatory to close the aperture to the container immediately after removing the transfer hardware; also, it is mandatory to minimize the time period when opening for insertion. While raising the tube, air will condense on the cold outer tube, and unless restricted, will run down the tube into the conduit. A commonly used technique to prevent this is to provide a suitable wiping ring between the tube and the conduit opening, such as an absorbent cloth. The cloth will then collect the major portion of condensed air, particularly if the removal of the tube is done quickly. A more positive method of preventing air from entering the container is the use of the ball valve

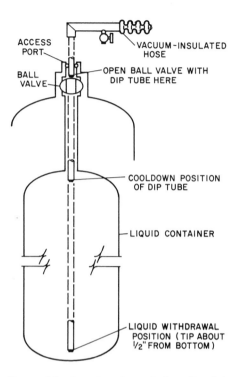

ACCESS PORT

VACUUM-INSULATED HOSE

BALL VALVE

OPEN BALL VALVE WITH DIP TUBE HERE

COOLDOWN POSITION OF DIP TUBE

LIQUID CONTAINER

LIQUID WITHDRAWAL POSITION (TIP ABOUT 1/2" FROM BOTTOM)

FIGURE 6.1.   *Insertion of transfer hose dip tube.*

[16] arrangement shown schematically in figure 6.1. This technique has the advantage of maintaining a slight positive pressure in the container at all times, since the O-ring seal to the tube is effected before the ball valve is opened for insertion of the tube, or vice versa on removal.

Most of the early liquid helium dewars had only a single aperture to the container, and some near disasters occurred due to plugging of this path by solid air. For this reason, dual relief paths have come into common use, and most manufactureres now supply containers with such an arrangement. An adapter is frequently used on single neck tube dewars to provide two relief paths, as discussed by Scott [17] and shown in figure 6.2.

For larger equipment, it is also recommended that dual relief paths be used. Often other design requirements will favor the use of two separate lines. One of these lines should be sized for the catastrophic requirement (either fire exposure or air condensation), while the second line should handle the relief requirement for loss of vacuum with helium, as described below.

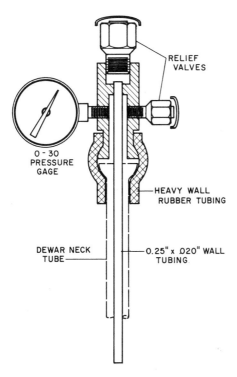

FIGURE 6.2. *Pressure relief device.*

By combining the operating techniques described above with the use of dual paths to suitable relief devices, the incidence of plugged containers has dropped to virtually zero. However, careless handling such as leaving one or both of these paths open to the atmosphere invites disaster. This is true for containers holding only cold gas as well as those holding liquid, because air can reach the low-temperature regions by diffusion, or by a reverse pressure differential caused by barometric or altitude variation. It is easy to overlook the fact that saturated helium gas at 4.2 K and 1 atm, if isolated by a solid air plug, can build to approximately 300 psi at 60 K, the approximate temperature at which a solid air plug might break. If a small amount of liquid is present in the container when the air plug is completed, the pressure can build to a much higher level, and thus rupture the container with extreme hazard to personnel. If a plugged container is suspected, move it to an isolated area, evacuate the area, erect warning signs, and notify the supplier immediately.

For those containers having an access path for insertion of transfer hardware, test for a plug can be made by inserting a $1/4$-in-diameter by 2 ft-long rod into the opening. If the path is plugged an obstruction will be felt. Means should be provided to prevent any inserted object from falling into the container. Also, should a plug be broken the outrush of vapor might expel the tool in a hazardous fashion if a method of limiting its travel is not applied. One method of relieving such a plug is to place a common crankcase heater into the neck and let it rest on the plug. Connect the heater to a 110-V circuit and from a distance turn on the heater. The heater will melt the plug and relieve the pressure. The remainder of the plug should then be reamed out, and the contents promptly emptied so the vessel can be returned to the supplier for checking.

Relief devices. To assure adequate sizing of relief devices and conduit paths to the inner container, it is necessary to predict the amount of heat which might be added to the helium. This becomes a matter of judgment as to the type of environment to which the insulation system will be exposed. The loss of vacuum insulation due to helium or air leakage has already been mentioned. For liquid nitrogen-shielded containers, a mechanical failure could admit liquid nitrogen to the insulation space, where it would come in intimate contact with the helium container. The container could be exposed to a fire, while simultaneously losing vacuum.

Scott [17] discusses the effect of failure on relief capacity requirements for 25-l liquid nitrogen-shielded dewars. Unpublished data by Schiffhauer [18] also indicates that a liquid nitrogen failure mode required greater relief capacity than vacuum deterioration with helium.

The CGA has a recommended guide to sizing relief devices for cryogenic containers [19]. The CGA equation estimates the total heat input to a vessel under fire conditions (including the effect of some insulation deterioration), considers the latent heat of vaporization of the lading, and converts the required relief rate to Q_a in ft^3/min of air at 60 F and 1 atm. The relief rate for air is one of the standard methods for rating relief devices, hence selection of a device with the required capacity from manufacturers' listings is straightforward.

A relief device should be sized to provide a flow of

$$Q_a = G_i U A^{0.82},$$

where:

$Q_a =$ minimum rated flow capacity of the relief device in ft³/min of air at 60 F and 1 atm,

$G_i =$ factor based on characteristics of the gas

$$= \frac{73.4 \times (1200 - t)}{LC} \left(\frac{ZT}{M}\right)^{1/2},$$

$U =$ total thermal conductance of the container insulating material at 100 F (Btu/hr·ft²·F) when saturated with gaseous nitrogen at atmospheric pressure. (Since the thermal conductivity of helium is much greater than that of nitrogen, the value of U should be based on helium for containers in helium service.)

$A =$ total outside surface area of the container in square feet,

$L =$ latent heat at flow conditions in Btu/lb,

$C =$ constant for gas or vapor related to ratio of specific heats (See ref. [19], fig. 2),

$Z =$ compressibility factor at flow conditions,

$T =$ temperature of gas at flow conditions in R,

$M =$ molecular weight of the gas,

$t =$ temperature of gas at flow conditions, F.

The CGA provides G_i values for some cryogenic fluids. The conventional CGA formula cannot usually be used for calculating G_i for helium, since the design pressure of the transport and storage container is usually well above helium's critical pressure. However, a G_i value of 52.5 has been adopted by the CGA for helium vessels with design pressures between 35 and 200 psig. This G_i value of 52.5 for helium is based on calculations and discussion given in Appendix A.

The size of a spring-loaded relief valve for loss of vacuum (i.e., when helium gas is in the insulation space) can be determined using the formula

$$Q_a = 4.5 \ (UA),$$

where Q_a and A are in the units above, and $U =$ thermal conductance in $\frac{\text{Btu}}{\text{hr·ft}^2\text{·F}}$ of the insulation at 1 atm of helium at $290 R$. Where the insulation is such that appreciable convection does not exist, U can be estimated by taking the ratio of the thermal conductivity to the insulation thickness. The factor 4.5 varies somewhat with pressure, so for safety a conservative value is used. Additional detail for this equation is given in Appendix A.

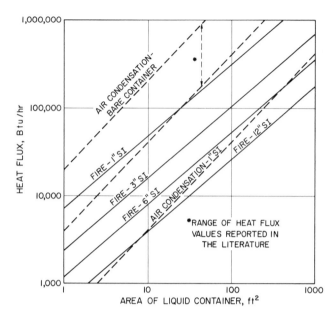

FIGURE 6.3. *Estimated total heat flux versus area for air condensation and fire conditions in multilayer (SI) insulated liquid
helium containers.*

It is quite possible that a flaw could develop in the outer jacket,
admitting air to the insulation space. Depending on the specific insulation
system, it is conceivable that the condensation of this air could add heat
to the helium at a greater rate than that occurring with fire exposure.

To illustrate, for one type of insulation system only, Frainier [20]
showed that air condensation on a liquid hydrogen container insulated
with 1 in of multilayer insulation has a heat flux of 400 Btu/hr-ft². Figure
6.3 summarizes the total heat flux as a function of liquid container area
for both air condensation and fire exposure. Heat flux due to fire exposure
is plotted for 1, 3, 6, and 12 in of multilayer (SI) insulation, and the
resulting comparison with heat flux due to air condensation for 1 in of
multilayer insulation shows that the fire condition represents the greater
relief device sizing requirement for all cases except large containers
having 6 to 12 in of insulation. For the latter case, it is also likely that
the 400 Btu/hr.-ft² would decrease appreciably, though this should be
determined experimentally.

The two dotted lines of figure 6.3 indicate the potential for very
large heat flux due to air condensation on a bare container. It can be

concluded that both air condensation and fire exposure should be carefully evaluated for the specific insulation system when sizing relief devices.

6.4.5. Operating Environment

In the last few years, the nature of liquid helium transportation has changed from an experienced scientist gently cradling a small flask while crossing the hallway between the liquefier and his research equipment, to the shipment by air, land, and sea of a wide variety of containers

FIGURE 6.4. *500-l liquid helium container.*
(Courtesy of Air Reduction Co.).

handled by workers who have never seen liquid helium before and who have not the slightest notion of its physical characteristics.

This vast change in handling procedure placed a severe challenge on designers of helium transport and storage equipment. At the start of commercial supply of liquid helium in 1959, the only available containers were the liquid nitrogen-shielded copper dewar containers typically used for laboratory operations. Fortunately, the 25-l size could be adapted for transport use by placing the container in a suitable shipping carton. Fiberboard shipping drums with shredded foam packing between the container and drum, and wooden boxes have been used, along with various types of shipping frames having rubber shock mounts. Experience in common carrier shipment of these packaged containers has been satisfactory.

New designs of containers have become available in recent years, and these generally are based on design and fabrication procedures consistent with DOT Specifications. The smaller containers usually use some form of packaging to reduce the loads imposed in common carrier handling. Figure 6.4 shows the shock mount arrangement used on a Hofman 500-l container.

Larger containers such as the Linde 7000-l Transport are mounted on semitrailers which provide appreciable cushioning, particularly when the new air-ride type of shock absorbing suspension is used.

Whenever a container of helium is shipped, make certain that (a) the liquid and gas phase valves are fully closed and capped; (b) all piping connections are tight; (c) the relief devices are properly in place and in satisfactory operating condition; (d) there are no frost buildups [which indicates container vacuum or insulation deterioration]; (e) container pressure is within an acceptable range; (f) container decals are properly in place and legible. Label the container with the following handling precautions and identification notices:

LIQUEFIED GAS CONTAINER

LIQUID HELIUM—LOW PRESSURE (up to 40 psia)

[or LIQUID HELIUM—PRESSURIZED (greater than 40 psia)]

KEEP CONTAINER UPRIGHT

DO NOT DROP

DO NOT BUMP

DO NOT LAY ON ITS SIDE;

(g) shipping papers are in order, including: necessary bill of lading, receiving instructions, delay enroute instructions, and the name and phone number of person(s) to be contacted in the event of a need of instructions or information; and (h) packaging of the container is provided, according to the needs of the specific container design.

Whenever a container of helium is received, inspect the container immediately to determine whether there are any breaks or leaks in the piping, or unusual frost formation. Check the pressure in the container to be certain that it is in the proper range for the specific container design, and that the relief device is operating properly. Test the smaller containers for neck plugs. Higher than normal loss of helium from the container can occur due to loss of container vacuum, low liquid nitrogen level (if liquid nitrogen shielded), or thermal oscillations (see chapter 5).

Altitude variation. Air shipment of liquid helium is a common occurrence, due to the large distances encountered between liquefier and customer. Such shipments can cause an appreciable variation in the atmospheric pressure immediately surrounding the helium container with typical variations from 8.2 to 12.2 psia at altitude, as pointed out by Van Meerbeke [21] and discussed in chapter 5. Care must be taken during descent of the aircraft that air does not flow into the container piping with consequent formation of a solid ice plug in the cold portion of the conduit.

There are several approaches to solving this problem, the most common being the use of an absolute pressure-relief device. Another approach consists of a heat exchanger coil which warms the gaseous helium prior to reaching the relief valve, thus greatly increasing the ability of the valve to resist backflow of air when the pressure difference is reversed. Still another common approach is to use a conventional spring-loaded relief valve with a setting sufficiently high that the container pressure is always greater than atmospheric. A 25-psia setting or greater is required, since the altitude variation can typically cause a 6 to 7 psi change in the ambient pressure (i.e., from 14.7 to 8.2 psia). This procedure has the potential of not releasing any helium from the container, so no-loss shipments are possible with suitably designed containers.

While the alternate approaches described above have been used successfully, the preferred arrangement for air shipment of small containers is the absolute pressure-relief valve. It works equally well with liquid nitrogen-shielded dewars, gaseous helium-shielded dewars, and gaseous helium-cooled multishielded dewars. The continuous evaporation permitted by this device also tends to reduce losses, and the pressure is controlled at the desired set point.

Weather. All transport containers are exposed to the elements, which can cause problems due to rain, snow, and freezing rain, etc. It is appropriate to protect the relief devices from these weather effects. This is sometimes accomplished by using weather shields, or protective housings. By specifying suitable positions of the relief device (i.e., outlet pointed down), adequate protection against moisture penetration and later freezeup can also be obtained. Frangible disks are usually fitted with a plastic blowoff cap on the outlet side to prevent undue corrosion with consequent premature failure. The plastic cap must be applied in such manner that it does not impede this relief path.

6.5. TRANSFER

Transfer operations provide a much sterner challenge to safe and efficient use of liquid helium than storage, because of the heat input experienced at the interfaces of the connecting conduit between the storage and receiving apparatus, and in the conduit and valves. Cooldown of the transfer elements and the receiving apparatus also contributes significant losses, even when precooled with liquid nitrogen. Evolution of a large amount of helium vapor when making such transfers requires adequately sized flow passages and relief devices to prevent over-pressurizing the apparatus. Figure 6.5 shows a typical transfer arrangement with a 100-l container supplying liquid helium to a cryosorption array located within a vacuum chamber. Note the vacuum-insulated transfer line used to transport the liquid helium from the supply container on the right to the array on the left. (The smaller container in front supplies liquid nitrogen to provide auxiliary refrigeration to minimize liquid helium consumption.)

Proper cooldown and purge of liquid helium equipment are essential to efficient and safe operations. Potential loss of liquid helium is best emphasized by examining the loss of liquid helium in cooling 1 lb of stainless steel, assuming no sensible heat recovery:

From	298K	to	78 K $-$ 14	liters
From	78K	to	4.2K $-$ 0.67	liters

FIGURE 6.5. *Liquid helium transfer from a Linde vessel (LS He-102) to cryosorption array in vacuum chamber.*
(Courtesy of Linde Division, Union Carbide Corporation).

Therefore, the weight of material to be cooled should be kept to a reasonable minimum, and precooling with liquid nitrogen should be used when feasible. Some principles and cautions to keep in mind in the precool operation are:

(a) Use of liquid nitrogen will greatly reduce the liquid helium cooldown loss, but the liquid nitrogen must be completely removed, followed by a helium gas purge. If not removed, the nitrogen will freeze at helium temperature with consequent operational problems and safety hazard due to plugged lines.

(b) Saturated nitrogen vapor at 139 R (77 K) in some cases may prove to be a good alternate cooldown medium since it avoids the need for liquid nitrogen removal.

(c) In some cases, particularly where a gaseous helium recirculation system is available, it may be advantageous to precool using helium gas cooled to 78 K by liquid nitrogen in a heat exchanger. This limits the purge operation to one initial step, and avoids any warmup which might occur when a gaseous helium purge follows a nitrogen cooldown operation.

(d) A trace system employing liquid nitrogen or cold gaseous nitrogen might be used to advantage, especially where intermittent

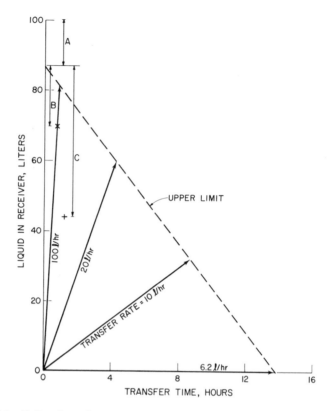

FIGURE 6.6.   *Helium loss when transferring from a 100-l supply container into a receiver vessel; transfer components have an assumed 15 Btu/hr heat flux, equivalent to a loss of 6.2 l/hr.*

Dotted line — indicates maximum recovery at transfer rates from 6.2 l/hr and up, with no cooldown of transfer line or receiver.

× — Experimental net recovery of 70 l = 100 − (A + B).

+ — Experimental net recovery of 43 l = 100 − (A + C).

A — Residual vapor in container.

B — Accumulated losses due to single cooldown of transfer line, and three 25-l containers from 78 K, plus steady heat leak to containers and transfer line.

C — Accumulated losses due to 14 repetitive transfers to a cold 3-l receiver with transfer line cooldown and steady heat leak.

transfers are required. The nitrogen should be removed and gaseous helium purged prior to liquid helium addition.

Chapter 5 discussed in considerable detail the many factors involved in the transfer of liquid helium including their effect on the loss of liquid helium during the process. Figure 6.6 illustrates some of the problems involved in the efficient use of liquid helium in typical operations. In this highly simplified transfer, conventional vacuum-insulated components, having a steady-state heat leak of 15 Btu/hr are used to provide a flow path from a 100-l supply container to the receiving vessel. For the purposes of this illustration, it is assumed that over the limited time period for the operation there is zero-heat leak to the supply and receiving vessels, no pressurizing or depressurizing effects (pressure remaining at 14.7 psia), and no cooldown loss in either the transfer components or the receiving vessel. The dotted line shows the upper limit of liquid helium captured in the receiving vessel for various rates of transfer (based on the amount of liquid helium *leaving* the supply container).

Also shown on figure 6.6 are the initial contents of the 100-l supply container, the 13.4 l which remain in the container as saturated vapor at 14.7 psia, and the loss due to the 15 Btu/hr steady-state heat leak to the transfer components for the total time of transfer. The two crosses represent results obtained in several typical operations. The upper cross shows that 70 l are recovered in the sequential fill of three 25-l nitrogen-shielded containers. In this operation, the transfer line is cooled only once, requiring a little less than 3 l, and three copper compartments are cooled from 78 K to 4.2 K, requiring about 8 l. For these low-pressure transfers (1 to 2 psig), depressurization and line losses described in chapter 5 are small compared to the precooling losses, and therefore are not indicated separately in these typical results.

The lower cross represents the loss incurred when a series of 14 refills are made to a relatively small receiving vessel in which the transfer components must be recooled for each transfer. This 3-l cooldown loss per transfer adds up to a sizable overall loss for such a recurring operation.

Generally speaking, liquid helium transfers should be made in a reasonably short time period, measured in minutes. Continuous transfers over a few hours should be avoided. The conventional transfer hoses, valves, and bayonets fit in well with short-term transfers, and have been designed for ruggedness and good adaptability at reasonable cost. When liquid helium must be transferred over a long time period or repeatedly transferred wherein the components warm up between transfers, design of special components should be considered.

The addition of necessary safety devices to containers and transfer lines may sometimes be detrimental to the thermal performance since they may cause thermal oscillations (chapter 5) in the piping which can

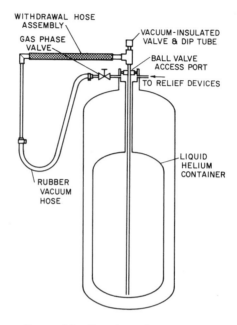

FIGURE 6.7. *Experimental arrangement*
used to avoid thermal oscillations.

contribute excessive amounts of heat. Short [22] describes a thermal oscillation damper for cryogenic containers. This device has been very useful in eliminating thermal oscillations in containers having concentric dual relief passages. Shal'nikov [23] describes the use of a short thread at the base of a withdrawal tube to remove thermal oscillations.

A technique for removing thermal oscillations, which sometimes occur in the insulated withdrawal tube path during periods of nonwithdrawal when retained in the container, is to provide a short, small-diameter jumper line between the liquid withdrawal tube outlet and the gas phase of the container as shown in figure 6.7. Both the liquid phase valve and the gas phase valve are then cracked or opened as required to remove the oscillations. The normal evaporation of helium from the container passes through the relief device provided for that purpose. Using this technique, overall loss from a container with the line inserted is only slightly greater than the loss from a container without the line inserted. This method of operation reduces the loss incurred in recooling the parts inserted into the container. The most efficient operation is therefore dependent on the frequency of withdrawal. Similar techniques can be used on transfer hardware that does not contain the liquid-line valve.

6.6. SAFETY IN CRYOSTAT DESIGN AND USE

The principles already elucidated for liquefaction, storage, and transport equipment should be adhered to in cryostat design. Safe operation is usually dependent upon safe design. The small-scale research apparatus holding only a few milliliters of liquid helium may be a bomb in disguise if the liquid is trapped. Therefore, this apparatus needs a safety review during the design as surely as does the large-volume apparatus holding hundreds of liters. Once again, however, firm recommendations are difficult, but some pointed reminders can be enumerated.

Standard procedures for laboratory safety are a required step in the safe operation [24, 25]. In addition to the usual considerations of safe laboratory practice with experimental apparatus, those intended for cryogenic service should have critical reviews in two areas: first, the materials of construction should be reviewed to ensure that materials are employed properly and that allowance has been made for the effect of temperature gradients on dissimilar materials, during cooldown, steady-state, and warmup; and second, the venting of the vapors evolved during all phases of operation should be determined to ensure adequate size of vent apertures and safety-relief valves and proper installation of vent lines. Obviously, if the apparatus employs liquid nitrogen as well as helium, the review should encompass this cryogen as well.

6.6.1. General Design Considerations

As a first step toward the design of safe apparatus, the ASME Boiler and Pressure Vessel Code [2] should be consulted. The various sections of this code provide information on material selection, joints, and formulae with safety factors for the design of a limited number of equipment configurations. The research equipment designer may find that his experimental requirements are in conflict with the codes and that his design must be non-code. These codes then give him a reference point from which he can gage the extent of his departure from sound engineering design practice. More importantly, they allow him to employ proven engineering practice for that portion of his apparatus which can be designed to code specifications.

The design of cryostats for helium service is covered in some detail by White [26] and by Rose-Innes [27] and in somewhat less detail in some parts of Hoare, Jackson, and Kurti [28] and by MacKinnon [29], Scott [30], and Din and Cockett [31]. Numerous designs of specific apparatus and design tips are reported in Review of Scientific Instruments, Journal of Scientific Instruments, Pribory i Tekhinka Eksperimenta, and Cryogenics, as well as other journals. Few of the authors give specific reference to safety features, although safety is implicit in many of the instructions.

The apparatus designer is frequently left to his own counsel or to locally prevailing procedures, either of which may or may not be adequate. In particular, as apparatus evolves and becomes more sophisticated, some simple, very effective safety aspects are sometimes designed out of the apparatus. When any experimental apparatus undergoes evolutionary development, a special check of safety features is in order, since safety is likely to be overlooked in the search for functional improvement.

The general desire in cryostat design is for an isothermal system at some specified temperature level having a minimum heat leak. These considerations usually lead to deep, narrow vessels which are of either glass or metal construction with high-vacuum thermal insulation. There are usually closed experimental spaces within these vessels which are suspended from a top cover by long, small cross-section support members, either tubular or solid. Frequently, these members, if tubular, form the principal opening to a boiling cyrogen and may represent a reasonable obstruction to the discharge of vapors from the system. In addition, sometimes there are radiation shields within or around the supports, which further obstruct the discharge path, particularly in the case of emergency venting. If the experimental requirements are such that venting may not be adequate, then the apparatus should be placed behind a shield to protect personnel in case of misadventure.

The designer should consult some of the standard works on equipment design [2, 32] and on methods of joining metals [33, 34, 35] in order to assess the strength and suitability of the particular joints to be used. When the designer employs a new technique of his own it must be thoroughly tested to insure that it will not contribute to or create an unsafe situation.

An admonition by Dr. Croft [5] relating to metal apparatus, that "nothing is safe for use until it has been hydraulically tested with water, oil, carbon tetrachloride, or some other suitable liquid," should be adhered to, although carbon tetrachloride is not a recommended testing liquid.

A final reminder is that the properties of materials found in many data books are measured values of a particular specimen or small numbers of specimens and do not, therefore, represent the variability in properties which may be encountered in practice. A safety factor must be used, and then the apparatus should be tested at above the working stress.

6.6.2. Mechanical Considerations

The configuration of components which are subjected to low temperatures and those which traverse large temperature gradients must be reviewed carefully. The forces resulting from thermal contraction must be considered, since the thermal contraction of most metals when cooled to or below liquid nitrogen temperature is sufficient to produce forces greater than the yield strength of the metal, if the member is restrained to its room temperature length. For example, consider a 304 stainless steel rod or tube restrained to its room temperature length and cooled to liquid nitrogen temperature [14, 36, 37]. The thermal contraction is

$$\left(\frac{L(139 \text{ R}) - L(528 \text{ R})}{L(528 \text{ R})} \right) = -285 \times 10^{-5} \text{ in/in.}$$

The modulus of elasticity of 304 stainless at 139 R is

$$Y = 29 \times 10^6 \text{ psi,}$$

so that the resulting stress is

$$P_{\text{Contraction}} = -Y \left(\frac{L(139 \text{ R}) - L(528 \text{ R})}{L(528 \text{ R})} \right)$$

$$= -(29 \times 10^6)(-285 \times 10^{-5}) = 82{,}500 \text{ psi}$$

while the yield strength of annealed 304 stainless ranges from 35,000 to 68,000 psi.

Other metals, such as 410 and 17–4 PH stainless, have sufficiently high yield strength that they can be restrained without yielding, but unfortunately they become brittle and should not be used in tension. There are, however, some metals, such as A–286 stainless and Invar, whose properties are such that they also can be restrained without exceeding their yield strengths, and they are not brittle.

If the member is in a thermal gradient, then the contraction will be less than for full cooling, and the stress level will be correspondingly lower, in many cases low enough to be safe. However, the designer must check to be sure. This determination requires knowledge of the thermal gradient in the member in order to arrive at an estimate of the length. The elasticity modulus is nearly constant with temperature, so that a single value can be used to determine the stress level once the contraction is known; this stress must then be compared to the *lowest* yield strength in the temperature range in question, in order to assess the design.

Dissimilar metals in a thermal gradient may also give rise to forces which will exceed the yield strength of the metals or which will distort the apparatus, thus increasing the heat leak or breaking other supports or instrumentation connections. Even when dissimilar metals are avoided or designed for, problems may arise during cooldown or emergency venting due to the asymmetrical thermal gradients which can exist if only one of several parallel tubes is used as a vent. Gaskets held by bolted flanges may loosen due to differential contraction of the components, i.e., bolts, flanges, and gaskets. Safe practice dictates that some form of elastic member be employed to ensure sealing.

Support members which are hollow and sealed must be used with caution, since small leaks into the sealed volume may result in a considerable volume of gas being condensed at the low temperature region with subsequent high pressure on warmup. Where slow warmup is expected because of massive components, small vent holes may suffice to release pressure, but for rapid warmup restricted volumes should be avoided.

6.6.3. Glass Apparatus

For many years the most common equipment for handling the lower boiling cryogens was glass apparatus, and even today many laboratories find it convenient and economical to employ glass in the construction of cryostats. Rose-Innes [27] discusses a typical glass cryostat and its use in some detail. Safe practice dictates that large pieces of glass be coated with a plastic film or taped with a plastic, cloth, or paper tape to restrain the fragments in event of breakage. While glass dewars usually implode upon breaking, as a result of the insulating vacuum in the jacket, they should nevertheless be protected, either by the above means or by placing them in a metal or plastic enclosure. When clear strips are left in glass dewars for observation of the liquid level, some protective cover between the observer and the strip should be provided.

Large glass apparatus should be annealed in a furnace before installation. Glass tubing that must be installed at the apparatus should be carefully annealed in situ to remove internal strain which may cause unexpected failure during use. Inspection with polarized light is recommended. If annealing is not possible, then connections should be made by flexible plastic tubing, rubber, or by ground glass joints.

Dewars which are moved frequently should be handled with extreme care as they may get scratched and break unexpectedly, since they are always under stress due to the vacuum. The sealoff tips should have a protective cover to guard against accidental bumping.

Most hard glasses such as Pyrex are quite permeable to gaseous helium at room temperature and above. The permeation rate is sufficiently high that, if warm dewars are left with helium in them, the vacuum deteriorates in a very short time and permanently sealed dewars are rendered useless. The common practice is to provide a pumpout connection at the top of the dewar and to evacuate them periodically. White [26] reports that dewars may be used some 100 hr or so between evacuations. The vacuum achieved need not be very high, since the helium-cooled inner sleeve of the dewar will cryopump the residual gases other than helium. In fact, many experimenters intentionally introduce a small quantity of air into the vacuum in order to enhance the higher temperature heat transfer and speed the cooldown. As indicated by both White and Rose-Innes, the connection between the dewar and the pumpout tap is best made with a short piece of plastic or rubber tubing. This serves as a safety relief as well as a flexible joint. If the dewar vacuum is permanently fused to a glass system, some form of blowout relief device should be provided between the dewar and the evacuation tap.

The common practice of attaching glass dewars to the dewar cap by a rubber sleeve provides very effective overpressure relief, since the thin rubber can sustain only slight internal pressures without ballooning. If, however, the glass dewars are sealed to the cap with O-rings or by the use of glass pipe flanges, then a safety relief device should be provided in the dewar cap, since these seals can sustain considerable internal pressure.

Glass manometers are frequently used in cryogenic apparatus for pressure measurement and control. They should always be constructed with catch basins at the ends to prevent fluid from being discharged into the apparatus or the room. Care should be exercised to avoid rapid pressure changes in systems with mercury manometers because of the considerable momentum of a rapidly moving column of mercury. As with all glass apparatus, safety shields should be employed.

6.6.4. Fill and Vent Procedures

Economical and safe transfer of liquid helium is in part a function of the design of the cryostat. In most transfer operations the total losses can be reduced by carrying out the transfer at low pressures and at moderate flow rates. There is a clear distinction, however, between filling an open volume such as a transport container and filling an experimental cryostat where the free volume for liquid is small and the surface of the included apparatus is large. There is a further distinction between the initial fill of any apparatus and the refill operation.

For initial fill, the cryostat should be designed to allow the vapors from the transferred liquid to pass over the apparatus to be cooled, in order to utilize the sensible refrigeration in the vapors and to warm the vapors up before discharge from the cryostat. The sensible heat to warm the helium vapor to room temperature is over 75 times the latent heat of vaporization. The recovery of this refrigeration is accompanied by an increase in the vapor volume, and the principal hazard in transfer is the large expansion of the cold vapor or liquid when warmed by the apparatus in the cryostat. The principal losses in transfer result from the entrainment of liquid in this large volume of vapor and the failure to recover the refrigeration in the effluent vapors. Thus, for the initial fill into a cryostat, the liquid should be introduced at the bottom of the liquid container and in a relatively open volume which will allow low vapor velocities to aid disengagement of the vapor and liquid phases during the early stages of transfer.

During refill of the liquid helium, the apparatus cooling problems do not exist, but there is an entrainment problem resulting from vapors which accompany the transferred helium. If the transfer line on refill is allowed to go to the bottom of the cryostat, this entrainment can be very large, mainly resulting from first rush of vapor that is produced in a warm transfer line. The entrainment can be greatly reduced by precooling the transfer line prior to insertion into the cryostat and then further reduced by inserting the transfer line only as far as the anticipated filled helium level, so that none of the two-phase liquid is discharged below the liquid level.

Sizing the vent opening in a cryostat is subject to some variability. For example, when large masses of metal must be cooled, the largest vapor evolution may occur during cooldown, and the amount of vapor will not necessarily be related to the liquid volume contained when the apparatus is full. Conversely, in some situations (such as cryostats for superconducting magnets), there may be considerable evolution during cooldown and, in addition, periods of high evolution during magnetic field discharge—both accidental and intentional. In other cases, the vent need handle only the small volume resulting from the usual low heat leak to well-designed cryostats.

One aspect of venting which should not be overlooked is warmup after an experiment is completed, since the 4.2 K saturated vapor in an "empty" cryostat will expand to about 100 times its volume at room temperature and thus could result in large pressure buildup, if confined. In laboratories where gaseous helium is recovered, there is no problem, since the cryostats are connected to a gas holder, but where helium is vented to the atmosphere a problem can develop. While it is fairly common practice to employ a narrow vent tube with a small wad of cotton or glass wool to prevent back diffusion of air, this is not a safe procedure, since barometric pressure changes can cause air transport into the cryostat. A positive relief valve is preferred, and it should be so arranged that the vapor passing through it is sufficiently warm that no atmospheric moisture can freeze on the valve and impair its opening or closing. The use of a slit rubber tube or "Bunsen" valve is not recommended, since the slits are quite prone to freezing open due to the rubber becoming stiff when only slightly cold gas is passing through the valve. They are totally unacceptable as emergency relief valves.

, The rate of vapor evolution is dependent upon the geometric arrangement and construction of the apparatus and the properties of the fluid. The heat transfer rate to boiling cryogens has been determined for simple geometries by a number of investigators, and a recent review by Brentari and Smith [39] provides data for use in equipment design. The data indicate that the peak nucleate pool boiling heat transfer in helium is about 1 W/cm^2 of surface area, which corresponds to an evaporation rate of 1.41 liquid liters per hour per square centimeter or about 10 l/hr of vapor at helium temperature, which could expand to 1000 l at room temperature, if an additional 80 W are available to warm the vapors to room temperature. An object 10 cm in diameter by 10 cm long could thus produce an evaporation rate of 440 liquid liters per hour. A liquid container of these dimensions would contain 785 cm³ and would be emptied in about 6 s if boiled at the peak nucleate flux rate producing about 5.5 l of vapor at helium temperature and about 550 l if warmed to room temperature. The warming of the vapor would require about 160×10^3 J (25kW for 6 s) compared to about 2×10^3 J (315 W for 6 s) needed for vaporization. Since in most apparatus this amount of heat is not available, emergency venting invariably produces cold vapor, and the design of vents must be suitable for cold vapors.

6.7. SUMMARY

The uses of liquid helium are extremely diverse, making it difficult to provide specific recommendations, but the following general principles will be helpful in planning safe and efficient operations:

a. Select an adequate thermal isolation system for the supply and receiving vessel, and transfer components.

b. Make certain that the degree of vacuum in the thermal isolation system is such that adequate performance will be achieved.

c. Consider precooling and purge requirements in the design of equipment, and use materials compatible with the operating temperature.

d. Where feasible, use adequate helium-content-monitoring devices. The low density of liquid helium, coupled with a varying liquid nitrogen weight, can completely mask the true helium content. Point sensors, or differential pressure gages, have been used successfully. If liquid helium equipment is overfilled, very high losses result.

e. Slowly insert transfer hardware, sensor probes, etc., to permit cooling with helium vapor rather than liquid helium. The energy input with the transfer hardware may be used to build the pressure required for transfer. Fast insertion will result in high vapor discharge accompaned by undesirable liquid entrainment.

f. When reducing the pressure of the liquid helium container, bleed off slowly from the gas phase to avoid liquid entrainment.

g. Use sufficient pressure difference to effect the transfer in a reasonably short time. However, use the lowest pressure consistent with the time requirement to minimize added losses due to pressurization (through addition of gaseous helium to maintain required pressure), transfer loss, pressure drop and depressurization, as discussed by Van Meerbeke [21]. For many operations, 0.5 to 1.0 psig is sufficient, though other operations require 3 psig or more.

h. Design equipment with adequate vapor vent paths and suitable safety devices. In sizing relief devices, include the additional heat input which can result from loss of vacuum, exposure to fire, air condensation, and when applicable, the energy input potential from other system characteristics such as that due to a cryogenic magnet going normal, etc.

i. Avoid transfer arrangements which permit gaseous helium to bubble through a pool of liquid.

j. Where periodic refills are required, some means of preventing entry of warm gaseous helium into the liquid helium container is desirable. This can be accomplished in a variety of ways, including use of liquid-nitrogen shielding and venting of gaseous helium from a location near the receiving vessel until the transfer line is cold.

APPENDIX A. SIZING OF RELIEF DEVICES

The Compressed Gas Association [19] provides information for sizing of relief devices for compressed gases, including pressurized liquid oxygen, nitrogen, and argon and liquefied hydrogen, in cargo, portable, and storage tanks. A value of G_i (the parameter used to size relief devices) is listed for each commodity and is dependent on the latent heat of vaporization and other physical properties of the specific fluid.

Sizing of relief devices for liquid helium containers is somewhat more complex, since the relieving pressure is usually above the critical pressure where no latent heat value exists. A method for handling helium is presented herein, a G_i value being computed in typical fashion, but based on L', an equivalent value used in place of the latent heat of vaporization. The units of L' are Btu/lb, where Btu's represent the total heat added to the vapor between temperatures T_1 and T_x per pound of efflux gas leaving the container at constant pressure, P. The L' varies significantly with T_x, and has its lowest value shortly after start of relief.

Sizing for Fire Condition

The basic equation for sizing relief devices is

$$Q_a = \frac{13.1 \ WC_a}{60 \ C} \left(\frac{ZTM_a}{MZ_aT_a}\right)^{1/2} \tag{6A-1}$$

where Q_a = scfm of air at 520 R (289 K) and 14.7 psia, required capacity of the relief device

W = lb/hr, required flow of the gas

C_a = Gas constant = 356 for air

C = Gas constant of the gas

Z_a = Compressibility factor = 1.0 for air at STP

Z = Compressibility factor for the gas at the flow condition

M_a = Molecular weight of air = 28.97

M = Molecular weight of the gas

T_a = Temperature of air at STP = 520 R

T = Temperature of the gas at the flow condition.

Also,

$$W = \frac{HA}{L}, \text{ lb/hr}, \tag{6A-2}$$

where H = Heat input in Btu/hr/ft^2
$\quad\quad A$ = Total outside area of the liquid container in ft^2
$\quad\quad L$ = Latent heat of gas in Btu/lb.

Source information for this earlier work [19] has shown that as the size of the container increases the fraction of the surface exposed to the open fire decreases, hence $A^{0.82}$ is used rather than A, and $HA^{0.82}$ then represents the total heat passing to the fluid in the container under fire conditions. For insulated containers,

$$HA^{0.82} = kA^{0.82}(t_2 - t)/l, \text{ in Btu/hr},$$

where k = Thermal conductivity of the insulation, Btu/hr ft F
$\quad\quad T_2$ = 1200 F
$\quad\quad t$ = Temperature of the gas at flow condition, F
$\quad\quad l$ = thickness of insulation, feet.

This can be expressed as

$$HA^{0.82} = UA^{0.82}(t_2 - t), \text{ in Btu/hr}, \tag{6A-3}$$

where U = Total thermal conductance of the container insulation system, Btu/hr/ft^2 F.

Substituting (6A-2) and (6A-3) for W in (6A-1), along with the other values defined,

$$Q_a = \frac{13.1}{60} \frac{UA^{0.82}(1200 - t)}{L} \frac{356}{C} \left(\frac{ZT\,28.97}{M(1.0)520}\right)^{1/2}$$

$$= \frac{18.3\,UA^{0.82}(1200 - t)}{LC} (ZT/M)^{1/2}. \tag{6A-4}$$

A factor G_i is defined as

$$G_i = \frac{73.4\,(1200 - t)}{LC} (ZT/M)^{1/2}, \tag{6A-5}$$

TABLE 6A-1. G_1 values for helium, for insulated containers

(Calculated from: $G_l = 0.097(1200 - t_x)\sqrt{Z_x T_x/L'}$)

Relief pressure psia	m_1	v_1	T_1	h_1	$m_x \left(= \dfrac{v_1 m_1}{v_x}\right)$	v_x	T_x	t_x
	lb	$\dfrac{ft^3}{lb}$	'R	$\dfrac{Btu}{lb}$	lb	$\dfrac{ft^3}{lb}$	°R	°F
100X............	1.0	0.1259	10	7.66	0.793	0.1589	12	−448
		.1589	12	10.92	.67	.2368	14	−446
		.2368	14	15.71	.742	.3200	16	−444
		.3200	16	19.91	.81	.3948	18	−442
		.3948	18	23.47	.85	.4642	20	−440
		.4652	20	26.72	.78	.5940	24	−436
		.5940	24	32.70	.765	.7765	30	−430
		.7765	30	41.08	.728	1.0661	40	−420
		1.0661	40	54.38	.792	1.3473	50	−410
		1.3473	50	67.31	.71	1.899	70·	−390
		1.899	70	92.72	.70	2.715	100	−360
		2.715	100	103.39	.668	4.0657	150	−310
		4.0657	150	192.77	.60	6.755	250	−210
		6.755	250	317.09	.627	10.78	400	−60
		10.78	400	503.29	.742	14.54	540	+80
50⊙............	1.0	0.1208	8	5.04	0.76	0.159	10	−450
		.159	10	8.19	.372	.4284	12	−448
		.4284	12	16.08	.724	.5913	14	−446
		.5913	14	19.79	.808	.7321	16	−444
		.7321	16	23.0	.848	.8628	18	−442
		.8628	18	25.97	.874	.9878	20	−440
160△............	1.0	0.1148	10	8.21	0.892	0.129	12	−448
		.129	12	10.47	.84	.1537	14	−446
		.1537	14	13.49	.802	.1918	16	−444
		.1918	16	17.30	.812	.2361	18	−442
		.2361	18	21.12	.844	.2803	20	−440
		.2803	20	24.67	.87	.323	22	−438
		.323	22	27.98	.887	.3645	24	−436

TABLE 6A-1. G_i *values for helium, for insulated containers* — Continued

(Calculated from: $G_i = 0.097(1200 - t_x)\sqrt{Z_x T_x/L'}$)

Relief pressure psia	h_x	$\dfrac{(m_1 + m_x)}{2}$	$(m_1 - m_x)$	$(h_x - h_1)$	$L'^{(1)}$	Z_x	G_i
	$\dfrac{Btu}{lb}$						
100X............	10.92	0.896	0.207	3.26	14.1	0.52	28.3
	15.71	.835	.33	4.79	12.1	.6	38.2
	19.91	.871	.258	4.20	14.2	.73	38.4
	23.47	.905	.19	3.56	16.9	.8	35.8
	26.72	.925	.15	3.25	20.0	.85	32.8
	32.70	.89	.22	5.98	24.2	.92	30.8
	41.08	.883	.235	8.38	31.4	.95	26.9
	54.38	.814	.272	13.30	39.8	1.0	25.0
	67.31	.896	.208	12.93	55.7		19.8
	92.72	.855	.29	25.41	75.0		17.2
	130.39	.85	.30	37.67	107		14.1
	192.77	.834	.332	62.38	157		11.5
	317.09	.80	.40	124.32	249		8.68
	503.29	.813	.373	186.20	406		6.02
	676.99	.871	.258	173.70	585		4.30
50○............	8.19	0.88	0.24	3.15	11.6	0.33	25.2
	16.08	.686	.628	7.89	8.6	.63	51.1
	19.79	.862	.276	3.71	11.6	.69	42.7
	23.0	.904	.192	3.21	15.1	.83	38.4
	25.97	.924	.152	2.97	18.0	.86	34.8
	28.82	.937	.126	2.85	21.2	.92	32.2
160△............	10.47	0.946	0.108	2.26	19.8	0.65	20.6
	13.49	.92	.16	3.02	17.4	.67	26.0
	17.30	.901	.198	3.81	17.3	.7	28.9
	21.12	.906	.188	3.82	18.4	.77	30.4
	24.67	.922	.156	3.55	21.0	.81	28.8
	27.98	.935	.13	3.31	23.8	.84	27.4
	31.12	.943	.113	3.14	26.2	.88	26.6

(1) $L' = \dfrac{(h_x - h_1)\,(m_1 + m_x)}{2(m_1 - m_x)}$

and also,

$$Q_a = G_i U A^{0.82}. \tag{6A-6}$$

Note that the value of G_i in (6A-5) is four times that indicated by comparison of (6A-4) and (6A-6). This factor of 4 has been introduced to permit use of a U value determined at 100 F instead of at the higher average temperature incurred under fire conditions, and to allow for some insulation performance deterioration under fire conditions.

For the specific case of sizing relief devices for insulated helium containers, it is proposed, where necessary, to substitute L' (as previously defined) for L, so that

$$G_i \text{ (Helium)} = \frac{73.4 \ (1200 - t)}{L' \times 378} \left(\frac{ZT}{4.00}\right)^{1/2}, \tag{6A-7}$$

where $C = 378$ for a monatomic gas at $k = C_p/C_v = 1.67$ at standard conditions, and

$$G_i \text{ (Helium)} = \frac{0.097 \ (1200 - t)}{L'} (ZT)^{1/2}, \tag{6A-8}$$

where t, Z, T, and L' are determined at the flowing conditions.

In the relief of helium vapor above the critical pressure, the following system can be visualized:

$$\left\{\begin{array}{l} m_1 = \text{lb helium} \\ \quad \text{vapor, at:} \\ \\ P_1, \text{psia} \\ T_1, \text{R} \\ h_1, \text{Btu/lb} \\ v_1, \text{ft}^3/\text{lb} \end{array}\right\} \rightarrow \left\{\begin{array}{l} m_x \text{ lb helium vapor} \\ \quad \text{remaining in} \\ \quad \text{container, at:} \\ P_x = P_1, \text{psia} \\ T_x, \text{R} \\ h_x, \text{Btu/lb} \\ v_x, \text{ft}^3/\text{lb} \end{array}\right\} + \left\{\begin{array}{l} (m_1 - m_x) \text{ lb helium vapor} \\ \quad \text{relieved through} \\ \quad \text{safety device, at:} \\ P_x = P_1, \text{psia} \\ T_1 \rightarrow T_x, \text{R} \\ h_1 \rightarrow h_x, \text{Btu/lb} \\ v_1 \rightarrow v_x, \text{ft}^3/\text{lb} \end{array}\right\}$$

The heat absorbed by the helium vapor for any such incremental step can be approximated by

$$q = m_x(h_x - h_1) + (m_1 - m_x)\frac{(h_x - h_1)}{2}, \text{ Btu.}$$

The heat absorbed per pound of helium vapor leaving the container is then:

$$L' = q/(m_1 - m_x) = \frac{m_x(h_x - h_1) + (m_1 - m_x)\frac{(h_x - h_1)}{2}}{(m_1 - m_x)}$$

$$L' = \frac{(h_x - h_1)(m_1 + m_x)}{2(m_1 - m_x)}, \frac{\text{Btu}}{\text{lb}}. \tag{6A-9}$$

Table 6A1 summarizes, for several pressures, L' and G_i values as determined by (6A-8) and (6A-9) for a number of incremental steps. The Z_x, T_x, and t_x values have been used in the calculation of G_i.

Figure 6A1 shows a plot of those G_i values as a function of T_x. Note that the G_i value peaks below 20 R for each of the several pressures investigated. Figure 6A2 shows a plot of L' versus T_1 for each of several pressures.

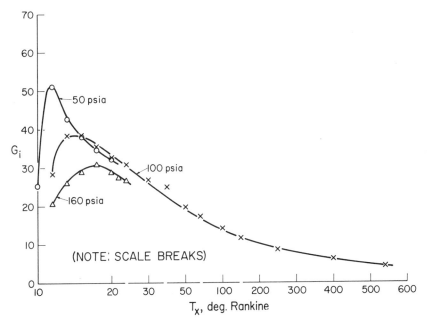

FIGURE 6A-1. *Values of G_i for sizing helium relief devices.*
Relief pressures of 50, 100 and 160 psia are indicated.

A G_i value of 52.5 for pressurized liquid helium is being added to table 1 of the CGA Pamphlets S–1.2 and S–1.3 for a set pressure of 200 psig. Per the footnote to this table, the same value could be used for lower settings of the relief device.

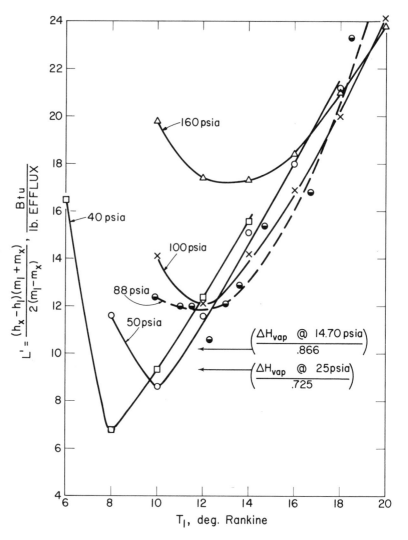

FIGURE 6A–2.   *Heat absorbed per pound efflux for a helium container relieving above the critical pressure.*
Relief pressures of 40, 50, 88, 100, and 160 psia are indicated.

The values of U and A used in the $Q_a = G_i U A^{0.82}$ formula would depend on the characteristics of the specific design with U being determined at 100 F with helium in the insulation space, and A the area in square feet of the liquid container.

Since most safety devices are rated in terms of free air flow (at 60 F and 14.7 psia), selection of the proper size of relief device is straightforward. Size of the piping between the container and the relief device should be no less than that of the device. Since no provision has been made in the calculation procedure for warmup of the cold vapor, the piping should be kept to minimum length.

A frangible disk would usually be used to meet this relief device requirement, and the pressure for rating the flow of the device should not exceed its nominal setting, or 1.2 times design pressure (plus 15 psi if vacuum insulation is used), whichever is less.

Loss of Vacuum (No Fire)

CGA Pamphlets S-1.2 and S-1.3 also specify that a safety relief valve be used on cryogenic containers, with a flow capacity sufficient to handle loss of vacuum in the insulation space with air or lading, whichever is greater. The following example for loss of vacuum with helium shows the recommended method for determining this requirement. From (6A-1) and substituting $C_a = 356$, $M_a = 28.97$, $Z_a = 1.0$, $T_a = 520$ R, we get

$$Q_a = \frac{18.3W}{C} (ZT/M)^{1/2}.$$

But for this condition,

$$W = \frac{HA}{L} = UA(100 - t)/L,$$

and for helium

$$Q_a = \frac{18.3UA(100 - t)}{378L} \left(\frac{ZT}{4.00}\right)^{1/2}$$

$$= 0.0244UA(100 - t)(ZT)^{1/2}/L.$$

At a relief pressure of 10 psig = 25 psia

$L = 6.72$ Btu/lb of helium vaporized, or

$$= 6.72 / \left(\frac{6.95 - 1.90}{6.95} \right) = \frac{6.72}{0.725} = 9.28 \text{ Btu/lb of helium efflux}$$

(where $0.725 = \frac{\rho_l - \rho_g}{\rho_l}$ at 25 psia) and $T = 8.7R$, $t = -451 \ F$, $Z = 1.0$,

$$Q_a = 0.0244 \, (U\dot{A}) \, (551) \, [1.0(8.7)]^{1/2} / 9.28$$

$$= 4.28 U A.$$

At a relief pressure of 70 psig$=85$ psia (this is above critical point), from figure 6A2, let $L' = 12$ Btu/lb efflux, and $T=15$ R, $t=-445$ F, $Z=1.0$; thus

$$Q_a = 0.0244 (UA) \, (545) [1.0(15)]^{1/2} / 12$$

$$= 4.2 U A.$$

At a relief pressure of 145 psig$=160$ psia (above critical point), from figure 6A2 let $L'=17$ Btu/lb efflux and $T=16$ R, $t=-444$ F, $Z=0.93$; thus

$$Q_a = 0.0244 (UA) \, (544) \, [0.93(16)]^{1/2} / 17$$

$$= 3.10 U A.$$

The Q_a requirement will vary with pressure. However, to streamline calculation procedures, assume

$$Q_a = 4.5 U A$$

where A is area of the liquid container.

Since the capacity of most relief valves is given as $Q_a = $ cfm of air at 520 R and 14.7 psia, selection of the required device from manufacturers' listing is straightforward. The calculation procedure does not consider warmup of the cold vapor, so piping length to the relief valve should be kept to a minimum.

REFERENCES

[1] M. G. Zabetakis, Safety with Cryogenic Fluids (Plenum Press, New York, N.Y., 1967).

[2] ASME Boiler and Pressure Vessel Code: Section II — Materials Specifications; Section VIII — Rules for Construction of Unfired Pressure Vessels; Section IX — Welding Qualifications (American Society of Mechanical Engineers, 345 East 47th Street, New York, N.Y. 10017).

[3] J. L. Cost, Design and construction for safety, A Summary Report of Cryogenic Safety Conference, Air Products, Inc., Allentown, Pa. (July 1959), pp. 31–40.

[4] G. M. Kintz and Frances C. Hill, Safety at gas processing plants, Bureau of Mines Bulletin 588, USGPO, Washington, D.C. (1960).

[5] A. J. Croft, Ancillary equipment for the production of liquid hydrogen and liquid helium, Experimental Cryophysics (ed. F. E. Hoare, L. C. Jackson, and N. Kurti, Butterworths, London, 1961), p. 115.

[6] Howard H. Fawcett and William S. Wood, Safety and Accident Prevention in Chemical Operations (John Wiley & Sons, New York, N.Y., 1965).

[7] A. Wexler, Storage and transfer of liquefied gases, Experimental Cryophysics (ed. F. E. Hoare, L. C. Jackson, and N. Kurti, Butterworths, London, 1961), p. 138.

[8] G. C. Nubel and H. K. Hover, A bulk liquid helium distribution system, Liquid Helium Technology (Intern. Inst. of Refrigeration, Commission 1, Bulletin 1966–5), p. 329.

[9] Interstate Commerce Commission Regulations, Tariff No. 19.

[10] CGA Docket 1204: Insulated Cargo Tank Specification for Low-Temperature Liquefied Gas, Requirements for semitrailers and truck-mounted tanks which remain on the chassis; CGA Docket 1127A: Insulated Portable Tank Specification for Low-Temperature Liquefied Gases, Requirements for tanks having gross volume in excess of 1000-pounds water.

[11] Restricted Articles Regulations, International Air Transport Association, Section IV, articles 865, 866 and 867; Section VI, articles 252 and 808.

[12] O. A. Hansen, Low temperature characteristics of metals, Refining Engineer (Dec. 1959), p. C–21.

[13] G. H. Zenner, Low temperature metals: A roundup, Chemical Eng. (Oct. 31, 1960).

[14] Cryogenic Materials Data Handbook, Technical Documentary Report No. ML–TDR–64–280, Air Force Materials Lab., Research and Technology Division, Air Force Systems Command, Wright-Patterson Air Force Base, Ohio.

[15] Aerospace Research Application Centers (ARAC), Indiana University, Bloomington, Indiana.

[16] J. A. Paivanas and P. E. Loveday, U.S. Patent No. 3,272,374.

[17] L. E. Scott, Neck plug hazards in liquid helium shipment, Advances in Cryogenic Engineering (ed. K. D. Timmerhaus, Plenum Press, New York, 1964), Vol. 9, p. 379.

[18] J. H. Schiffhauer, Relief device requirements for nitrogen-shielded liquid helium dewars, unpublished.

[19] Safety Relief Device Standards, Pamphlet S–1, Parts 2 and 3, Compressed Gas Association, 500 Fifth Avenue, New York, N.Y. (also see chapter 5).

[20] R. J. Frainier, Liquid hydrogen containers: loss of vacuum with air, unpublished.

[21] R. C. Van Meerbeke, Commercial handling of liquid helium dewars, Liquid Helium Technology (Intern. Inst. of Refrigeration, Commission 1, Bulletin 1966–5), p. 303.

[22] A. J. Short, U.S. Patent No. 3,298,187.

[23] A. I. Shal'nikov, The prevention of sonic vibrations in helium siphons, Cryogenics **6**, No. 5, 299 (October 1966).

[24] H. A. J. Pieters and J. W. Creyghton, Safety in the Chemical Laboratory (Academic Press, New York, 1957).

[25] The General Safety Committee of the Manufacturing Chemists Association, Inc., Guide for Safety in the Chemical Laboratory (D. Van Nostrand Co., Inc., New York, 1954).

[26] G. K. White, Experimental Techniques in Low Temperature Physics (Oxford Univ. Press, 1959).

[27] A. C. Rose-Innes, Low Temperature Techniques (D. Van Nostrand Co., Inc., London, 1964).

[28] F. E. Hoare, L. C. Jackson and N. Kurti, Experimental Cryophysics (Butterworths, London, 1961).

[29] Lachlan MacKinnon, Experimental Physics at Low Temperatures (Wayne State Univ. Press, Detroit, Mich., 1966).

[30] R. B. Scott, Cryogenic Engineering (D. Van Nostrand Co., Inc., Princeton, N.J., 1959).

[31] F. Din and A. H. Cockett, Low Temperature Techniques (Geo. Newnes Ltd., London, 1960).

[32] J. Strong, Procedures in Experimental Physics (Prentice-Hall, New York, 1938).

[33] American Welding Society Inc., Brazing Manual (Reinhold Publ. Corp., New York, 1963).

[34] H. H. Manko, Solders and Soldering (McGraw-Hill Book Co., New York, 1964).

[35] J. F. Lancaster, The Metallurgy of Welding, Brazing and Soldering (Elsevier Publ. Corp., New York, 1965).

[36] Victor J. Johnson (ed.), A Compendium of the Properties of Materials at Low Temperatures, Part II—Properties of Solids (Wright Patterson Air Force Base, Ohio, WADD Tech. Note 60-56, 1960).

[37] R. M. McClintock and H. P. Gibbons, Mechanical Properties of Structural Materials at Low Temperatures—A Compilation from the Literature, NBS Mono. 13 (1960).

[38] G. K. White, Experimental Techniques in Low Temperature Physics (Oxford Univ. Press, 1959).

[39] E. G. Brentari and R. V. Smith, Nucleate and film pool boiling design correlations for O_2, N_2, H_2, and He, Advances in Cryogenic Engineering (ed. K. D. Timmerhaus, Plenum Press, New York, 1965), Vol. **10B**, p. 325.

CHAPTER 7

Cryoelectronics

James W. Meyer [1] and Robert A. Kamper [2]

[1] MIT Lincoln Laboratory, Lexington, Mass. 02173 (operated with support from the U.S. Air Force).
[2] Cryogenics Division, NBS Institute for Basic Standards, Boulder, Colo. 80302.

7.1. INTRODUCTION

At present, cryoelectronics show great potential for the future and some solid achievement in the past. There is a promising future because of many cryolectronic devices of comparatively recent invention, and recently refrigeration has become sufficiently convenient to be practicable in many situations quite outside an elaborately equipped low-temperature laboratory. Convenient as it has become, however, refrigeration still has a nontrivial cost in money, maintenance, and power, so there has to be good reason to choose a device working at a low temperature rather than some other device performing the same function at ambient temperature. Such reasons do exist: the maser amplifier has won acceptance because of its exceptionally low noise level; the superconducting linear accelerator is being built in the hope that its electrical loss will be so small that it can run at a power level unattainable at ambient temperature; and superconducting computer memories are being developed to an advanced state in the hope that their sheer simplicity will make them so much cheaper to fabricate than their present day rivals that it will become worthwhile to use them when a sufficiently large memory is required. Some recent developments in this field promise an advantage in speed also.

In this chapter we will describe briefly some of the physical phenomena which seem to be particularly significant for electronics, and outline the principles of operation of some of the presently more important devices. We will also give some examples of successful applications. There are some devices, such as the tunnel diode and the field effect transistor, which are normally used at ambient temperature but still work perfectly well when cold. We have not discussed these unless, like the paramp, they have had extensive use at low temperatures or involve principles which are important for other purely cryoelectronic devices. We have to admit that our choice has been a little bit arbitrary.

We have grouped the cryoelectronic devices under three headings: Quantum Devices, which we take to mean devices involving transitions between the energy levels of paramagnetic impurities in crystals; Semiconductor Devices; and Superconductor Devices. This is not a profound way to categorize them (for example, many of the superconductor devices are distinctly quantum mechanical) but it serves to introduce some order into the chapter. In a final section we describe a few cryoelectronic devices which are presently in use in the field.

7.2. QUANTUM DEVICES

7.2.1. The Solid-State Maser

This is a low noise microwave amplifier which can significantly improve the sensitivity of a microwave receiver when it is used as a pre-amplifier. It has been used in radio and radar astronomy systems, in space communication ground terminals, in deep space instrumentation, in missile range tracking equipment, in ballistic missile defense radars, and in reentry physics research radars. In each case the improved system performance justified the inconvenience of low-temperature operation.

The physical phenomenon upon which the maser depends [1–5] [3] is the paramagnetism of unpaired electrons in the metallic ions of some salts and oxides. This is associated with the presence of closely spaced energy levels which can be split apart by the action of an applied magnetic field. A flux density of the order of 0.1 to 1 tesla (T) causes a splitting corresponding to a quantum of microwave energy in most paramagnetic materials. Such a field is conveniently available from either an iron-core electromagnet or a superconducting solenoid. The occupation of these energy levels is governed by Boltzmann statistics. At high temperatures, energy levels spaced as closely as these are very nearly equally occupied. It is only at temperatures in the liquid helium range that there are substantial differences in energy level occupation. Figure 7.1 depicts the relative population of three energy levels in thermal equilibrium at a temperature T. The lower the temperature, the greater is the preference for E_1 rather than E_2 and E_3. If we apply microwave power at a frequency f which satisfies the resonance condition $hf = E_3 - E_1$, we can induce transitions between these energy levels. As we increase the applied power we disturb the occupation of E_1 and E_3 until we reach a point where both levels are equally occupied and no further absorption of power can take place. We say that we have "saturated" the transition. Depending upon the details of the way the system relaxes toward equilibrium, it is possible in this way to achieve a situation in which the population of E_3 exceeds that of E_2. Now microwave energy at a frequency resonant with $E_3 - E_2$ will stimulate radiation of energy stored in the excess popu-

---

[3] Figures in brackets indicate the literature references at the end of this chapter.

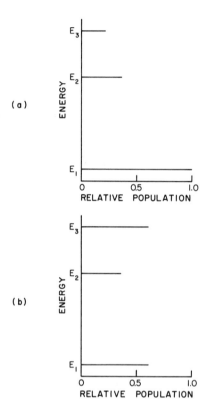

FIGURE 7.1. *Distribution of spins in a system of three energy levels.*

(a) In thermal equilibrium at a temperature $T = (E_2 - E_1)/k$.

(b) With the transition $E_3 - E_1$ saturated, assuming no relaxation into E_2.

lation of E_3. The available power clearly depends upon the difference in population of E_3 and E_2, since stimulated emission and absorption through the same transition are equally probable. If this available power exceeds the loss in the microwave hardware, we get coherent amplification of the stimulating wave. Spontaneous emission, which is incoherent and generates noise in the system, depends upon the occupation of E_3 and the frequency of the radiation.

From these elementary considerations we can draw several important conclusions. Clearly we improve the operation if we increase the equilibrium occupation of the lowest level E_1. We do this by going to lower temperatures. Increasing the separation of the energy levels would help too, but this requires that we raise the frequency of the saturating power into a range where high power sources become very expensive. We also observe that at a lower temperature the population of E_3 required to maintain a given excess over that of E_2 is smaller, so noise from spontaneous emission can be reduced. The power required to saturate a resonance is proportional to the relaxation rate, which also falls when the temperature is reduced.

The reduction of these simple principles to practice requires ingenuity on the part of the microwave engineer. We shall not go into the details of his problems here, except for some specific examples of hardware which has been used in practical applications. We point out, however, that refrigeration requirements for a maser are quite small, typically of the order of one watt at the low temperature including all heat leaks and the power dissipated by the maser itself.

The maser is one of the most sensitive amplifiers we can construct. We talk about the noise power developed by an amplifying system in terms of an effective noise temperature T_n. This means that the noise power from an amplifier with bandwidth B is equivalent to that from a noise source at the input terminals of power $P_n = kT_nB$. Contributions to this noise temperature come from the black and grey body absorbers and emitters in the system as well as the active device itself. Microwave plumbing, for example, which absorbs 10 percent of the microwave energy and is in equilibrium at a temperature of 300 K can contribute 30 K to the system noise temperature. This example shows the importance of reducing circuit losses or the temperature or both.

A carefully constructed waveguide termination which absorbs essentially all incident power and is maintained at a known low temperature can be used for an absolute standard noise source [6, 7] for measuring the performance of very low noise devices such as the maser. Some ingenuity is required to construct a radiometer to make full use of the available accuracy of this standard of very small power levels.

In the microwave region, Planck's radiation formula can be simplified, and the minimum achievable noise temperature as limited by spontaneous emission noise is [8] $T_n = hf/k$. Figure 7.2 shows the variation of this minimum noise temperature with frequency. Throughout the

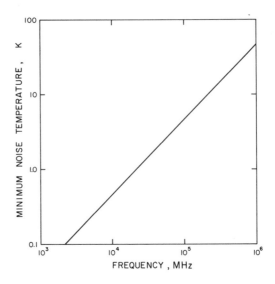

FIGURE 7.2. *Minimum theoretical noise temperature plotted against frequency.*

radio and microwave region of the spectrum it does not exceed a few degrees, but in the visible region it rises to some thousands of degrees.

A number of masers have been operated below the lambda point of liquid helium. Not only does this very low temperature help to improve the overall performance in terms of gain, bandwidth, and noise, but also the superfluid maintains a very stable temperature and eliminates potential problems resulting from bubbling or rapid boiling of liquid helium.

7.2.2. The Photon Counter

Bloembergen [4] and Weber [3] independently suggested a device which in principle can detect radiation with arbitrarily small noise. Although not yet realized in practice, there is no reason to suppose that it cannot be developed. In principle it is similar to the maser. Its action is to replace each incoming photon with another of higher energy which is therefore easier to detect. Consider the three-level system shown in

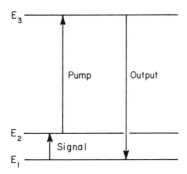

FIGURE 7.3. *Energy level system illustrating the action of the quantum counter.*

figure 7.3 in which the spacing between E_2 and the ground state E_1 is resonant with the incoming signal. The temperature must be low enough so that in equilibrium only E_1 is significantly occupied. A powerful microwave oscillator supplies "pump" power at a frequency resonant with $E_3 - E_2$, but since E_2 and E_3 are normally almost unoccupied it induces transitions at a negligible rate. When an incoming photon is absorbed by the system it induces a transition from E_1 to E_2. The pump is then able to induce a further transition up to E_3. Provided that a system has been chosen with favorable transition probabilities, most of these events will result in the system relaxing by spontaneous emission of a photon whose energy is equal to $E_3 - E_1$. Thus the net result of the whole process is the absorption of N photons of energy $E_2 - E_1$ followed by the emission of ηN photons of energy $E_3 - E_1$, where η is the quantum efficiency of the device.

One might therefore regard this device as an amplifier with power gain $\eta (E_3 - E_1)/(E_2 - E_1)$. However, it has the property that the phases of the output and input signals are independent. This raises an interesting question which has been discussed by Heffner [8], who pointed out that according to the quantum mechanical uncertainty principle the phase of a wave and the number of quanta associated with it can never be determined simultaneously with arbitrary precision. Thus the noise in an amplifier, which represents fluctuations in the number of quanta, is necessary in order to preserve information about the phase. This sets a lower limit to the attainable noise temperature of a phase sensitive amplifier. The photon counter we have been discussing avoids this limit by losing the phase of the signal completely.

7.3. SEMICONDUCTOR DEVICES

7.3.1. The Parametric Amplifier

The semiconductor diode parametric amplifier [9] has given the solid-state maser some of its stiffest competition for application to field problems. A major reason for this is that, unlike the maser, the parametric amplifier can operate over a temperature range from near absolute zero to ambient. The noise is of course worse at higher temperatures, but the fact that it will operate at all should the refrigeration fail is a great practical advantage.

Any amplifier requires a source of power that can be used to increase the signal power. The maser uses microwave power to store energy in the excited levels of a paramagnetic crystal, and the parametric amplifier is similar in that it too is driven by microwave power at a frequency higher than that of the signal. There are other similarities but attempts to describe both devices with a common fundamental theory have been unsuccessful.

In the parametric amplifier (or paramp) the power source is used to vary (pump) one of the circuit parameters of a combination of resonant circuits [10]. Such a variation of any component, such as a capacitor or inductor, which is capable of storing energy, can result in amplification of a signal of a suitable frequency.

To understand paramp action in its simplest form let us consider the resonant circuit shown in figure 7.4, in which the capacitor is variable. As the circuit resonates the capacitor is alternately charged and discharged through the inductor, twice per cycle with alternating polarities. The simplest way to decrease the capacitance is to increase the separation of the capacitor plates, and when they are charged this requires mechanical work against their electrostatic attraction, which increases the stored energy of the system. By separating the plates in those parts of the cycle when they are charged and restoring their original positions when the are discharged, it is possible to supply energy continuously to the system and sustain the oscillation of the circuit. The same principle is used by a child pumping a swing.

This simplest example, with the pump frequency double the signal frequency, is known as a degenerate paramp. A more complex arrangement could have a circuit resonant at the signal frequency f_s coupled to another circuit resonant at an idler frequency f_i by a coupling which varies at the pump frequency f_p. If $f_p = f_s + f_i$ this arrangement also sup-

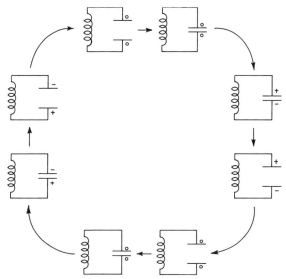

FIGURE 7.4. *The action of a degenerate parametric ampli-*
fier, pumped by moving the capacitor plates at twice the
resonant frequency of the circuit.

plies energy to the signal. It has the advantage that the presence of the
idler circuit removes the need for fixing the phase of the pump relative
to that of the signal. This is the arrangement normally used for microwave work. In order to achieve stable amplification, rather than oscillation, it is necessary to separate the input and output signals, which can
be accomplished by means of isolators and circulators. Another possibility is the so-called "up-converter" mode, in which the output is taken
at the idler frequency.

The variable reactance commonly used in paramps is the varactor
diode. A junction between p and n-type semiconductors normally contains a depletion region, with very few charge carriers, which increases
in width when a reverse bias voltage is applied. The material in this
region has a high resistivity and therefore acts as the dielectric in a
capacitor whose "plates" are the conducting p and n-type regions on
either side. The variation of capacitance of this arrangement with reverse bias voltage is used to drive the paramp.

There are two main sources of noise in the paramp. The first is the
varactor diode itself, whose leakage resistance generates Johnson noise.
The shot noise from the leakage current is usually negligible. Reducing
the temperature reduces the Johnson noise provided that the diode
resistance does not increase too much. The second source of noise is

the idler circuit, which receives noise generated elsewhere and also generates some of its own in lossy components. The amount of this noise coupled into the signal circuit depends upon the ratio of idler to signal frequencies. It can be reduced by making this ratio large and by cooling the idler circuit.

The ratio of idler to signal frequencies is limited by diode loss, which becomes more serious at higher frequencies. In practice there is therefore an optimum idler frequency.

In general cooling a semiconductor to a low temperature raises its resistivity by "freezing out" the carriers. However, the diodes used for varactors are usually so heavily doped that this problem does not arise, and they work quite well at low temperatures. Diodes made of GaAs and InSb have been used successfully in the liquid helium temperature range to make very low noise amplifiers.

There are other variations of the paramp principle and other possibilities for the active element besides the varactor diode. In particular, several up-converters have been made with the incoming signal at zero frequency, or direct current. They can be used as preamplifiers in extremely sensitive systems for measuring small steady voltages. One device of this type was developed by Hille, Reid, and Beer [11]. The active element consists of a pair of coils separated by a sheet of bismuth. At low temperatures the skin depth for alternating currents in the bismuth varies with an applied magnetic field because of magnetoresistance. The resulting variation in the mutual inductance of the coils is sufficient for efficient paramp action. Another way to modulate the mutual inductance of two sets of coils is to move them mechanically. This principle was used by Ries and Satterthwaite [12] to create a device with a sensitivity of 4×10^{-14} V with a time constant of 1 s. The coils were made of superconducting wire to reduce the input impedance. One set was mounted on an electrically driven tuning fork to provide the motion.

We will describe other parametric amplifiers in section 7.4.

7.3.2. Radiation Detectors

In general, perfectly adequate detectors for light of visible or shorter wavelengths can be made to operate at ambient temperature [13]. The fundamental reason for this is that the quanta of radiation are large compared to kT, when T is the ambient temperature, so it is relatively easy to find processes which can be driven by the radiation but not by available thermal energy. In the far infrared, however, the situation is different, and the best available detectors for this region of the spectrum all operate at a low temperature [13, 14].

In most infrared detectors, the radiation causes a change in the electrical resistance of the active element, which is detected by maintaining a steady current and observing the change in voltage. It is usual to chop the incident radiation with a rotating shutter, and detect variations of voltage at the chopping frequency, in order to discriminate against background radiation. Because of the low conversion efficiency of present-day transducers, this requires a very low-noise, low frequency preamplifier. The overall sensitivity of the complete detector could be improved either by a radical improvement in transducers, or by using a preamplifier with lower noise [15]. One of the future contributions of cryoelectronics may be directed to this problem.

There are several mechanisms by which absorption of infrared radiation can affect the resistivity of a semiconductor. The simplest is used in the bolometer, where the incident radiation raises the temperature of the semiconductor and affects the resistivity through its temperature dependence. This simple principle has been developed into a very sensitive instrument by Low [16]. Putley [17] has developed a refinement of the principle in which only the energy distribution (and hence temperature) of the conduction electrons is affected by the radiation. The temperature of the crystal lattice does not need to change, so the effective heat capacity of the device is very small. In photoconductive detectors [13, 18] the radiation excites current carriers out of bound states and thereby increases the conductivity of the semiconductor. For long wavelengths the bound states must be very close to the conduction band in energy, so a low temperature is necessary to avoid masking the photoconductive effect with thermal excitations. Arndt and Hartwig [19] have developed a variation of this detector in which the semiconductor is placed in a resonant microwave cavity. The carriers which are excited by the incident radiation affect the real part of the dielectric permittivity and hence the resonant frequency of the cavity. The resulting phase shift in microwave transmission or reflection by the cavity can be detected with a microwave bridge. The sensitivity of this system can be increased greatly using a superconducting microwave cavity.

We will mention some superconducting infrared detectors in section 7.4.

7.3.3. The Cryosar

This device was developed for use as a computer memory [20]. Its name is an acronym for low temperature switching by avalanche breakdown and recombination. In compensated crystals of germanium at temperatures below 10 K, impact ionization of the impurities gives rise to a negative resistance characteristic in the bulk material, which can be used to make a simple bistable device. It is switched by voltage pulses of appropriate size, applied through ohmic contacts.

Although this device promises to be fast, compact, and simple to fabricate, it has not yet been used in a practical computer.

7.4. SUPERCONDUCTOR DEVICES

7.4.1. Some Useful Properties of Superconductors

The most striking property of superconductors, for which they are named, is the absence of electrical resistance at all temperatures below the characteristic critical temperature, provided that they are not exposed to an excessive current or magnetic field. Small magnetic fields and currents do not permeate the bulk of a superconductor. They are confined to a surface region whose thickness, known as the penetration depth, is of the order of 1000 Å. This penetration depth is sensitive to magnetic fields and may be altered significantly in a thin film, which can retain its superconductivity in the presence of magnetic fields strong enough to drive a thick specimen of the same metal into the normal state. This results in a nonlinear response to electromagnetic radiation.

In addition to these properties of isolated superconductors, there are some fascinating phenomena which are observed when a weak link is formed between two superconductors. In practice this can be achieved quite simply by touching lightly together two pieces of superconducting metal which have been exposed to normal atmospheric corrosion. The properties of such a junction depend strongly on the contact pressure and are usually improved by shaping one of the superconductors to a fine point. Another technique is to form a thin uniform layer of oxide or other insulator on the smooth surface of a thin film of one superconductor and then to deposit a thin film of the second superconductor on top. There are various mechanisms for conduction of electric current across these structures, but the most striking effects are due to the quantum mechanical tunnel effect [21, 22], and other contributions to the current tend to have nuisance value only and must be suppressed as much as possible in a well-fabricated junction.

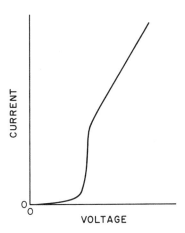

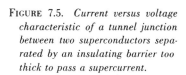

FIGURE 7.5. *Current versus voltage characteristic of a tunnel junction between two superconductors separated by an insulating barrier too thick to pass a supercurrent.*

VOLTAGE

If the insulating barrier in a tunnel junction between two identical superconductors is rather thick, the current versus voltage characteristic typically looks like the curve shown in figure 7.5. For small voltage, the current is very small and temperature dependent, tending to zero at zero temperature. As the voltage is increased, there is a well defined value of the order of a millivolt at which the current increases sharply, and thereafter the junction has an ohmic response. This characteristic curve is controlled mainly by the influence of the energy gap for excitations in superconductors, and may be modified by the presence of electromagnetic radiation [23] or ultrasound [24, 25] of sufficiently high frequency.

A very thin insulating barrier permits the two superconductors to influence each other enough to create various effects due to quantum mechanical phase coherence, first predicted by B. D. Josephson [26] and subsequently verified when the experimental difficulties were overcome. Briefly, these effects consist of the passage of electric current across the junction without dissipation: a direct current can flow at zero voltage; when the junction is biased to a finite voltage, the energy gained by each electron pair as the current flows is radiated away as a quantum of electromagnetic radiation, the frequency f being given by $hf = 2eV$ where h is Planck's constant, e is the electron charge, and V is the bias voltage. The d-c effect at zero bias may be distinguished from a simple metallic short in the junction by its extreme sensitivity to a magnetic field, which disturbs the phase coherence. The maximum current I_c which can flow at zero bias through a typical thin film junction, covering about 1 mm square, is plotted against the strength of a magnetic field,

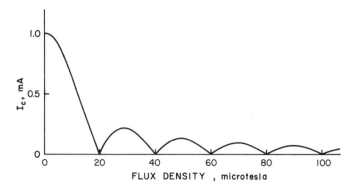

FIGURE 7.6.   *Maximum supercurrent* I_c *plotted against applied magnetic field for an ideal rectangular Josephson junction.*
The positions of the nodes depend upon the dimensions of the junction.

applied in the plane of the junction, in figure 7.6. The Josephson effect is clearly a rich source of potential devices.

7.4.2. Superconducting Switches

The earliest and, at the time of writing, most developed superconducting switch is the Cryotron [27]. In its present form [28] it consists of two thin overlapping superconducting films, on a suitable substrate, which are separated by an insulating layer too thick for leakage by electron tunneling. These two films are in the form of narrow strips and are known as the "gate" and the "control." The gate can be switched between the superconductive and resistive states by the magnetic field due to a current in the control strip, which is designed to remain always in the superconductive state. The gate could also be switched by its own current if it were large enough, and it is meaningful to talk of a current gain defined as the ratio of gate current to control current required to switch the gate into the resistive state. If this gain exceeds unity it is possible to devise many computer circuits [29], both for logic and for storage, in which the paths taken by electric current in a superconducting network are controlled by cryotrons.

Although cryotrons can be combined to form bistable circuits suitable for computer memories, more compact devices for this purpose have been devised. One of the most promising of these is the continuous film memory described by Burns [30]. This consists of a sheet of superconducting tin covered on one side by a square grid of insulated strips

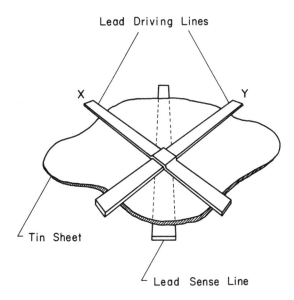

FIGURE 7.7. *Single cell of a continuous film computer memory.*

of lead. Each intersection of this grid forms one storage cell, and there is an insulated sense line on the other side of the sheet consisting of a strip of lead which passes over every cell on the sheet. A single cell of this arrangement is shown in figure 7.7. The memory is operated by pulses of current in the X and Y strips of the grid. The amplitude of these pulses must be adjusted so that only the combined current in both X and Y strips of a cell creates sufficient magnetic field to switch the cell by driving the nearby part of the tin sheet into the normal state and thereby trapping a loop of magnetic flux. Once this metastable loop of flux is established, a current pulse in either the X or the Y strip can drive the tin normal again, and induce a voltage pulse in the sense line, only if its direction is such that its magnetic field adds to the flux loop. A single pulse in the opposite direction does not communicate with the sense line.

Units with 16,384 cells together with cryotrons to drive the switching currents have been made on a single sheet in a very compact arrangement [30]. Burns argues that the chief advantage of this type of memory is that the price per bit of storage falls rapidly as the size of the memory increases. He estimates that a memory of about 13 million bits arranged on 50 sheets would cost about one cent per bit, a very

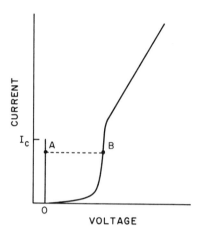

FIGURE 7.8. *Current versus voltage characteristic of a Josephson junction between superconducting thin films.* The operating points of interest for the tunneling cryotron are marked A and B.

competitive price. The speed of these memories would be limited by the cryotron circuits that drive them.

The speed of a cryotron circuit is limited by the resistance and inductance of the gate in the normal state and by the time required for the superconducting to normal state transition. Matisoo [31] has reported a new type of cryotron which promises to be much faster than the device we described earlier in this section. The improved performance is obtained by replacing the gate film with a Josephson junction. The control strip is retained. The current versus voltage characteristic of the gate with zero control current is shown in figure 7.8. A gate current less than I_c (see fig. 7.8) would normally be passed with zero voltage at an operating point such as A. The effect of a control current of the right sense is to reduce I_c, switching the cryotron into the finite voltage operating point B. If there is a second cryotron connected in parallel the current would then be transferred to it in a time which can be as small as a few hundred picoseconds. After the transfer of current the first cryotron would be free to switch back into the zero voltage mode, but if all the connections are superconducting the current would remain in its new path until it is disturbed again by the introduction of resistance into the circuit. Thus the combination of two such cryotrons forms a bistable device with a very fast switching time.

One disadvantage of this device is that Josephson junctions are difficult to fabricate with a high success rate. However, a development effort equivalent to a small fraction of that which transistors received should solve this problem.

7.4.3. Superconducting Amplifiers

Because of their nonlinear response to currents and magnetic fields, superconductors lend themselves very readily to parametric amplification. Clorfeine [32] and Bura [33] have both reported parametric microwave amplifiers in which the mixing of signal and pump frequencies is achieved by nonlinear transmission through superconducting thin films. Point contact Josephson junctions have also been used for microwave mixing [34].

One striking achievement was reported by Zimmerman and Silver [35], who used a point contact Josephson junction as the active element in a parametric up-converter. The input signal was the oscillation of the junction itself under the influence of a very small bias voltage. They were able to convert a detectable signal up to 30 MHz, with an input at 1 Hz. The amplitude of the input could not exceed the bias voltage of 2×10^{-15} V, which could be measured by measuring the frequency of oscillation. Such a sensitivity can only be achieved in a superconducting circuit.

Another superconducting device which can function as the active element in a parametric amplifier is the Ryotron [36, 37]. This device is superficially similar to the cryotron, in that it consists of a pair of superconducting strips, the "gate" and the "control," in close proximity. However, the function of these strips is different. The gate always remains in the superconducting state during normal operation, and its important property is its self inductance, which is influenced by the tendency of the control strip to screen the magnetic field due to the gate current. The device operates when a large current is passed through the control strip, driving it into the normal state and allowing magnetic flux to penetrate it. By careful attention to geometry it is possible to cause the inductance of the gate to change by over two orders of magnitude when the control switches into the normal state. This switching can be accomplished in a time of the order of a nanosecond, giving a broad bandwidth for parametric applications. It is also possible to use the ryotron to steer currents in a superconducting network just like a cryotron, and it has the same potential for logic circuits.

In contrast to these parametric amplifiers, Newhouse and Edwards [38] have developed a broadband, linear amplifier based on the cryotron. The switching of the gate of a cryotron from the superconducting to the resistive state does not happen instantaneously, but occupies a finite range of control current. If the cryotron is biased into the center of this range, and kept there by a feedback circuit incorporating a low-pass filter, then the gate resistance is a very sensitive function of the control current for frequencies above the cutoff of the filter. The gain of the cryotron used in this mode is of course much greater than the "current gain" commonly used to describe the switching mode.

These amplifiers usually have a low input impedance and excellent noise characteristics. Newhouse and Edwards [38] report a minimum detectable signal of 1.3×10^{-18} V for an amplifier operating at 100 Hz with a bandwidth of 10 Hz. The source resistance was less than 3×10^{-9} Ω and the operating temperature was 3.6 K.

7.4.4. Superconducting D-C Instruments

We have already mentioned two excellent instruments for measuring very small, steady voltages: namely, Ries and Satterthwaite's parametric amplifier [12] with vibrating coils (sec. 7.3.1) and Zimmerman and Silver's detector [35] using parametric up-conversion of oscillations due to the Josephson effect (sec. 7.4.3). The performance of these instruments is unsurpassed at the time of writing.

An interesting low-level null detector has been developed by Clarke [39]. In essence, the input circuit is a short piece of superconducting niobium wire, with negligible resistance and a small inductance. Any current which flows in this wire is sensed by the effect its accompanying magnetic field has on the critical current of a Josephson-like junction between the wire and another superconductor. Clarke formed these junctions by freezing a blob of lead-tin solder onto the niobium wire. The solder does not wet the niobium but instead forms an electrical connection which behaves like a multiple point-contact Josephson junction. It is possible to form junctions of this type whose critical current, or resistance for currents slightly over critical, is a well defined periodic function of the current in the niobium wire. If a voltage is applied to the niobium wire a current builds up linearly with time until it becomes large enough to have a detectable effect on the junction. Allowing a time of one second, Clarke found he could detect 10^{-14} V.

In addition to these very sensitive low-level instruments, the Josephson effect may make a significant contribution to precise measurements of fundamental quantities. Parker, Taylor, and Langenberg [40] have measured the relationship between frequency and voltage, $hf = 2 eV$, to an accuracy of a few parts per million, deriving a new value for the constant $2e/h$ from their results. Assuming that there is no unknown electrodynamic correction to be applied to this quantity, they used it to calculate a new value for the fine structure constant, $\alpha = e^2/\hbar c$, which resolved a long-standing discrepancy between the theoretical and experimental values for the hyperfine splitting of the ground state of the hydrogen atom.

Their experience with this measurement suggested to them that the Josephson effect might be used with advantage to maintain a standard volt by frequency to voltage conversion [41]. Among the advantages they listed were the simplicity of the equipment, the lack of stringent requirements on the preparation of the junction and experimental conditions, and the ready availability of very accurately known frequencies.

A companion to this idea was Meservey's [42] suggestion that the quantum of magnetic flux, $h/2e$, should be used as a fundamental electromagnetic unit. The volt could then be derived from it by reversing the emphasis of Parker, Taylor, and Langenberg's measurement [40], and the ampere could be derived from it by a direct measurement of the flux density generated by a precisely made solenoid. This would be accomplished by using the Josephson effect to count the flux quanta linking a superconducting circuit of known area.

7.4.5. Superconducting Radiation Detectors

As we mentioned in the introduction to this chapter, it is only necessary to use a cold detector for radiation of long wavelength. Both the detectors we describe in this section were designed for the far infrared.

The older of the pair is the superconducting bolometer, which was developed into a working instrument by Martin and Bloor [43]. It consists of a thin superconducting film, on a very light substrate, connected to the helium bath through a thermal resistance. The transition from the superconductive to the normal resistive state occupies a finite range of temperature, and in this range the resistance of the film is a very sensitive function of temperature. Martin and Bloor found that the minimum incident power detectable by its heating effect on this structure was 10^{-12} W (noise equivalent power), with a time constant of 1.25 s. In order to achieve its sensitivity this detector suffers from the rather slow response time of 15 ms, which can be a disadvantage for some applications.

Grimes, Richards, and Shapiro [44] showed that this situation can be improved, as always, by making use of the Josephson effect. The junctions they used were point contacts with current versus voltage characteristics as shown in figure 7.9. (Note the difference from the thin film junctions illustrated in fig. 7.8.) They found that the maximum current at zero voltage, as well as the nearby part of the curve, were

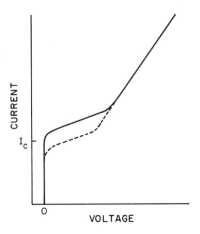

FIGURE 7.9.   *Current versus voltage char-*
acteristic of a point contact Josephson
junction (solid curve).
Long wavelength radiation causes the characteristic
to follow the dotted curve.

sensitive to irradiation with far infrared, which would cause the curve
to shift as shown in figure 7.9. By biasing the junction to a suitable operating point, they were able to detect 5×10^{-13} W (noise equivalent
power) with a time constant of one second. The response time was less
than 10 ns and the detector was sensitive to radiation of any wavelength
shorter than 300 μm (corresponding to a quantum of about twice the
energy gap of the superconductor they used). The difficulty of concentrating a reasonably large portion of the incident radiation onto the very
small junction was overcome with a metal light pipe.

7.4.6. Passive Superconducting Circuit Elements

The obvious benefit of superconductivity to passive circuit elements
is to reduce loss and hence reduce power consumption and permit tuned
circuits of narrower bandwidth. In this connection we should remark
that superconductors show zero resistance only for direct current. Alternating currents suffer loss through hysteresis effects and, at higher
frequencies, through the presence of thermally excited carriers which
behave as if they were in the normal state. This latter mechanism becomes stronger as the frequency is increased, but still allows superconductors to show superior performance to normal metals for wavelengths through the millimeter region.

The most ambitious use of superconducting passive circuits to date is in the linear accelerator, described in chapter 8. Its performance will be improved by several orders of magnitude as a direct result of using superconducting microwave cavities.

There has been some work on superconducting radiofrequency filters. A filter based on circuits with a Q of 500,000 at 27 MHz has been reported [45]. It was made of superconducting Nb_3Sn and had a working temperature of 15 K.

Superconducting pulse delay lines seem to be very promising. The reduction in loss in the line yields a wider bandwidth and hence less distortion of sharp pulses [46]. Quite a crudely made coaxial line, with a niobium inner conductor, teflon dielectric and lead outer conductor, operating at 4 K, was found to permit a pulse rise time of 500 ps in a length sufficient to give a delay of 2 μs.

Large coils carrying heavy currents store a great deal of energy inductively. This is a source of embarrassment to the designers of stable superconducting magnets, but it is the cheapest way to store energy in megajoule quantities for release in short pulses. If the cycle time is short it is unnecessary to use a superconducting coil, and there may be some advantage in using a coil of normal metal, cooled to reduce its resistivity somewhat [47].

Another property which superconductors have is that in the form of thin filaments they can pass large currents with very few carriers. Little [48] has shown that when they do so the energy stored as kinetic energy of the electrons contributes a significant amount to the self-inductance of the circuit. This offers a solution to a problem which has troubled the designers of miniature integrated circuits: that of making inductors of very small physical size.

7.4.7. Superconducting Magnetometers and Gravimeters

The superconducting magnetometers which have been proposed or built fall into two classes. Either they depend upon sensing the persistent current induced in a superconducting loop or they depend upon counting flux quanta in a quantum interference device. Both kinds really measure changes in field and need precautions to set the zero for absolute measurements.

Since a superconducting loop has zero resistance, it follows from Lenz's law that if it is placed in a magnetic field a persistent electric current must flow so as to keep the magnetic flux linking the loop constant. Regardless of the geometry of the loop, this current is linearly related to the change of field, provided the superconductor remains always in the superconducting state. Several schemes have been used to detect this persistent current nondestructively. If the self inductance L of part of the circuit carrying a current I is modulated an emf equal to d/dt (LI) appears, which can be coupled out of the circuit by means of a transformer. The modulation can be accomplished by moving a superconducting ground plane mounted on a vibrating quartz crystal close to the loop [49], or by driving a superconducting core in a small coil repeatedly through its transition temperature [49, 50]. Some advantage can be gained by tuning the circuit to resonate at the modulation frequency. With a wire loop of radius 1 cm a calculated sensitivity [49] of 10^{-14} T should be achievable with a bandwidth of 1 Hz. Another sensitive detector of the induced persistent current, which does not require modulation, is the Clarke [39] null-detector which we mentioned in section 7.4.4. By using a two-stage detector it might be possible to achieve even greater sensitivity than is feasible by the modulation technique.

The classic flux-quantum counter [51] depends upon the fact that the Josephson current which crosses an insulating barrier is proportional to sin φ, where φ is the local difference in quantum mechanical phase across the barrier. If two such barriers are connected together in a superconducting ring, as shown in figure 7.10, then the total quantum mechanical phase difference integrated round the ring is equal to the number of flux quanta $(h/2e)$ enclosed multiplied by 2π. Most of this phase difference appears across the barriers, so it follows that if they are identical and if the ring encloses an integral number of flux quanta the Josephson currents through the two barriers must be equal and opposite. For a half-integral number of flux quanta the two currents will flow in the same sense. Thus the maximum current that the two-branch structure shown in figure 7.10 can pass with zero voltage is a periodic function of the magnetic flux linking the ring, the period being one flux quantum.

Recently Mercereau [52] has shown that it is possible to count flux quanta entering a weak superconducting ring without constructing such an elaborate device as the double junction ring we have described. The achievable sensitivity appears to be comparable to that of the other superconducting magnetometers we have described.

Closely related to these magnetometers is Prothero and Goodkind's superconducting gravimeter [53]. This is a device for detecting changes in the acceleration g due to gravity over a long period of time. It consists of a superconducting ball which is levitated by a magnetic field.

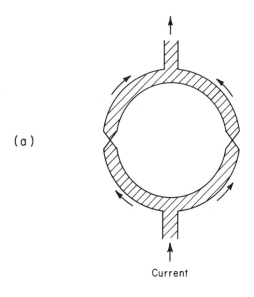

(a)

Current

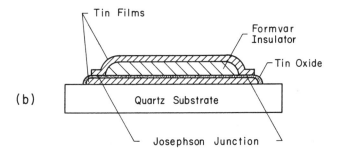

(b)

FIGURE 7.10.   *Quantum interferometers for counting quanta of magnetic flux.*

(a) Ideal, with point contacts

(b) Practical version with thin film junctions described in ref. [51].

The field gradient required to keep the ball in position is proportional to *g* and is maintained by a sensitive servo loop. The position of the ball is sensed both by measuring the capacitance between it and some fixed plates and by using a sensitive magnetometer to detect the distortion of magnetic field it causes. The advantage they hope to obtain over the more usual spring balance is in long-term stability. In principle, this device is perfectly stable and it is designed for a sensitivity of 10^{-12} *g*.

7.5. WORKING DEVICES

In this section we describe a few examples of cryogenic devices which have been used in the field because their performance warranted the inconvenience of keeping them cold. This inconvenience will hopefully be reduced by the development of compact, reliable refrigerators to handle the rather modest heat loads from these devices.

7.5.1. Working Masers and Paramps

An early application of the solid-state maser followed Bloembergen's suggestion [1] that it would be useful in radio telescopes. The residual background temperature of the universe appears to be only about 3 K when measured by microwave radiometry, a discovery which owes an obvious debt to cryoelectronics [54, 55]. Although the background temperature seen by most radio telescopes exceeds this, it is low enough so that faint sources may be picked out by a sensitive instrument without being swamped.

A UHF solid-state maser [56] was used with the Millstone radar at the Lincoln Laboratory in an attempt to make a radar observation of the planet Venus. Operating at a temperature of 1.6 K, it gave a gain of 10 dB with a bandwidth of 100 kHz.

A self-contained package including a ruby maser with a closed cycle refrigerator has been developed at the Jet Propulsion Laboratory [57]. It gives a gain of 37 dB with a bandwidth of 18 MHz centered on 2295 MHz. The operating temperature is 4.5 K and the noise temperature is 15 K. The whole package weighs 200 kg.

Masers were used in the Telstar satellite communication experiments [58]. They gave gains near 30 dB at 4170 MHz with a bandwidth of 25 MHz. The noise temperature was 3.5 K at an operating temperature of 4.2 K, indicating very efficient design.

An experimental transportable ground terminal for space communications at the Lincoln Laboratory incorporates a parametric preamplifier [59] with two channels, in the band between 7.7 and 8.4 GHz. Each channel consists of a two-stage paramp using gallium arsenide varactor diodes. It has an overall noise temperature of 55 K.

Helium-cooled masers and paramps have even been used in missile tracking and defense radars, for which reliability is at a premium.

7.5.2. Working Radiation Detectors

Many of the infrared detectors we described earlier in this chapter have seen considerable service in spectroscopy, and some of them are available as commercial instruments.

The superconducting bolometer [43], for example, is the workhorse of a productive group of infrared spectroscopists at Queen Mary College in London [60]. Low's germanium bolometer [16] is available as an optional detector with several commercial spectrometers. The performance and commercial availability of many photoconductive detectors have been summarized by Putley [61].

Infrared detectors are also used occasionally in astronomy. Westphal, et al. [62], have used a crystal of germanium doped with mercury for this purpose. It was cooled to 20 K with liquid hydrogen and used in the wavelength range from 8 to 14 μm. The reason for this choice was to take advantage of a "window" in the atmospheric absorption spectrum in order to make observations on the planets which would help to reveal the compositions of their atmospheres.

7.5.3. Conclusion

In looking over the list of ingenious devices we have mentioned in this chapter, it seems that rather a small proportion have won present-day acceptance in pragmatic engineering. Many of the others offer remarkable performance which we do not know how to use yet. No doubt the all-round advance in technology will one day create problems requiring these elegant solutions.

REFERENCES

[1] N. Bloembergen, Proposal for a new type solid state maser, Phys. Rev. **104**, 324 (1956).

[2] J. R. Singer, Masers (John Wiley & Sons, Inc., New York, 1959).

[3] J. Weber, Masers, Rev. Modern Phys. **31**, 681 (1959).

[4] N. Bloembergen, Solid state masers, Progress in Low Temperature Physics (ed. C. J. Gorter, North Holland Publ. Co., Amsterdam, 1961), Vol. **III**, p. 396.

[5] A. E. Siegman, Microwave Solid-State Masers, (McGraw-Hill Book Co., Inc., New York, N.Y., 1964).

[6] C. T. Stelzried, Temperature calibration of microwave thermal noise sources, IEEE Trans. **MTT-13**, 128 (1965).

[7] C. Trembath, D. F. Wait, G. Engen, and W. Foote, The NBS Helium-Cooled Microwave Noise Standard, to be published.

[8] H. Heffner, The physical aspects of low noise electronics, Low Noise Electronics (ed. K. Endresen, Pergamon Press, Ltd., London, 1962), p. 3.

[9] W. W. Mumford, Some notes on the history of parametric transducers, Proc. IRE **48**, 848 (1960).

[10] W. H. Louisell, Coupled Mode and Parametric Electronics (John Wiley & Sons, Inc., New York, N.Y., 1960).

[11] P. F. Hille, F. J. Reid, and A. C. Beer, Amplification by magnetic control of skin depth, Solid State Electronics **9**, 453 (1966).

[12] R. P. Ries and C. B. Satterthwaite, A superconducting parametric amplifier for the measurement of small DC voltages, Rev. Sci. Instr. **38**, 1203 (1967).

[13] R. A. Smith, Detectors for ultraviolet, visible, and infrared radiation, Appl. Opt. **4**, 631 (1965).

[14] P. Bratt, W. Engeler, H. Levinstein, A. MacRae, and J. Pehek, A status report on infrared detectors, Infrared Phys. **1**, 27 (1961).

[15] E. H. Putley, The ultimate sensitivity of sub-mm detectors, Infrared Phys. **4**, 1 (1964).

[16] F. J. Low, Low-temperature germanium bolometer, J. Opt. Soc. Am. **51**, 1300 (1961).

[17] E. H. Putley, Indium antimonide submillimeter photoconductive detectors, Appl. Opt. **4**, 649 (1965).

[18] H. Levinstein, Extrinsic detectors, Appl. Opt. **4**, 639 (1965).

[19] G. D. Arndt, W. H. Hartwig and J. L. Stone, Photodielectric detector using a superconducting cavity, J. Appl. Phys. **39**, 2653 (1968).

[20] A. L. McWhorter and R. H. Rediker, The cryosar—A new low-temperature computer component, Proc. IRE **47**, 1207 (1959).

[21] I. Giaever, Energy gap in superconductors measured by electron tunneling, Phys. Rev. Letters **5**, 147 (1960).

[22] B. D. Josephson, Supercurrents through barriers, Advances in Physics **14**, 419 (1965).

[23] A. H. Dayem and R. J. Martin, Quantum interaction of microwave radiation with tunneling between superconductors, Phys. Rev. Letters **8**, 246 (1962).

[24] Y. Goldstein, B. Abeles, and R. W. Cohen, Tunneling induced by longitudinal microwave phonons in Al-Pb, Al-Sn, and Pb-Pb superconducting diodes, Phys. Rev. **151**, 349 (1966).

[25] W. Eisenmenger and A. H. Dayem, Quantum generation and detection of incoherent phonons in superconductors, Phys. Rev. Letters **18**, 125 (1967).

[26] B. D. Josephson, Possible new effects in superconductive tunneling, Physics Letters **1**, 251 (1962).

[27] D. A. Buck, The cryotron – a superconductive computer component, Proc. IRE **44**, 482 (1956).

[28] J. M. Lock, Superconductive switching, Reports on Progress in Physics **25**, 37 (1962).

[29] J. D. Barnard, F. A. Behnke, A. B. Lindquist, and R. R. Seeber, Structure of a cryogenic associative processor, Proc. IEEE **52**, 1182 (1964).

[30] L. L. Burns, Cryoelectric memories, Proc. IEEE **52**, 1164 (1964). See also: J.D. Barnard, R. H. Blumberg, and H. L. Caswell, Operation of the cryogenic continuous film memory cell, Proc. IEEE **52**, 1177 (1964).

[31] J. Matisoo, The tunneling cryotron – a superconductive logic element based on electron tunneling, Proc. IEEE **55**, 172 (1967).

[32] A. S. Clorfeine, Microwave amplification with superconductors, Proc. IEEE **52**, 844 (1964). See also; A. S. Clorfeine, Nonlinear reactance and frequency conversion in superconducting films at millimeter wavelengths, Appl. Phys. Letters **4**, 131 (1964).

[33] P. Bura, Parametric amplification with superconducting films, Proc. IEEE **54**, 687 (1966).

[34] G. K. Gaule, R. L. Ross, and K. Schwidtal, Microwave mixing with weakly coupled superconductors, Symp. Physics of Superconducting Devices, Charlottesville, Va. (1967). Available as an ONR report.

[35] J. E. Zimmerman and A. H. Silver, High sensitivity superconducting detector, Appl. Superconductivity Conf., Austin, Tex. (1967). To be published. See also: A. H. Silver, J. E. Zimmerman, and R. A. Kamper, Contribution of thermal noise to the line-width of Josephson radiation from superconducting point contacts, Appl. Phys. Letters **11**, 209 (1967).

[36] R. A. Gange, The cryotron – a new cryogenic device, Proc. IEEE **52**, 1216 (1964).

[37] J. C. Miller, C. M. Wine, and L. S. Cosentino, The ryotron – a variable inductance cryogenic device, Proc. IEEE **52**, 1223 (1964).

[38] V. L. Newhouse and H. H. Edwards, An ultrasensitive linear cryotron amplifier, Proc. IEEE **52**, 1191 (1964).

[39] J. Clarke, A superconducting galvanometer employing Josephson tunneling, Phil. Mag. **13**, 115 (1966). See also: J. Clarke, The measurement of small voltages using a quantum interference device, Symp. Physics of Superconducting Devices, Charlottesville, Va. (1967). Available as an ONR report.

[40] W. H. Parker, B. N. Taylor, and D. N. Langenberg, Measurement of $2e/h$ using the AC Josephson effect and its implications for quantum electrodynamics, Phys. Rev. Letters **18**, 287 (1967).

[41] B. N. Taylor, W. H. Parker, D. N. Langenberg, and A. Denenstein, On the use of the AC Josephson effect to maintain standards of electromotive force, Metrologia **3**, 89 (1967).

[42] R. Meservey, Proposed absolute ammeter using flux quantization, J. Appl. Phys. **39**, 2598 (1968).

[43] D. H. Martin and D. Bloor, The application of superconductivity to the detection of radiant energy, Cryogenics **1**, 159 (1961).

[44] C. C. Grimes, P. L. Richards, and S. Shapiro, Far infrared response of point-contact Josephson junctions, Phys. Rev. Letters **17**, 431 (1966). See also: S. Shapiro, Josephson effect far infrared detector, Symp. Physics of Superconducting Devices, Charlottesville, Va. (1967). Available as an ONR report.

[45] K. Siegel, R. Domchick, and F. R. Arams, High circuit Q's with niobium stannide at radio frequencies, Symp. Physics of Superconducting Devices, Charlottesville, Va. (1967). Available as an ONR report.

[46] R. J. Allen and N. S. Nahman, Analysis and performance of superconductive coaxial transmission lines, Proc. IEEE **52,** 1147 (1964).

[47] V. Arp, Cryogenic coil for megajoule energy storage, Proc. Intern. Symp. Magnet Technology, Stanford, Calif. (1965).

[48] W. A. Little, Device application of super-inductors, Symp. Physics of Superconducting Devices, Charlottesville, Va. (1967). Available as an ONR report.

[49] J. M. Pierce, A persistent current magnetometer with novel applications, Symp. Physics of Superconducting Devices, Charlottesville, Va. (1967). Available as an ONR report.

[50] B. S. Deaver and W. S. Goree, Some techniques for sensitive magnetic measurements using superconducting circuits and magnetic shields, Rev. Sci. Instr. **38,** 311 (1967).

[51] R. C. Jaklevic, J. Lambe, J. E. Mercereau, and A. H. Silver, Macroscopic quantum interference in superconductors, Phys. Rev. **140,** A1628 (1965).

[52] J. E. Mercereau, Modulated flux flow in superconducting films, Symp. Physics of Superconducting Devices, Charlottesville, Va. (1967). Available as an ONR report.

[53] W. M. Prothero, Jr., and J. M. Goodkind, A superconducting gravimeter, Symp. Physics of Superconducting Devices, Charlottesville, Va. (1967). Available as an ONR report.

[54] R. A. Stokes, R. B. Partridge, and D. T. Wilkinson, New measurements of the cosmic microwave background at $\lambda = 3.2$ cm and $\lambda = 1.58$ cm — Evidence in support of a black body spectrum, Phys. Rev. Letters **19,** 1199 (1967). This paper contains references to the earlier work.

[55] R. H. Dicke, Gravitation and the universe, Science J. **2,** 95 (Oct. 1966).

[56] R. H. Kingston, A UHF solid state maser, Proc. IRE **46,** 916 (1958).

[57] R. C. Clauss, W. Higa, C. Stelzried, and E. Wiebe, Total system noise temperature: 15 K, IEEE Trans. **MTT-12,** 619 (1964).

[58] W. J. Tabor and J. T. Sibilia, Masers for the Telstar Satellite communications experiment, Bell Syst. Tech. J. **42,** 1863 (1963).

[59] L. W. Bowles, Parametric amplifiers in the Lincoln experimental terminal, Nerem Record **7,** 212 (1965) (Published by E. E. Witschi, Jr., Newton, Mass.) See also: C. Blake, L. W. Bowles and E. P. McCurley, Helium-cooled parametric amplifier, Appl. Phys. Letters **2,** 17 (1963).

[60] D. Bloor, J. J. Dean, G. O. Jones, D. H. Martin, P. A. Mawer, and C. H. Perry, Spectroscopy at extreme infrared wavelengths, Proc. Roy. Soc. **A260,** 510 (1961).

[61] E. H. Putley, Solid state devices for infrared detection, J. Sci. Instr. **43,** 857 (1966).

[62] J. A. Westphal, B. C. Murray and D. E. Martz, An 8–14 micron infrared astronomical photometer, Appl. Opt. **2,** 749 (1963).

CHAPTER 8

Applications

Robert A. Kamper, R. H. Kropschot, and A. F. Schmidt [1]

[1] Cryogenics Division, NBS Institute for Basic Standards, Boulder, Colo. 80302.

Low-temperature research utilizing liquid helium has revealed many unique properties of matter which are currently being exploited for technological applications. These applications have stimulated much of the work discussed in the earlier chapters. Thus it appears appropriate to present a brief description of some of these uses and to indicate how the field may develop in the future. The reader is requested to bear in mind that the material presented here is not meant to provide a comprehensive treatment of the subject and therefore selected references are provided as a guide for further study. The intention is to illustrate the use of liquid or cooled gaseous helium for specific applications.

The chapter is divided into six major subdivisions where the individual applications are discussed. Perhaps the most exciting and far-reaching low-temperature development is in the area of high-field superconducting magnets. These and non-superconducting cryogenic magnets are described in the first section. The second section describes how superconducting resonance cavities can be utilized to construct high-energy linear particle accelerators. The third section describes the use of liquid helium in bubble chambers as a detection device for high-energy physics investigations. The fourth section explains the use of helium cooled surfaces for the production of high and ultra high vacuum by cryopumping. The last two sections deal with non-condensable gas injection and some other applications in missile and space systems.

8.1. MAGNETS

8.1.1. Introduction

The reason for operating an electromagnet at a low temperature is to avoid the cost and inconvenience of supplying and dissipating a large quantity of power. This can be achieved by making the windings of either a superconductor or a very pure metal whose resistivity falls to a very small, but nonzero, value at low temperatures. Both alternatives have been used successfully to achieve flux densities over 10 tesla (100 kilogauss) [1, 2].[2] They offer great promise for applications such as magnetohydrodynamic generators, plasma containers, satellite radiation shields, particle accelerators, and research tools, where the cost, power consumption or weight of the power supply for a conventional magnet, working at or above ambient temperature, would be unacceptable. We will discuss these two alternatives separately, concentrating mainly on the limitations set by the properties of materials.

8.1.2. Superconductors

Superconductors may be classified into several types according to their behavior in a magnetic field. In general, persistent currents flow which partly screen a steady applied field from the interior of a thick superconducting body. Figure 8.1 shows how the resulting magnetic moment, M, per unit volume of a specimen with zero demagnetizing coefficient varies with the applied field H for the different types.

Figures 8.1(a) and 8.1(b) represent two ideal types to which very carefully prepared specimens of real metals may approximate. They differ in that the surface energy at a phase boundary, between superconducting and normal regions of the same metal, is positive in (a) and negative in (b). Abrikosov [3] has called them ideal superconductors of type I and type II respectively. He has shown that the main features of their behavior are described very well by a phenomenological theory of superconductivity due to Ginzburg and Landau [4]. According to this theory the difference between type I and type II behavior depends upon the value of a dimensionless parameter κ which is equal to the ratio of two lengths, λ/ξ, where λ is the depth of penetration of a weak magnetic field into the surface of the superconductor and ξ is the characteristic distance within which the wave functions of the electrons change, from

---

[2] Figures in brackets refer to the literature references at the end of this chapter.

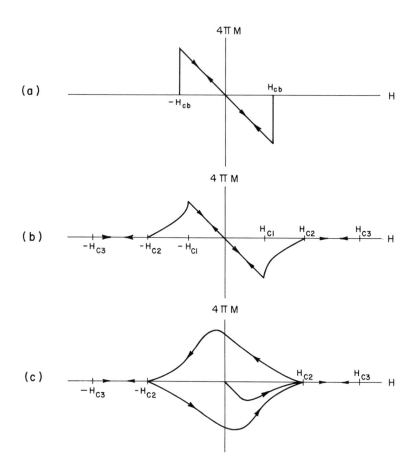

FIGURE 8.1. *Curves of volume magnetization* M *versus field* H, *illustrating the difference between the types of superconductors:* (a) *ideal type I,* (b) *ideal type II, and* (c) *hard.*

the superconducting to the normal state, at a phase boundary. A type I superconductor has $\kappa < 1/\sqrt{2}$ while a type II has $\kappa > 1/\sqrt{2}$.

In ideal type I superconductors the screening currents are confined to a surface layer of depth λ (typically 10^{-5} to 10^{-6} cm) and totally exclude the field from the interior. When the applied field exceeds the critical field H_{cb} the whole superconductor makes an abrupt transition to the normal state. Good specimens of most pure superconducting elements (e.g., tin, indium, lead, etc.) fall into this class.

The maximum current that can be carried without resistance by a type I superconducting wire is just that current which brings the total field at any point on the surface of the wire up to the critical value H_{cb} (Silsbee rule). This critical current decreases in an applied field and falls to zero at $\frac{1}{2}H_{cb}$ (the factor of $\frac{1}{2}$ is the demagnetizing factor) for a circular wire in a transverse field. Since H_{cb} is typically a few hundreths of a tesla, this sets a severe limit to the usefulness of this type of superconductor. There has, however, been a proposal to use type I superconductors for power transmission [5], the equipment being designed so as to limit the maximum field to less than H_{cb}.

The above remarks refer to thick specimens. If one dimension of a superconductor, perpendicular to the field direction, is of the order of the penetration depth λ or less, the critical field is increased. For example, the Ginzberg-Landau theory predicts that a film of thickness $2d(d \ll \lambda)$ with a small value of κ would have a critical tangential field H_c where

$$H_c = \sqrt{6} \ (\lambda/d)H_{cb}. \tag{8.1}$$

The Silsbee rule for critical current no longer applies. Instead, the critical current density J_c tends to the value

$$J_c = \frac{4 \times 10^{-8}}{3 \sqrt{6}} \cdot \frac{H_{cb}}{\lambda} \left[1 - \left(\frac{H}{H_c} \right)^2 \right]^{3/2} \text{ MKS units} \tag{8.2}$$

in the limit of small d. This is typically of the order of 10^8 A/m^2 when $H \ll H_c$. There have been proposals [6] to make superconducting magnets with thin film windings. A successful thin film magnet would require very careful attention to geometry, because the critical perpendicular field [7] is just $\sqrt{2} \ \kappa \ H_{cb}$, which is less than H_{cb} for a type I superconductor.

Type II superconductors behave like type I in small magnetic fields. When the applied field exceeds a lower critical field $H_{c1}(< H_{cb})$, however, they assume a mixed state in which the metal behaves as if it were finely divided into superconducting and normal phases, allowing partial penetration of the magnetic field into the interior. This mixed state persists up to a second critical field $H_{c2} = \sqrt{2}\kappa H_{cb}$ at which the interior of a thick specimen is essentially in the normal state, but superconductivity persists as a sheath on surfaces parallel to the field [8] up to an upper critical field $H_{c3} = 1.69\,H_{c2}$. Good specimens of niobium and many well annealed, single-phase alloys approximate to this type.

Below H_{c1} it is expected that type II superconductors carry transport currents on the surface, like a type I superconductor, but in the mixed state above H_{c1} current paths in the interior would be mobile and unstable against Lorentz forces, at least in transverse fields [9]. There is experimental evidence that defect free type II superconductors do indeed obey the Silsbee rule in transverse fields [10,11], with H_{c1} as the limiting surface field, while a longitudinal field can enhance the critical current by creating a force-free current path [12].

The behavior represented by figures 8.1(a) and 8.1(b) corresponds to true equilibrium, so the same magnetization curves are obtained in both increasing and decreasing fields.

The so-called "hard" superconductors are characterized by inhomogeneous structures due to the presence of several metallurgical phases, lattice defects, or variations in composition. They usually behave as shown in figure 8.1(c). They may be regarded as extreme type II superconductors with the mixed state stabilized against Lorentz forces by the irregularities in their structure, resulting in both magnetic hysteresis and the ability to carry substantial transport currents distributed over the entire cross section of a wire [13, 14]. These irregularities also have the effect of decreasing the effective value of ξ and hence increasing H_{c2}. There is, however, an upper limit to this effect which is imposed by the paramagnetism of the conduction electrons in the normal state [15, 16, 17]. It is unlikely that any superconductor will be found to withstand flux densities in excess of 50 T (500 kG).

Typical examples of hard superconductors which have been successfully used in electromagnets are cold-worked alloys of niobium with zirconium or titanium and the intermetallic compound Nb_3Sn. They have all been observed to carry distributed current densities of the order of 10 A/m^2 at 4 K without resistance. The Nb-Zr alloys will carry significant current densities in flux densities up to about 7 T (70 kG) while Nb-Ti and Nb$_3$Sn can be used over 10 T (100 kG) [18, 19].

There is now a considerable quantity of literature on the design of superconducting magnets [18–22, 2]. The choice of superconductor depends upon convenience and the performance required. The Nb-Zr and Nb-Ti alloys are both ductile and can be wound into coils very easily. Nb$_3$Sn, which can show a better performance, is very brittle. It is necessary either to use a very thin layer deposited on a flexible substrate or to wind the coil with the mixed but unreacted elements and form the compound afterwards by heat treatment.

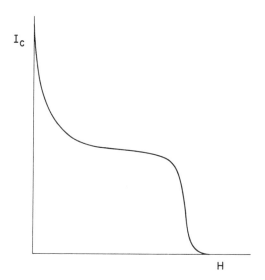

FIGURE 8.2. *Typical variation of critical current* I$_c$ *with transverse field* H *for a short sample of a hard superconducting wire.*

The design of the magnet then requires a knowledge of the critical current of the chosen wire as a function of transverse field at the working temperature. Figure 8.2 represents a typical curve measured with a short sample. Unfortunately, unless special precautions are taken, a long length of the same wire wound into a coil would probably not perform as well as figure 8.2 would suggest, especially in the low field, high current range. Various explanations have been proposed for this degradation effect [19], but the one currently in favor was suggested by Riermersma, Hulm, and Chandrasekhar [23, 18]. The magnetization curve for a hard superconductor is not usually observed as the smooth curve represented in figure 8.1(c), especially in the low field region. Instead, magnetic flux is observed to enter and leave the superconductor in a series of irregular steps known as "flux jumps." These are irreversible and release pulses of heat. In a coil, a flux jump at one point may precipitate flux jumps in neighboring windings and nucleate a region in the normal state. If the coil were carrying a sufficiently large current, the resulting Joule heat could then spread this region throughout the windings, driving them into the normal state without exceeding the critical steady current (at the working temperature) at any point.

Stekly [24] suggested that a magnet could be stabilized against this effect by having the superconducting wire in electrical contact with a copper strip throughout its length, to share the current during flux jumps. His original criterion for the thickness of the copper was that it should be capable of carrying the full current while remaining below the zero current transition temperature of the superconductor, albeit with a vigorous temporary boiloff of helium. However it was subsequently found that considerably less copper is required [25, 26], resulting in a big improvement in the winding packing factor. Using this principle it is possible to construct a magnet with a technologically useful overall current density which is free of the degradation effect.

Another aspect of the transition to the normal state which requires attention is the protection of the magnet from damage. Electrical transients in a large, unprotected coil are capable of causing breakdown of the insulation of the wire and local heating sufficient to spoil the heat treatment of the metal. Smith [27] has discussed several protection schemes. Stekly's stabilized coils are also completely protected and offer a solution to the problem which should be acceptable for large magnets, which do not require high current densities.

The use of hard superconducting coils with alternating current is severely limited by hysteresis loss [14, 28–30]. This could conceivably create a problem when running up the current in a large superconducting magnet. A certain amount of heat will be liberated by the irreversible process of attaining the final field and current distribution within the superconducting metal, and provision must be made to absorb it. The quantity involved is of the order of Q where [14]

$$Q \approx tJB \text{ J/m}^3 \tag{8.3}$$

where t is the thickness of the wire in meters, J is the maximum current density in A/m^2, and B is the final flux density in tesla.

The prospects and achievements in superconducting magnet technology at the time of writing have been reviewed by Laverick [31].

8.1.3. Non-superconductors

We turn now to magnets using non-superconducting metals at low temperature. A general discussion of these has been given by Taylor and Post [32]. Corruccini [33] has also discussed the choice of metal. The success of this type of magnet depends upon the reduction in the electric resistance of the windings, with a decrease in the working temperature, overcompensating for the work required to extract a given quantity of joule heat.

The three major contributions to the resistivity of a metal are:

  (a) scattering of electrons by lattice vibrations;
  (b) scattering by impurities, dislocations, grain boundaries, etc;
  (c) magnetoresistance.

To a first approximation, these three contributions may be simply added together.

For most pure metals in attainable magnetic fields, (a) dominates the other two at room temperature. It may be reduced to an arbitrarily small amount by reducing the temperature.

The residual resistivity to which a metal tends at very low temperature and zero magnetic field is a measure of (b). It can be reduced by purifying and annealing. For an optimum cryogenic magnet material the residual resistivity must be negligible compared to the other two contributions under working conditions, but in practice the cost of refining may force a compromise which falls short of this.

The relative change in resistivity $\Delta\rho/\rho$ due to magnetoresistance in a field H usually scales approximately as a function of H/ρ when ρ is changed either by changing the temperature or adding impurities, although there are exceptions to this rule especially for very pure metals at low temperature. The exact form of this function is a property of each individual metal and depends on the relative orientation of the field, current and crystal axes. For many metals the magnetoresistance is proportional to $(H/\rho)^2$ at low fields, and it may or may not saturate at a constant value $\Delta\rho/\rho \approx 2$ or 3 at high fields depending on the electronic structure. Thus the magnetoresistance in a given field in general increases as the contribution of scattering to the resistivity is reduced, and it imposes the ultimate limit on the attainable efficiency of a magnet.

The choice of metal for a cryogenic magnet must depend upon the use for which it is intended. If it is only to be used intermittently, its chief advantage over a room-temperature magnet would be the lower capital cost of the power supply, and the chief consideration in choosing the winding metal would be a balance of its resistivity under working conditions against its cost. For a more or less continuously running magnet, however, the cost and power consumption of refrigerating plant become more important. The total power consumption at a given current density would then become a more important consideration. This is the sum of the power delivered by the power supply and the power required by the refrigerator (or liquefier) to remove it in the form of joule heat. There are only six metals with which low-temperature operation is known to offer any advantage over copper at room temperature in this respect [33], assuming a magnet sustaining field of the order of 10 T. They are: aluminum, sodium, indium, lithium, copper, and beryllium [34]. Of these, aluminum and sodium are distinctly better than the others. For very pure samples, the optimum working temperatures [32] are about 17 K for aluminum and 10 K for sodium. At these temperatures they both require a total power consumption as low as 10 percent of that required to sustain the same current density in copper at room temperature. It should be emphasized, however, that this does not represent a direct comparison of the performance of actual magnets, since there is no reason why an optimum room-temperature magnet should work at the same current density as a cryogenic magnet for the same purpose.

The very pure metals used in cryogenic magnets are usually very weak mechanically, especially as they must be used in an annealed state. The problem of supporting the windings against Lorentz forces while maintaining cooling channels for efficient heat transfer may become acute. It is usually necessary to interleave the windings with a stronger metal.

Designs and working cryogenic magnets have been reported in the literature by Taylor and Post [32], Purcell and Payne [35], Laurence and Coles [2], and Laquer [21].

8.2. LINEAR ACCELERATORS

Liquid helium, below about 2.18 K, has many strange characteristics which are not possessed by any other material and therefore it has
been given the name "superfluid." It has been suggested [36, 37] that the
use of the nearly zero electrical resistance of superconductors (exactly
zero for direct current only) and the superfluid helium properties will
revolutionize the construction of high energy particle accelerators. The
Stanford University group has constructed a 5 ft (1.5 m) long accelerator
of the type which will accelerate electrons to about 6 Mev (and probably
to 10 Mev with improved injection) and are constructing a 500 ft (150 m)
long machine.

The schematic of a bi-periodic $\pi/2$ mode accelerator is shown in
figure 8.3. It consists of a series of microwave cavities connected together so the entire system resonates as a single unit. The electric field
in the short cavities is small while the field in the other cavities is along
the axis of the accelerator and alternates periodically in time. The distance from one accelerating cavity to the next is adjusted such that the
electrons will obtain maximum acceleration.

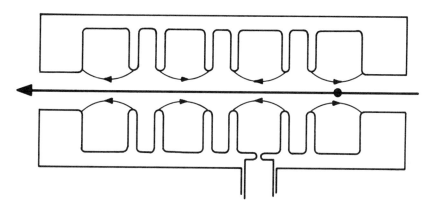

FIGURE 8.3.   *Standing wave bi-periodic $\pi/2$ mode accelerator.*

The major advantage of using a superconducting cavity is its low
electrical surface resistance R (zero only for direct current) or high Q.
The Q of a cavity is proportional to $1/R$ and is an exponential function
of temperature [38] as shown in figure 8.4. Using very careful preparation
techniques, McAshan has been able to obtain residual Q's of about
18×10^9 for lead and 15×10^9 for niobium.

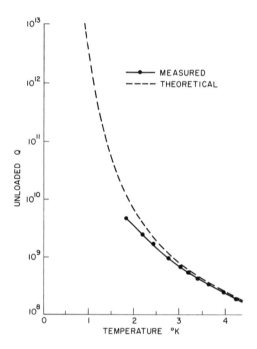

FIGURE 8.4. *Experimental and theoretical* Q *of a lead superconducting cavity as a function of temperature.*

The lower the temperature the smaller the power dissipation and therefore superfluid helium will be used to cool the accelerator. Helium below the superfluid transition or λ point has a very high thermal conductivity and estimates indicate that refrigeration at the center of the 500 ft (150 m) accelerator will be practical using a helium thermal bus bar. A 9-in (23 cm)-diam tube of helium at 1.8 K will keep the accelerator to within ± 0.03 K over its entire length. It would require a 100 ft (30 m) diameter copper bar to do an equivalent job [37].

Superfluid helium, which has fascinated and entertained low temperature physicists for about 40 years is being put to work. Professor Fairbanks and his group are utilizing the high thermal conductivity and specific heat to do a job which would be extremely difficult in other ways.

8.3. BUBBLE CHAMBERS

8.3.1. Introduction

Helium bubble chambers are used as targets and detectors of high energy particles for selected nuclear physics experiments. The bubble chamber, as first suggested by Glaser [39], consists of a container of liquid under sufficient pressure to be sub-cooled. When the pressure is reduced to below the normal boiling condition (superheated), the bubbles nucleate around charged particles [40]. Bubble tracks define the trajectory of charged particles traversing the liquid. The chamber is constructed with one or more windows to permit photographing the events and the entire unit is placed in a magnetic field so that the charged particles will have curved paths which in turn determine their momenta [41]. Bubble chambers combine many of the advantages of cloud chambers and nuclear emulsions to give a high-density detection device. Hydrogen and deuterium chambers have been used extensively as universal detectors and are the backbone of the high-energy nuclear physics detection and analysis system [42, 43].

8.3.2. Helium Chambers

Liquid helium chambers are of specialized interest in the study of particular events which occur in high energy physics reactions. For example, when a beam of K^- particles impinges upon the helium chamber, some of the interesting events include the measurement of the lifetime of $_\Lambda H^3$ and $_\Lambda H^4$ and the binding energies of $_\Lambda He^4$ and $_\Lambda H^4$, where the Λ indicates unstable excited states of the atoms known as hyper-nuclei. Also of particular interest is the study of the decay modes of these hyper-nuclei such as $K^- + He^4 \rightarrow {}_\Lambda H^3 + n + \pi^0$ and the subsequent decay of $_\Lambda H^3$.

Figure 8.5 shows a cut-away view of the Argonne-Carnegie Tech 10-in. helium bubble chamber. Table 8.1 gives the characteristics of this and other existing helium chambers.

The operating conditions for good quality bubble tracks is a fluid temperature of about 3.5 K and an operating pressure which varies between about 200 and 500 torr. As a high-energy charged particle passes through the liquid it ionizes some of the atoms giving rise to free electrons. These electrons are nucleation sites for boiling in a superheated

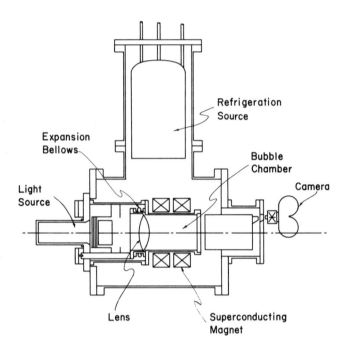

FIGURE 8.5. *Schematic of the Argonne-Carnegie Tech 10-in helium bubble chamber.*
Particles enter at right angles to the optical system.

TABLE 8.1.

Source	Vol ℓ^*	Expansion system	Field	Refrig	Reference
Duke Univ................	3	Piston		He reservoir	[44]
Rome.......................	4	Piston		He reservoir	[45]
Oxford/NIRNS...........	150	Bellows	20Kg	80 W refrig	[46]
Argonne...................	20	Bellows	45Kg	He reservoir	[47]
Northwestern.............	45	Bellows	28Kg	He reservoir	[48]

*These values are approximately the volume available for photographing. The value for thermodynamic calculations will be larger.

liquid and bubbles will grow if their radius is greater than the critical
value r_c where

$$r_c = \frac{2\sigma}{\delta P},$$

σ is the surface tension, $\delta P = P_l - P_v$, P_l is the pressure of the liquid
and P_v is the saturated vapor pressure in the bubble. The critical radius
for helium is approximately 1×10^{-6} cm.

Figure 8.6(a) shows a schematic of an ideal pressure-time cycle
(solid line) and an actual (dotted line) pressure-time cycle. The expansion is not an equilibrium process and therefore cannot be represented
on a conventional pressure-volume or temperature-entropy diagram.
However, it is useful to use such a diagram for estimating the amount of
refrigeration which will be required. Figure 8.6(b) is a schematic of a
temperature-entropy diagram for liquid expansion. The area inside the
curve must be estimated in order to adequately size the external
refrigerator.

The external refrigerator must be sized such that it will cool the
entire chamber to operating temperature in a reasonable time, remove
heat transferred to the chamber from external sources, and remove the
work of compression during operation. The work of compression for
existing chambers is of the order of 0.05 to 0.2 joules/pulse/liter. The
specific value is dependent upon the irreversibility of the expansion cycle
and conceivably could be made much less than existing values by careful
cryogenic design. Although gas expansion has been frequently used for
hydrogen, it has not been used in helium chambers because of helium's
low heat of vaporization and the large refrigeration load it would cause.
Small work of compression is desirable primarily because of the greater
ease of maintaining temperature stability as well as the high cost of
refrigeration. Heat from external sources can be reduced greatly by
use of nitrogen-cooled radiation shields, but in any case it can be estimated accurately from knowledge of the physical properties of the
materials of construction.

A uniform temperature within the chamber yields uniform track
densities and thus allows particle energy determination using bubble
densities. Whereas, small chambers can operate using a reservoir of
liquid and only the latent heat of vaporization, a large refrigeration load
or an extended time of operation will very easily justify the capital
investment for integral refrigeration which utilizes the enthalpy of the
cold gas in the cycle [49].

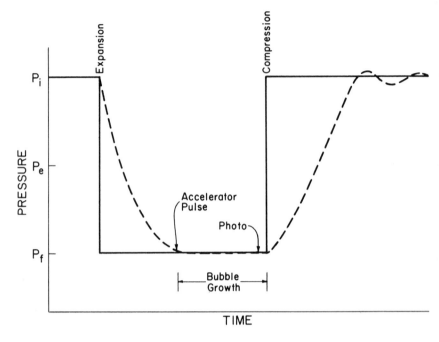

FIGURE 8.6(a). *Schematic of pressure-time cycle for bubble chamber operation.*

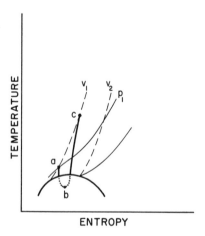

FIGURE 8.6(b). *Temperature-entropy diagram for liquid expansion.*

Process is non-equilibrium and therefore cannot be traced point by point.

8.4. CRYOPUMPING

8.4.1. Introduction

The production of high- and ultra-high vacuum can be enhanced through the utilization of cryogenic cooling, where the gas is condensed, sorbed or trapped on a low temperature surface [50–57]. Alternate schemes for producing high vacuums include ion, sublimation, and sputter type pumps which operate on the similar principle of capture or retention of mass from the gas phase, as well as the more conventional momentum transfer, mass removal pumping techniques. The principal advantages of the cryopump over these other pumping schemes are: simplicity, high pumping efficiency, low ultimate pressures, no moving parts, no premature shut-downs due to burn-out of filament needed for ionizing current, no heavy magnets or high voltages, etc. It is a technique that provides a clean, oil-free system in which the pumping capabilities for atmospheric gases closely match their respective partial pressures in the atmosphere. Limitations include: the necessary size requirements of cryosurface areas, cryosurface capacity (operation time between periods of surface regeneration), temperature rise across the deposit due to the heat of condensation, unfavorable thermal properties of the deposit, and the limited ability to pump certain low boiling point gases. Even the removal of gases which are normally termed non-condensable can be augmented by cryogenic cooling. The cryogenic cooling of a plane surface can increase the pumping capacity of that surface; however, more effective utilization of this scheme is realized by providing extended surfaces such as molecular sieves, silica gel, charcoal or the solid particles of a condensed gas.

Three major research areas where cryogenic pumping is beneficial are space chambers, low density wind tunnels, and high altitude air samplers.

8.4.2. Space Simulation Chambers

It has not proven feasible, nor is it possible at this time, to simulate either individually or collectively all of the various aspects of a true space environment. However, during the past half-decade or so, considerable strides have been made in the development of chambers capable of accommodating and producing many of the extreme conditions of space [58–70]. The high cost of space flight coupled with the consequences of insufficient reliability have dictated the necessity for simulation testing on the ground.

306–922 O–68—23

Inasmuch as this discussion is primarily concerned with the several effects of refrigeration on simulations as afforded by liquid helium or cold helium gas, the principal environmental conditions of interest are associated with the low temperature and pressure of space.

The infinite heat sink of space is known to have an effective temperature as low as that of liquid helium. This, in itself, is not a criterion which requires that a simulated space radiation heat sink be at this temperature, since the fourth power Stefan-Boltzmann radiation law indicates that only small error can be derived by substituting sink temperatures on the order of 80–100 K (providing that the radiating test body is maintained no lower than 300 K). Of greater importance is the fact that surfaces cooled to a temperature only slightly greater than absolute zero are able to provide increased molecular retention capability, thereby reducing the reflection or rebounding of gas molecules back to the test piece from the chamber walls after originally departing from that surface. The value of an extremely low temperature is in the establishment of a molecular sink more closely approximating the infinity of space. In certain small systems or experiments where true temperature and pressure simulation is deemed necessary, liquid helium has been used as the cryopanel refrigerant in large quantities and with attendant cost. This is possible at the few facilities fortunate enough to possess sizeable helium liquefaction capability, but even then it is expensive and requires good justification.

In order to achieve the extreme high vacuum (or low pressure) of space, it is generally recognized that various cryopumping techniques are invaluable, if not indispensable. With the exception of neon, hydrogen, and helium, all of the constituents of air have vapor pressures less than 10^{-10} torr at a temperature of 20 K, which is the normal boiling point of hydrogen. Assuming that the process of cryogenic condensation will be used to take out the primary gas load in a typical cryopumped simulator, and assuming that cryo-sorption, -trapping, -gettering, or some other method is used to remove the noncondensables, it is seen then that the temperature of liquid hydrogen may be considered an upper limit to many test requirements. However, although liquid hydrogen is now in plentiful supply and reasonably inexpensive, its use constitutes a safety hazard which is not warranted for such an application. Instead, dense helium gas refrigeration usually is adopted at a working temperature level of 10–20 K. In order to minimize the heat load and hence the appreciable cost of low-temperature refrigeration to the helium cooled cryopanel, a liquid nitrogen-cooled thermal shroud or

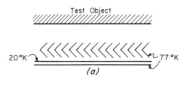

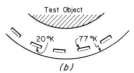

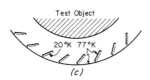

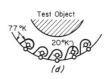

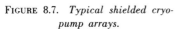

FIGURE 8.7. *Typical shielded cryo-*
pump arrays.

In each geometrical arrangement illustrated here, the liquid nitrogen cooled radiation shielding is positioned to maximize pumping speed of the helium cooled cryopump condenser surface while minimizing the high temperature thermal radiation load.

shield is provided to intercept incident radiation. Typical shielded cryopump arrays are shown in figure 8.7. As one example, each of the 39-ft spherical General Electric Valley Forge space simulators [71, 72] shown in figure 8.8 consist of a 1-kW (below 20 K) helium gas cryopanel surrounded by a 150-kW liquid nitrogen shroud in two of the chambers and a 300-kW nitrogen shroud in the third.

The origin of gases to be evacuated from a space chamber generally consists of (a) an initial or residual volume of air in the chamber, (b) desorption from the chamber walls and test body, and (c) leaks. However, a somewhat different category of near-space propulsion testing requires also that rocket-exhaust products be collected and condensed on an appropriate cryogenically-cooled surface. The AEDC Engine Test Cell J-2(A) [73] (figs. 8.9 and 8.10) consists of an 18-ft (5.5 m) diam by 32-ft (9.8 m) long nitrogen-cooled vacuum chamber equipped with a gaseous helium refrigerated system of cryoplates capable of absorbing a 1-kW heat load at a maximum refrigerant return temperature of 18 K.

FIGURE 8.8.   *39-ft diam General Electric space test chambers (Valley Forge, Pa.).*

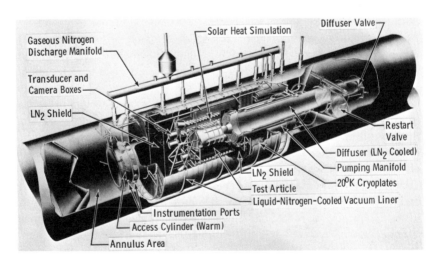

FIGURE 8.9.   *AEDC Propulsion Engine Test Cell (J–2A).*

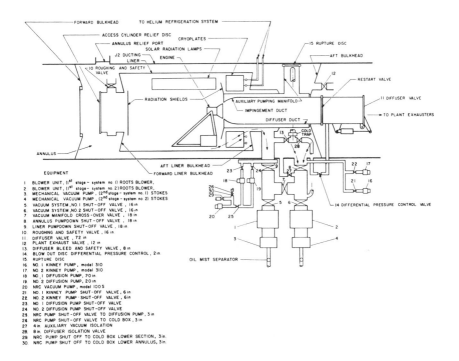

FIGURE 8.10.   *AEDC Propulsion Engine Test Cell (J-2A).*

8.4.3. Low-Density Wind Tunnels

As a result of intensified interest in the exploration of space and the upper atmosphere, it has become increasingly desirable to develop large low-density wind tunnels [74] capable of operating over extensive periods of time at hypersonic velocities in the transitional flow regime, i.e., altitude range between 200,000 ft (60 km) and 500,000 ft (150 km). In this region between continuum and free-molecule flow, neither of the bounding flow regime concepts have been sufficient to provide quantitative design information or to explain certain aerodynamic phenomena.

The first large-scale application of cryopumping occurred in the spring of 1959 when the University of Southern California low-density wind tunnel [75] became fully operational. A helium refrigerator, originally constructed as part of a refrigerated liquid hydrogen transport dewar, was used to cool the condenser. The information obtained on this system has been invaluable in designing more recent cryotunnels.

The choice of refrigerants for such application is usually limited to neon, hydrogen, or helium using either an open or closed refrigeration cycle. Closed cycle systems are more economical over the long run whereas an open cycle would require only moderate capital investment but high operating cost. In view of the potential safety hazard of hydrogen, and the low-temperature limitation and cost of neon, helium refrigeration appears to offer the best solution for a large cryopump.

In addition to the primary cryosurface considerations, tunnel design criteria require that liquid nitrogen-cooled precoolers be installed upstream of the final condenser in order to decrease the refrigeration load (by reducing the heat content of the flowing gas) on this condenser; a liquid nitrogen-cooled shroud is also furnished to protect the primary element from thermal radiation. The importance of this is illustrated by the fact that approximately 70 percent of the available refrigerator power in the early USC tunnel was dissipated in radiation losses, leaving only the remaining 30 percent to useful condensation. To alleviate the problem of non-condensables in the tunnel working fluid stream, it has been found desirable to substitute high-purity nitrogen for the atmospheric air. For testing purposes, its properties are similar to air, and it is readily condensed on the cryosurface. Also, to increase the useful operating time of a cryotunnel, means have been considered to remove

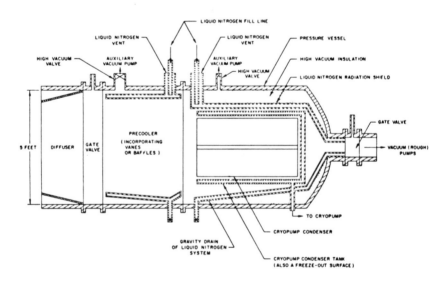

FIGURE 8.11.   *AVCO precooler and cryopump condenser.*

the built-up condensate on the cold surface(s). Periodic scraping, or a flexible surface, would permit continuous operation if desired. The AVCO tunnel design [76] suggests radiative heating of the cryodeposit in such a manner that a minimum amount of heat is transferred to the cooling fins. This causes the condensate temperature to be raised above its triple point, permitting it to drip off and be removed in the liquid phase. A schematic layout of the AVCO hardware is presented in figures 8.11 and 8.12.

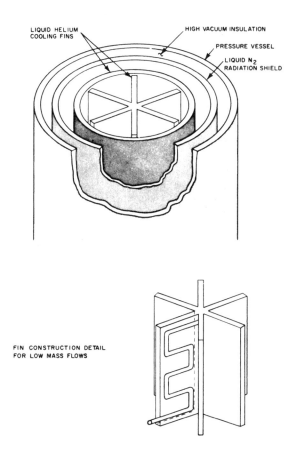

FIGURE 8.12. *AVCO condenser fin arrangement and construction detail.*

8.4.4. High-Altitude Air-Sampling Cryoprobe

Included in a variety of devices which have been, or are being, developed in the interest of examining the constituents of the upper atmosphere are several which make use of cryogenic collection techniques. One of these, the Nesco cryoprobe [77], has been designed to collect a whole-air sample volume (including particulate matter) of up to 800,000 ft³ (20,000 m³) within an altitude range of 300,000 to 400,000 ft (90 to 120 km). As part of the USAF's air-launched, air-recoverable rocket (ALARR) program, the payload is fitted to a Genie rocket booster and launched by supersonic aircraft; recovery is accomplished using a conventional air-snatch technique, with the sampler then flown to the laboratory for sample evaluation and analysis [78].

FIGURE 8.13. *Nesco cryoprobe paddle deployment.*

In-flight cryopumping is achieved by a large helium-cooled parasol (development of which is shown in fig. 8.13) unfurled by centrifugal force to sweep the prescribed flight path in 30 to 60 s. After sampling, the collector surface is refolded and stored in its original nosepiece. Approximately 20 lb (9.1 kg) of indium — a metal having the highest specific heat capacity of any useful to the program — are fabricated into 0.05 in (1.3 mm) blades which then are sandwiched between 0.015 in (0.38 mm) gold-plated aluminum face sheets; the plating improves bonding to the indium and provides a highly reflective surface for solar heat rejection. On the basis of both theoretical and experimental analysis, it has been determined that no shock wave forms at the face of the blades as long as the temperature does not exceed 32 to 38 K in the applicable sampling altitude range. Therefore the temperature of 4 K when deployed can rise to something less than 32 K with small decrease in efficiency. The cryoprobe functions first as a vacuum-insulated dewar, retaining liquid helium about the sampling paddles for several hours prior to the actual collection period. Following collection, the condensate turns to gas with rising temperature and the container becomes a low-pressure vessel.

8.5. NON-CONDENSABLE GAS INJECTION

8.5.1. Introduction

The involvement of cryogenic propellants in missiles and space vehicles has provided the aerospace industry with a multitude of problems, and solutions for several of these have relied upon the availability and unique characteristics of helium. As a result of its low boiling point or non-condensability, low solubility, low molecular weight, and, because it is inert, helium has many cryopropellant applications.

In this section, examination is made of the use of low-temperature helium gas injection as a cryogenic fluid conditioning technique. If a non-condensable gas is bubbled through a volume of liquid, evaporative cooling — the vaporization of some of the liquid into the gas bubbles — causes the temperature of the liquid to be lowered. When properly applied to a tank or pipeline of liquid hydrogen or liquid oxygen, for example, injected helium is able to refrigerate and thereby reduce the temperature of the liquid [79–82], suppress geysering [83], and create or maintain solid or solid-liquid propellant mixtures [84, 85]. Various cryogenic propellant stages of the Saturn family of space vehicles make use of helium injection as a means of conditioning propellant in the suction lines of the pumps. Several gas injection-based methods are described below.

8.5.2. Injection Cooling

The liquid duct connecting the bottom of the cryopropellant tank to the rocket engine-feeding turbopump furnishes the physical system for a variety of undesirable phenomena. The combined effect of suction line length, diameter, and environmental heating is able to cause an excessive temperature rise in the contained fluid which either can be objectionable or impossible to accommodate by the vehicle system.

Should insufficient net positive suction head (pump inlet total pressure minus vapor pressure) be available to the pump, cavitation may occur and the mission will be jeopardized; since vapor pressure is a function of temperature, this latter quantity must be controlled in some way to maintain the liquid in a sufficiently subcooled condition.

If, due to ambient heating at anytime prior to launch, the column of liquid becomes superheated, geysering can result from a violent generation of vapor caused by the release of superheat, which forces liquid from the line upward into the propellant tank. Cooling from the vaporization process, and colder liquid falling back through the residual vapor, sets up a condition wherein the momentum of dropping liquid must be absorbed by the bottom of the fluid column. This results in a large pressure spike — at times a factor of ten or more greater than the initial pressure — which can be extremely destructive to the confining hardware. A mechanism to refrigerate (or somehow adjust the temperature of) this pipe of liquid therefore becomes necessary to preserve the integrity of the fluid system. Injection cooling can be used to reduce or eliminate both cavitation and geysering.

A more recent development of this technique concerns the formation and maintenance of solid-liquid (slush) mixtures of cryogen. The advantages of creating and using such mixtures lie in their ability to absorb more heat before any evaporation occurs — i.e., to provide an increased heat sink — and to require a smaller container volume due to greater density of the solid relative to the liquid. Injection cooling is not considered to be an economically justifiable large-scale production method, but it may well be an excellent way to upgrade the mixture within a thin-walled space vehicle propellant compartment. Upgrading is necessary because of the uncertain, or long, periods of ground-hold or standby time, imperfect tank insulation characteristics, and a possible requirement to increase the solid percentage above a flowable mixture.

Gas injection cooling is accomplished in the following manner [81, 82]. Assuming that the non-condensable helium gas being injected into a liquid cryogen is pure, then the partial pressure of the cryogen within any given helium bubble is zero. A portion of the liquid is required to evaporate into the gas bubble since a difference has been established between the vapor pressure of the cryogenic fluid surrounding the bubble and the partial pressure of the cryogen within the bubble. The natural result of vaporization is a cooling effect whereby heat is extracted from the liquid and its temperature decreased accordingly.

A heat balance of the given control volume of figure 8.14 yields

$$q = q_1 + q_2 - q_3$$

where q is the total system heat flux, q_1 the environmental heat flux, q_2 the injected helium heat flux, and q_3 the evaporative cooling rate. Using the simplifying assumptions of instantaneous cool-down of helium gas to the temperature of liquid cryogen and instantaneous diffusion of cryogen vapor into the helium gas (the model does not apply for a system where

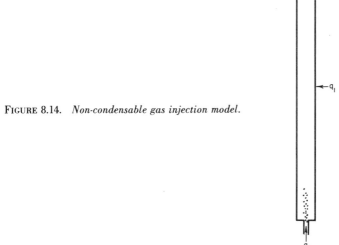

FIGURE 8.14. *Non-condensable gas injection model.*

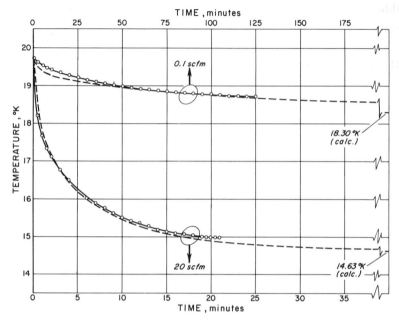

FIGURE 8.15. *Comparison between calculated and experimental temperature his-tories for different injection gas flow rates.*

Solid line experimental, dotted theoretical. (20 scfm ≈ 0.57 m³/min.)

significant diffusion of gas to liquid occurs), a comparison of experiment and theory is shown in figure 8.15. The correlation is quite good for two rather extreme values of injection flow rate -0.1 scfm (0.0028 m³/min) and 20 scfm (0.57 m³/min) of helium into liquid hydrogen.

Figure 8.16 is a graphical representation of the analytical model for a specific helium injection flow rate of 10 scfm (0.28 m³/min). An environmental heating load q_1 of 2.7 W/m² of wetted column wall area is used as an example but substitution may be made for any value. Also, since the injected helium heat flux q_2 and the evaporative cooling rate q_3 vary directly as the injected gas flow rate, these curves may be altered by simple ratio, e.g., $(q_2)_{20 \text{ scfm}} = (2q_2)_{10 \text{ scfm}}$, and $(q_3)_{20 \text{ scfm}} = (2q_3)_{10 \text{ scfm}}$. The curves are useful in predicting the minimum theoretical temperature attainable for a given set of conditions. That is, for a specified gas flow rate and a known system heat load, the minimum temperature may be found simply by setting $dT/d\theta$ (and therefore q) equal to zero, from which $q_1 + q_2 - q_3 = 0$; graphically (fig. 8.16 or equivalent), the temperature at $q_1 + q_2 = q_3$ is the desired temperature.

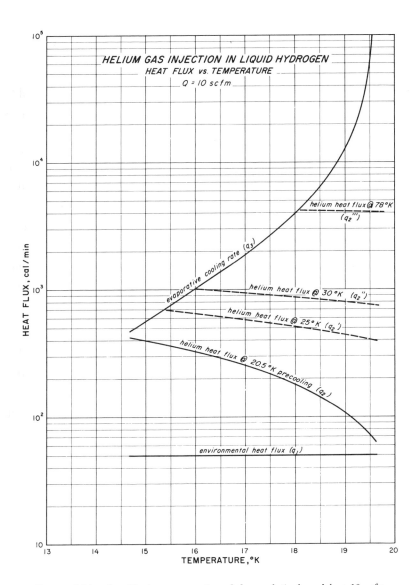

FIGURE 8.16. *Graphical representation of the analytical model at 10 scfm
(0.28 m³/min).*

8.5.3. Thermal and Helium Lift Pumping

Where more than one column of liquid may be considered usable in a fluid conditioning system — many space vehicles are now equipped with multiple propellant lines due to the parallel clustering of both engines and propellant tanks — several liquid recirculation schemes have been developed where in a given set of two lines each is interconnected near the bottom. Whether one tank, or several manifolded tanks, are used to supply these line combinations makes little difference as long as a continuous circulation path is provided (see fig. 8.17) from tank(s) to line A through connector to line B to tank(s), etc. Since we are concerned with vehicle standby and engine prestart suction line fluid conditioning (i.e., dead-ended lines with nonoperative pumps), line A will be designated "feed" and line B "return".

Assume now that the two ducts are filled with liquid at different temperatures and that they open into a common tank filled with liquid at the colder temperature. Density differentials in the lines due to this temperature difference then cause a natural convection, or *thermal pumping*, process to be established which moves fluid from the cold column into the warm column, warm fluid into the tank, and cold tank

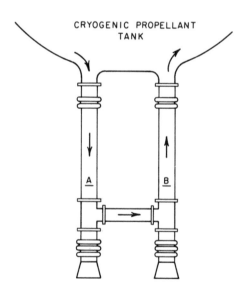

FIGURE 8.17.   *Thermal and helium lift pumping model.*

liquid down into the colder line as replenishment. This continues as long as the feed and return line temperatures are different, which is a function of the normal ambient heat flux to the columns and a continuing supply of cold liquid from the propellant tanks.

If it is found that the natural circulation process outlined above is not quite sufficient to do the job, and that it is undesirable or impossible to insulate the cold line and/or adjust line sizes, restrictions, etc., then it becomes necessary to implement the flow by some other means. By injecting helium gas into the bottom of the return line, the effective mean density of the two-component fluid system within this line is decreased, with subsequent increase in density differential between lines and concomitant rise in flow driving force. From the previous section on injection cooling, it will be recalled that the evaporative cooling effect of non-condensable gas introduced here eliminates geysering by temperature reduction of the affected (return) line liquid. Also, it has been verified experimentally that flow oscillations in such a system at low (filling or draining) propellant tank head are stabilized due to the accelerated flow rate and subcooled liquid resulting from injection.

Analysis of this so-called *helium lift pumping* process is complicated because of the interdependency of several variables — two-phase flow, liquid-gas interfacial mass transfer, etc. However, computer programs have been written by a group at the NASA-Marshall Space Flight Center which predict steady state recirculation flowrates and temperature distributions for both helium lift and thermal pumping systems. Extensive analytical and experimental investigations of these systems at Marshall have proven the feasibility for space vehicle application [86].

8.6. OTHER APPLICATIONS IN MISSILE AND SPACE SYSTEMS

Because of the many desirable properties of helium which were listed in a previous section, the fluid enjoys multi-faceted utilization in space vehicle applications [87, 88].

As propellant pressurant in a pump-fed engine system, the gas is used to displace the liquid fuel or oxidizer and to guarantee that propellant reaches the pump at a required pressure and usable fluid condition. The fact that helium is an inert gas, non-condensable and only very slightly soluble (therefore non-contaminating) in these propellants, and is of low molecular weight, identifies several good reasons for its choice of suitability as a pressurization gas. The helium is carried on-board in high pressure vessels, either external to, or within, the propellant tanks. For an internal configuration the gas loading is maximized since the fluid density is increased by a low temperature environment; however, subsequent to use, the temperature of the gas should be increased for efficient use at low density. Heat exchange is accomplished generally at some point in the connecting line between high pressure gas storage and tank ullage where the heat sink of the cold helium gas can, perhaps, be used to some advantage.

In the liquid hydrogen-fueled Centaur upper stage, liquid helium is employed as a pre-launch engine coolant [89]. The requirement here is based upon a need for near-operating temperatures of engine hardware prior to ignition to forestall the possibility of turbopump cavitation and overspeeding. A previous solution was to bleed liquid hydrogen from the fuel tank in flight after booster separation, but this procedure involved a valuable time period of roughly one-half minute and additional propellant to be carried solely for its refrigeration capacity. Results of the decision to pre-chill the engine with liquid helium on the ground before launching shortened the in-flight chilldown time by a factor of four and permitted a payload increase of 50 lb. At the expense of additional development time, a refrigerated helium gas system could have been devised to accomplish the same purpose.

Because of its low condensing point temperature, helium gas is also of value in certain extensive space travel pneumatic control systems where any long term exposure to a low temperature environment might freeze the more conventional actuating fluids. Cryogenic gas bearings are often lubricated with helium gas if the rotating device is required to operate at very low temperatures. The characteristics of helium previously mentioned as being beneficial for a pressurant are equally advantageous in purging operations which ultimately involve the handling of cryogens. Helium purge gas does not freeze, contaminate, or react with subsequently introduced low boiling point fluids.

REFERENCES

l] W. D. Coles, E. R. Schrader, and P. A. Thompson, A 14-tesla 15-centimeter-bore superconductive magnet, Advances in Cryogenic Engineering (ed. K. D. Timmerhaus, Plenum Press, New York, N.Y., 1968), Vol. **13**, p. 142.

[2] J. C. Laurence and W. D. Coles, Design, Construction, and Performance of Cryogenically Cooled and Superconducting Electromagnets, Proc. Symp. Magnet Technology, Stanford, Calif. (1965), p. 574.

[3] A. A. Abrikosov, On the magnetic properties of superconductors of the second group, Zhur. Eksp. i Teoret. Fiz. **32**, 1442 (1957). [Transl. in Soviet Phys.–JETP **5**, 1174 (1957)].

[4] V. L. Ginzburg and L. D. Landau, On the theory of superconductivity, Zhur. Eksp. i. Teoret. Fiz. **12**, 1064 (1950).

[5] R. McFee, Superconducting power transformers – A feasibility study, Elec. Eng. **80**, 754 (1961); **81**, 122 (1962).

[6] R. H. Kropschot and V. D. Arp, Superconducting magnets, Cryogenics **2**, 1 (1961). See also: Advances in Cryogenic Engineering **6**, 166 (1961).

[7] M. Tinkham, Effect of fluxoid quantization on transitions of superconducting films, Phys. Rev. **129**, 2413 (1963).

[8] D. Saint-James and P. G. deGennes, Onset of superconductivity in decreasing fields, Phys. Letters **7**, 306 (1963).

[9] C. J. Gorter, Note on the superconductivity of alloys, Phys. Letters **1**, 69 (1962).

[10] R. A. Kamper, The critical current of a superconductor of the second kind, Phys. Letters **5**, 9 (1963).

[11] J. W. Heaton and A. C. Rose-Innes, Current Capacity of a superconductor of the second kind, Appl. Phys. Letters **2**, 196 (1963).

[12] J. W. Heaton and A. C. Rose-Innes, Critical currents of a superconductor of the second kind, Cryogenics **4**, 85 (1964).

[13] C. P. Bean, Magnetization of hard superconductors, Phys. Rev. Letters **8**, 250 (1962).

[14] H. London, Alternating current losses in superconductors of the second kind, Phys. Letters **6**, 162 (1963).

[15] A. M. Clogston, Upper limit for the critical field in hard superconductors, Phys. Rev. Letters **9**, 266 (1962).

[16] B. S. Chandrasekhar, A note on the maximum critical field of high-field superconductors, Appl. Phys. Letters **1**, 7 (1962).

[17] R. A. Kamper, R. S. Collier, and Y. Ohori, Influence of spin paramagnetism on superconductivity, Phys. Rev. **137**, A75 (1965).

[18] H. T. Coffey, J. K. Hulm, W. T. Reynolds, D. K. Fox, and R. E. Span, A protected 100 kG superconducting magnet, J. Appl. Phys. **36**, 128 (1965).

[19] T. G. Berlincourt, High magnetic fields by means of superconductors, Brit. J. Appl. Phys. **14**, 9 (1963).

[20] D. B. Montgomery, Superconducting Magnets, IEEE Spectrum (Feb. 1964), p. 103.

[21] High Magnetic Fields (ed. H. H. Kolm, B. Lax, F. Bitter, and R. G. Mills, M.I.T. Press and John Wiley & Sons, Inc., 1962).

[22] C. Laverick, Superconducting Magnets, Nucleonics **24**, 46 (1966).

[23] H. Riemersma, J. K. Hulm, and B. S. Chandrasekhar, Flux jumping and degradation in superconducting solenoids, Advances in Cryogenic Engineering (ed. K. D. Timmerhaus, Plenum Press, New York, 1964), Vol. **9**, p. 329.

[24] A. R. Kantrowitz and Z. J. J. Stekly, A new principle for the construction of stabilized superconducting coils, Appl. Phys. Letters **6**, 56 (1965).

[25] Z. J. J. Stekly and J. L. Zar, Stable Superconducting Coils, IEEE Trans. Nucl. Sci. **NS-12**, 367 (1965).

[26] C. Laverick, G. M. Lobell, J. R. Purcell, and J. M. Brooks, Use of aluminum in super-conducting cables, Rev. Sci. Instr. **37**, 806 (1966).

[27] P. F. Smith, Protection of superconducting coils, Rev. Sci. Instr. **34**, 368 (1963).

[28] R. A. Kamper, A.C. loss in superconducting lead-bismuth, Phys. Letters **2**, 290 (1962).

[29] C. H. Jones and H. L. Schenk, A.C. losses in hard superconductors, Advances in Cryogenic Engineering (ed. K. D. Timmerhaus, Plenum Press, New York, 1963), Vol. **8**, p. 579.

[30] T. A. Buchhold, The nature of the surface losses of superconductors at low frequencies, Cryogenics **3**, 141 (1963).

[31] C. Laverick, The future of superconducting magnets, IEEE Trans. Nucl. Sci. **NS-14**, 361 (1967).

[32] R. F. Post and C. E. Taylor, Air core cryogenic magnet coils for fusion research and high-energy nuclear physics applications, Advances in Cryogenic Engineering (ed. K. D. Timmerhaus, Plenum Press, New York, 1960), Vol. **5**, p. 13. (See also ref. [21].)

[33] R. J. Corruccini, The electrical properties of aluminum for cryogenic electromagnets, NBS Tech. Note 218 (1964).

[34] P. Burnier, Cryogenics and aluminum in electrical manufacturing, Advances in Cryogenic Engineering (ed. K. D. Timmerhaus, Plenum Press, New York, 1966), Vol. **11**, p. 668.

[35] J. R. Purcell and E. G. Payne, High-field liquid H_2-cooled aluminum-wound magnet, Rev. Sci. Instr. **34**, 893 (1963).

[36] H. A. Schwettman, J. P. Turneaure, W. M. Fairbanks, T. I. Smith, M. S. McAshan, P. B. Wilson, and E. E. Chambers, The 1967 U.S. National Particle Accelerator Conference (to be published).

[37] W. M. Fairbanks, A superconducting linear accelerator and the use of superconductivity in some fundamental experiments in physics, Proc. Symp. Physics of Superconducting Devices (ed. B. S. Deaver, Jr., Univ. of Virginia, April 28–29, 1967), p. A–1.

[38] M. S. McAshan, The application of superconductors in the construction of high-Q Microwave cavities, Proc. Symp. Physics of Superconducting Devices (ed. B. S. Deaver, Jr., Univ. of Virginia, April 28–29, 1967), p. C–1.

[39] Donald A. Glaser, The bubble chamber, Handbuch der Physik (ed. S. Flugge, Springer, Berlin, 1958), Vol. **45**, p. 314.

[40] F. Seitz, On the theory of the bubble chamber, Phys. Fluids **1**, 2 (1958).

[41] D. F. Shaw, Hydrogen and helium bubble chambers, Cryogenics **4**, 193 (1964).

[42] R. P. Shutt, Recent advances in the bubble chamber technique, Nuclear Instr. Methods **20**, 71 (1963).

[43] N. C. Barford, Low temperature bubble chambers, Progress in Cryogenics **2**, 88 (1960).

[44] M. M. Block, W. M. Fairbanks, E. M. Harth, T. Kikuchi, C. Meltzer, and J. Leitner, Proc. Intern. Conf. High-Energy Accelerators and Instrumentation (C.E.R.N., Geneva, 1959), p. 461.

[45] E. Di Capua, U. Dore, G. C. Gialanella, P. Guidoni and I. Laakso, Nuclear Instr. and Methods **15**, 273 (1962).

[46] J. Moffatt, Nuclear Physics Laboratory, Oxford (1960) (unpublished report) (see ref. 41).

[47] E. G. Pewitt, M. Derrick, T. H. Fields, L. Hyman, C. Laverick, K. B. Martin, J. G. Fetkovich, and J. McKenzie, The 19th Intern. Conference on High Energy Physics, Dubna, U.S.S.R. (1964).

[48] M. M. Block, Northwestern University (unpublished data).

[49] D. B. Mann, Chapter 2.

[50] H. Adam, The significance of cryogenic techniques for the production of low pressures, Rev. Soc. Roy. Belge Ingrs. Ind. 11 457 (1963).

[51] J. P. Dawson and J. D. Haygood, Cryopumping, Cryogenics 5, 57 (1965).

[52] P. J. Gareis and G. F. Hagenbach, Cryosorption, Ind. Eng. Chem. 57, 27 (1965).

[53] E. L. Garwin, Cryogenic pumping and space simulation, Advances in Cryogenic Engineering (ed. K. D. Timmerhaus, Plenum Press, New York, 1963), Vol. 8, p. 37.

[54] E. L. Garwin, Cryogenic pumping and space simulation, Cryogenic Technology (ed. R. W. Vance, John Wiley & Sons, Inc., New York, 1963), p. 332.

[55] G. F. Hagenbach, Cryogenic vacuum pumps, Ind. Res. 7, 67–68, 70–72, 74 (1965).

[56] P. B. Henault, P. J. Fennema, and B. A. Buffham, Cryogenic pumping, J. Environmental Sci. 6, 15 (1963).

[57] L. O. Mullen and M. J. Hiza, The role of cryogenics in the production of high and ultra-high vacuum, Cryogenics 4, 387 (1964).

[58] J. L. Aberle and A. J. Westbrock, Liquid helium and nitrogen supply systems for space simulators, Advances in Cryogenic Engineering (ed. K. D. Timmerhaus, Plenum Press, New York, 1963), Vol. 8, p. 190.

[59] C. W. Alstrom, Design of extreme high vacuum facilities, Test Eng. 11, 28–30, 34, 41 (1964).

[60] N. C. Breddy and H. J. Smith, Some problems in space simulation chamber design, Vacuum 13, 449 (1963).

[61] E. E. Callaghan, Hard vacuums and cryogenics, Machine Design 34, 162 (1962).

[62] I. Farkass and G. W. Horn, Cryogenic pumping in space simulators, A.I.Ch.E., 56th Annual Meeting, Symp. Molecular Properties at Cryogenic Temperatures, Houston, Tex. (1963).

[63] S. Giles, Cryogenic pumping systems, Test Eng. 12, 38 (1964).

[64] B. H. Goethert and H. M. Cook, High ground for aerospace simulation, Astronaut. Aeronaut. 2, 96 (1964).

[65] R. A. Hindle, Space simulation, ASME Paper No. 62–AV–34 (1962).

[66] R. T. Hollingsworth, A survey of large space chambers, NASA Tech. Note D–1673 (1963).

[67] H. Mark and R. D. Sommers, The combined use of liquid and gaseous helium to provide near actual space environment, Advances in Cryogenic Engineering (ed. K. D. Timmerhaus, Plenum Press, New York, 1963), Vol. 8, p. 93.

[68] V. Outmann and J. C. McLane, Jr., Testing in the simulated space environment — an assessment, AIAA Paper No. 65–474 (1965).

[69] J. C. Simons, Jr., and M. P. Hnilicka, Future trends in space simulation — the role of vacuum and cryotechniques, Inst. Environ. Sci. Proc. (1963), p. 363.

[70] K. D. Timmerhaus, Cryogenics in space simulation, Test Eng. 12, 26, 28–29, 34, 42 (1964).

[71] J. Richman, Space simulation facility, Test Eng. 11, 16–18, 22 (1964).

[72] J. Richman and C. B. Hood, Report on three 32,000 cu. ft. space simulation systems, Trans. 9th Natl. Vacuum Symp. (ed. G. H. Bancroft, MacMillan Co., New York, 1962), p. 282.

[73] J. R. Reeves, Jr., General description and performance of the propulsion engine test cell (J–2A), Arnold Engineering Development Center, Arnold AF Station, Tennessee, Report No. AEDC–TDR–64–138 (1964).

[74] W. A. Clayden and R. B. Reynolds, Cryopumped low density wind tunnels, Vacuum 13, 461 (1963).

[75] J. G. Everton, Operational characteristics of a cryopump used in a low density wind tunnel, Trans. 9th Natl. Vacuum Symp. (ed. G. H. Bancroft, MacMillan Co., New York, 1962), p. 227.

[76] B. D. Henshall and E. M. Brower, A cryogenic hypersonic low-density wind tunnel, Advances in Cryogenic Engineering (ed. K. D. Timmerhaus, Plenum Press, New York, 1962), Vol. 7, p. 73.

[77] National Engineering Science Company, Cryogenic air sampler for high altitude application, NESCO Rept. SN 100A–1 (1964).

[78] C. M. Plattner, Super-cooled paddles used in high altitude air sampler, Aviation Week and Space Technology 82, 44–45, 47 (1965).

[79] P. S. Larsen, J. A. Clark, W. O. Randolph, and J. L. Vaniman, Cooling of cryogenic liquids by gas injection, Advances in Cryogenic Engineering (ed. K. D. Timmerhaus, Plenum Press, New York, 1963), Vol. 8, p. 507.

[80] F. W. Lytle and J. T. Stoner, Cryogenic cooling by noncondensible-gas injection, Science 148, 3678, 1721 (1965).

[81] W. O. Randolph and J. L. Vaniman, Sub-cooling of cryogenic liquids by injection of non-condensing gas, NASA-Marshall Space Flight Center, MTP–S&M–P–61–19 (1961).

[82] A. F. Schmidt, Experimental investigation of liquid-hydrogen cooling by helium gas injection, Advances in Cryogenic Engineering (ed. K. D. Timmerhaus, Plenum Press, New York, 1963), Vol. 8, p. 521.

[83] S. K. Morgan and H. F. Brady, Elimination of the geysering effect in missiles, Advances in Cryogenic Engineering (ed. K. D. Timmerhaus, Plenum Press, New York, 1962), Vol. 7, p. 206.

[84] G. J. Caras, Slush hydrogen, Redstone Scientific Information Center, Redstone Arsenal, Alabama, Report No. RSIC–288 (1964).

[85] R. R. Carney, R. F. Dwyer, H. M. Long, and L. R. Niendorf, Theoretical, experimental, and analytical examination of sub-cooled and solid hydrogen, Air Force Tech. Doc. Rept. No. APL-TDR 64–22 (1964).

[86] H. F. Trucks and W. O. Randolph, Analytical and experimental investigation of thermal and helium lift – pumping recirculation systems, Advances in Cryogenic Engineering (ed. K. D. Timmerhaus, Plenum Press, New York, 1965), Vol. 10, p. 341.

[87] W. M. Deaton, Helium for missiles and space vehicles, Missile Liquid Propellants Symp., Hershey, Pa. (1964).

[88] Rocket Propellant and Pressurization Systems (ed. Elliot Ring, Prentice-Hall, Inc., Englewood Cliffs, N.J., 1964).

[89] J. J. Gilbeau, D. L. Martindale, and K. R. Burton, A large-scale storage and transfer system for distribution of liquid helium as a refrigerant medium, Advances in Cryogenic Engineering (ed. K. D. Timmerhaus, Plenum Press, New York, 1965), Vol. 10, p. 428.

Author Index

Subject Index

NBS TECHNICAL PUBLICATIONS

PERIODICALS

JOURNAL OF RESEARCH reports National Bureau of Standards research and development in physics, mathematics, chemistry, and engineering. Comprehensive scientific papers give complete details of the work, including laboratory data, experimental procedures, and theoretical and mathematical analyses. Illustrated with photographs, drawings, and charts.

Published in three sections, available separately:

● **Physics and Chemistry**

Papers of interest primarily to scientists working in these fields. This section covers a broad range of physical and chemical research, with major emphasis on standards of physical measurement, fundamental constants, and properties of matter. Issued six times a year. Annual subscription: Domestic, $5.00; foreign, $6.00*.

●**Mathematical Sciences**

Studies and compilations designed mainly for the mathematician and theoretical physicist. Topics in mathematical statistics, theory of experiment design, numerical analysis, theoretical physics and chemistry, logical design and programming of computers and computer systems. Short numerical tables. Issued quarterly. Annual subscription: Domestic, $2.25; foreign, $2.75*.

●**Engineering and Instrumentation**

Reporting results of interest chiefly to the engineer and the applied scientist. This section includes many of the new developments in instrumentation resulting from the Bureau's work in physical measurement, data processing, and development of test methods. It will also cover some of the work in acoustics, applied mechanics, building research, and cryogenic engineering. Issued quarterly. Annual subscription: Domestic, $2.75; foreign, $3.50*.

TECHNICAL NEWS BULLETIN

The best single source of information concerning the Bureau's research, developmental, cooperative and publication activities, this monthly publication is designed for the industry-oriented individual whose daily work involves intimate contact with science and technology—*for engineers, chemists, physicists, research managers, product-development managers, and company executives.* Annual subscription: Domestic, $1.50; foreign, $2.25.*

NONPERIODICALS

Applied Mathematics Series. Mathematical tables, manuals, and studies.

Building Science Series. Research results, test methods, and performance criteria of building materials, components, systems, and structures.

Handbooks. Recommended codes of engineering and industrial practice (including safety codes) developed in cooperation with interested industries, professional organizations, and regulatory bodies.

Special Publications. Proceedings of NBS conferences, bibliographies, annual reports, wall charts, pamphlets, etc.

Monographs. Major contributions to the technical literature on various subjects related to the Bureau's scientific and technical activities.

National Standard Reference Data Series. NSRDS provides quantitative data on the physical and chemical properties of materials, compiled from the world's literature and critically evaluated.

Product Standards. Provide requirements for sizes, types, quality and methods for testing various industrial products. These standards are developed cooperatively with interested Government and industry groups and provide the basis for common understanding of product characteristics for both buyers and sellers. Their use is voluntary.

Technical Notes. This series consists of communications and reports (covering both other agency and NBS-sponsored work) of limited or transitory interest.

CLEARINGHOUSE

The Clearinghouse for Federal Scientific and Technical Information, operated by NBS, supplies unclassified information related to Government-generated science and technology in defense, space, atomic energy, and other national programs. For further information on Clearinghouse services, write:

Clearinghouse
U.S. Department of Commerce
Springfield, Virginia 22151

Order NBS publications from:
Superintendent of Documents
Government Printing Office
Washington, D.C. 20402

---

*Difference in price is due to extra cost of foreign mailing.